The Oblivion

of

Richard Trevithick

by

Philip M. Hosken

Published by The Trevithick Society
for the study of Cornish industrial archaeology and history

ISBN 978 0 904040 89 0

Printed and bound by T. J. International
Trecerus Industrial Estate, Padstow PL28 8RW

Typeset, layout and design by Peninsula Projects
c/o PO Box 62, Camborne TR14 7ZN

Cover design © Sean Croft

The Oblivion of Richard Trevithick

Richard Trevithick 1771-1833

Contents

The Oblivion of Trevithick, the Missing Years

The Oblivion of Trevithick

The Missing Years in the history of steam engineering endeavour are those between the conclusion of James Watt's extended patent on the steam engine in 1800 and the dawn of the Railway Age in 1830.

During this vital time there was feverish activity in the production of steam engines as industrialists demanded the new, more efficient, compact, high-pressure engines and manufacturers rushed to supply them.

In all this excitement, few historians accurately recorded how the new technology had emerged. The history of steam engineering is left with a gap that has been too often filled by crediting Watt with something he did not do and subsequent engineers with having invented the engines they merely built.

This is the story of Richard Trevithick, engineer, 1771-1833.

Author's note

Richard Trevithick and his third son Francis, who prepared his long awaited biography, provide us with little or no documentary evidence of his personal life. Trevithick was concerned with little more than his work. In his notebooks and letters he explained his mechanical contrivances, their operation and the financial and legal problems he encountered. We are subsequently left with a Trevithick who is not based on fact but on the imagination of writers through the years. As far as his private life is concerned, we have to draw such conclusions as we can from the scant information between the lines of his letters and from the actions and correspondence of his family, friends and acquaintances.

This book was motivated by two issues; the discovery that Francis Trevithick, in his hagiography, *The Life of Richard Trevithick*, had corrected the spelling and other errors in his father's letters, and the almost total obscurity of Trevithick in the public understanding of steam engine development. I was also very aware of the gaps in Trevithick's life story that many publications, the media and the World Wide Web have tended to fill with unfounded assumptions and errors. So prevalent have these inaccuracies become and so easy is it now to publish and replicate such myths that many of the reported high points in the life of Trevithick are based upon unsubstantiated legend, romanticism and conjecture. This means the Trevithick most people know is a fictitious character, but that is the case with many people in history.

Some authors have made remarks that they may have withdrawn. For instance, Trevithick's 1804 railway locomotive is described as 'of a very primitive design'.[1] It is not surprising that it was described as 'primitive', it was the very first railway locomotive in the world and it was built a year before the Battle of Trafalgar in which Admiral Lord Nelson sailed his wooden flagship propelled by the wind. While that author gives the impression that Trevithick's design and workmanship were crude, the technology was incredibly advanced for the day. With the benefit of hindsight, Trevithick's boiler design was sometimes described as inefficient. Those critics overlooked his patent of 1815 for a tubular, super heated boiler and that of 1832 in which he comprehensively established this advanced form of power.[2]

I have been advised that this book is longer than it need be; that may well be the case but you have bought it in full knowledge of the fact and I trust you will enjoy reading it to the end. My purpose has been to provide you with evidence that has hitherto lain dormant and offer some reason for its significance. Sometimes that is not easy, but we must separate what is important from a lot of chaff. I have not attempted to write a biography of Trevithick but have tried to link the facts I have found in a form that will enable readers to draw their own conclusions. Many characters appear on the following pages, most live concurrent lives but not all are acquainted with each other. This means that it is virtually impossible to write a story that flows like a novel from beginning to end. I have, therefore, divided the book into three main sections and trust that you will be able to combine these in your mind.

This story of Trevithick's life cannot be told without examining those of a number of people who appear from time to time, many of whom were unknown to the inventor. These people were generally divided into two groups. The first was composed of his family and others who appreciated his ability and tolerated his shortcomings; they were willing to support and encourage him. The second saw his ability but, under the cloak of friendliness, were keen to capitalise on it for the benefit of their interests. When assessing Trevithick's life we should adopt his view of the things he saw as important; by doing so we will be able to follow the significant development of the steam engine. It could be fairly said that Trevithick was 'driven by his engine' and that all his decisions were connected to its progress and application. We also speculate whether Trevithick truly appreciated what his friends did for him, sometimes we wonder if he even noticed.

In the following pages, we meet Richard Trevithick's father, also called Richard and John Harvey, a far-sighted Cornish blacksmith who founded Harvey's Foundry at Hayle and became Trevithick's father-in-law. There is Harvey's son Henry, who played a great part in Trevithick's life but whose kindness was never fully acknowledged. Trevithick's relatives include his wife, Jane, who was Henry's sister and his cousin Andrew Vivian, who would do as much as he could for Trevithick but also appears to have not been appreciated. Jane's brother-in-law, William West, was a skilled craftsman who helped Trevithick until he became tired of his annoying ways.

Then we break away from the main characters in Trevithick's family to meet Davies Giddy (to become Davies Gilbert later in life) who answered Trevithick's torrent of technical questions, was a Member of Parliament, scholar, Fellow, later President of the Royal Society and friend of Humphry Davy. Gilbert also tried to impose his will and scholarship on Jonathan Hornblower, Junior, and Thomasin Dennis. Gilbert had a number of friends including Dr Beddoes and his fiery wife Anna. Many engineers came into Trevithick's life and Français Auguste Vuille, later to become Don Francisco Uville, arrived from Peru. Of course, the lives of James Watt, his business partner Matthew Boulton and their engineer, William Murdoch, are examined in relationship to Trevithick and, like Davies Gilbert, they have a section of this book to themselves.

Technical details of the steam engine can be found in numerous books and are avoided here. There are some explanations of the significant improvements to be found in Trevithick's design over the failings of those who preceded him and, in some cases, followed him. There has been the opportunity to mention some people whose contribution to early steam has, like Trevithick's, been either overlooked or misrepresented.

So much has been written about Cornwall's steam engineering and its manufacturing industries that it has been impossible to consult it all. To reduce the amount of repeated fiction there has been in recent years research has been restricted to publications prior to the mid-nineteenth century where most have a purity that is subsequently missing elsewhere. More recent works have been used where the author has simply not relied on hearsay and imagination. People's memories deteriorated over the years and became more disappointing than they cared to admit.

The main source of information about Trevithick has been the biography written by his son, Francis and published in 1872. It has been used by everyone and there are comments about the book along the way. It is a good source of technical knowledge and has been used for that purpose. 'Most biographies are written with intent either to make the man a demigod or else to damn him as a rogue who has hoodwinked the world.'[3] That may well be the case.

It was, of course, impossible to study the period without coming across the industrious and resourceful works of Samuel Smiles who set about recording the activities and lives of the engineers and others. From his research and imagination Smiles has provided storytellers with a solid base of information that we are unlikely to find elsewhere. John Griffiths, author of *The 3rd Man,* an account of William Murdoch's life, says, 'Nor was Smiles one to spoil an 'improving story' by taking too much notice of the facts … his life of Watt did most to authenticate the myths'.[4]

There are some assumptions based on the facts but these have been made clear. In many cases the factual revelations might be more interesting than the legends.

There is kindness and unkindness, both of which are deserved. As it is often the case where people only seek sensationalism, the kindness will probably pass unobserved. I have set out to write the truth and, as Dr John Paris said in his biography of Sir Humphry Davy, 'I am writing history, not a eulogy'. I am sure there are those who will wish to add more facts and their own conclusions; they are very welcome to do so and I hope this may only be the beginning of our search for that intriguing subject, 'The truth about Trevithick'.

Philip Marrack Hosken
Marek Resruth
2011

References

'SB Papers' refers to the copious notes made by the late Stephen Buckland, moliere, during his many years of extensive but mainly un-indexed study of Trevithick's activities. They are held by the Trevithick Society, Cornwall, UK. CRO: Cornwall Record Office, RCM/RIC: Royal Cornwall Museum, ODNB: Oxford Dictionary of National Biography.

1. http://en.wikipedia.org/wiki/Richard_Trevithick.
2. *Life of Trevithick* Volume 2 Francis Trevithick 1872 p 380
3. *Gainsborough* Elbert Hubbard 1902 pp 73 & 84.
4. *The 3rd Man* John Griffiths p 349

Acknowledgements
I am grateful for the assistance I have received from so many people whilst researching this book. I am particularly appreciative to all those people who also said that this book had to be written. If I have left you out of this list I do apologise but, believe me, I am grateful.

Sean Croft; John Day; John & Ann Dickinson; Richard Green; Roger Harris; Vivian Hony; Susan W. Howard, USA; Peter Jones; Peter Joseph; Mary Mills; Sheila Oats; Barrie Osborne; Dr Sanjay Rana; Kingsley Rickard; staffs at Cornwall Studies Centre, Redruth, the Cornwall Record Office and the Courtney Library, Royal Institution of Cornwall, Truro, the Maritime Museum, Falmouth and the Dartford Museum; Dr Mike Still; Brian Sullivan; David Thomas; Martin Thompson; Graham Thorne, Michael Tonking; Robert Vale; Dr Ian Weslake-Hill; Colin Wheeler.

The assistance of the Quiller-Couch Memorial Fund is gratefully acknowledged.

Introduction

While the high-pressure steam engine has served mankind for many generations its true inventor is barely known. Here we will examine the man who provided the means to power industries and transport during the crucial century in which access to steam power changed the world, the Victorian Age when the British Empire became a financial and military power.

While Thomas Newcomen and James Watt provided the initial engines for the Industrial Revolution it was Richard Trevithick's ingenuity that supplied most of its power. This is not an account of Trevithick's many inventions; there are already sufficient books to explain his outstanding contribution. Here we hope to discover what sort of man he was, how he lived his life, how he was treated and how he reacted to other people. We will seek to answer the hoary question why he was overlooked for so long.

Against a background of inventive genius there are stories of faith and deceit. There is no trial so only the reader can decide whether there has been any injustice. When apportioning blame for the oblivion of Trevithick few people in this book are innocent; even Trevithick must bear some of the blame; but what of the others? Was there a determination to ensure that he never received recognition or did he simply not blend with the establishment?

Much has already been written about Trevithick's ability and character. Those who praise the former invariably go on to criticise the latter. Praise and criticism are usually based on comparison with the achievements and failings of others. Often one hears the easily applied criticism that Trevithick was 'his own worst enemy'. Anyone who could be so described is unlikely to have the ability to do anything about it.

At the conclusion of a lengthy article on the advantages of high-pressure, expansive steam and its application in Cornish pumping engines, the following paragraph, repeated later this book, stated in 1839,

> It is not unaccountable that oblivion should often encloud the memory of the greatest practical geniuses, for their early labours are hidden in the obscurity of the study or the workshop, and then, after battling against the efforts of the malignant, or the immovable resistance of solidarity, the inventor is long dead before the contest is ended, or his works are successfully established … Often, too, where a name survives, we are led to distrust, when, like that of an Arkwright, it has supplanted the rightful owner.[5]

Because Trevithick never made a fortune from his inventions many storytellers find it easy to pillory him as a failure. Trevithick's brilliance, determination and fortitude are frequently overlooked as writers attribute the appearance of his remarkable locomotives on road and rail to others. They then adopt the familiar theme of repetitive writers by castigating him for not having become a wealthy man who cared better for his family.

It would be fair to say that those who know something of Trevithick hold the view that he was an exceedingly clever man with a fixation about the possibilities of steam as the power to drive virtually everything. That quality is combined with an obsession about the operational ability of his engine and his almost total lack of interest in anything else. In many ways his exploits and character were exemplary, a role model for many young Cornishmen. We have not found any examples in his character of unfaithfulness, deception, financial irregularity, brutality, drunkenness or the whole host of over-indulgent failings that one could attribute to many famous people, some of whom are found on these pages.

Writers have portrayed James Watt as having invented and then developed the steam engine and locomotive. Many have also supposed that it was Watt's alleged belligerent nature, accredited to him during his years in Cornwall, which had excluded Trevithick from his place in the history of steam engine development. Watt, who it is true, had little time for Trevithick, Cornwall or Cornish folk in general, barely stood in Trevithick's way and that it was trusted sources much nearer to Trevithick's home who struck the most damaging blows. Furthermore, many of those same people and James Watt junior contributed much of the myth surrounding Watt's achievements.

One thing becomes very clear as the stories unravel; other than Watt's improvements to the atmospheric engine, the design and development of steam engines was almost entirely a West Country province until the manufacture of Trevithick-type engines was expanded throughout the world.

Most inventors disappear into obscurity as their creations fail to work or are replaced by more successful designs. This was not the case with Trevithick's effort. His was the invention that alone replaced the work of others; it was the machine that Man had sought for a thousand years, it was the definitive design, it performed from the outset and has been copied profusely to this day.

We have to be grateful that we are looking at a period in history when it was customary to communicate by letter and to retain those letters. Hand-written letters had become a sophisticated form of correspondence and in each one the observer can detect shades of the writer's education, beliefs and mood; the truth is not always found. The writers enjoyed finding eloquent ways of expressing personal feelings and compliments, or displaying the lack of both. That is something that is sadly absent from the temporal electronic and throwaway paper communications of today.

The following pages will contain a fresh look at the life of Trevithick. They will question, and maybe answer, how he managed to achieve so much and yet was still seeking fulfilment at the end.

The reader may be confused by the repetition of names. We immediately come across two Richard Trevithicks, there were more but they do not play a significant part in the story. There were two John Trevithicks who were mysteriously missing from Francis's biography, two prominent William Wests and a couple of John Harveys. Then there were the two Jonathan Hornblowers in a family that was designed to confuse, a pair of John Halls, two Andrew Vivians in a family full of Johns, two Matthew Boultons, a couple of James Watts and a few more; it is very confusing and not surprising that there have been mistakes. The Harveys, who feature in the administration of Harvey & Co. after the death of Henry Harvey, were not his descendants but those of his sister Anne who married a John Harvey from Helston; he was no relation although he bore the same name as her father. Her husband John was in association with a mercer called Nicholas Harvey of Helston, who was also not believed to be a relative and is not the Nicholas Owen Harvey who is mentioned later. Authors frequently muddle these characters and history suffers.

As a rough guide to values, using the Retail Price Index, £100 in 1800 would be a little more than £5,000 two centuries later, *i.e.*, multiply any figure by 50. This does not apply to financial income or property values where the multiplier is about 800. See www.measuringworth.com

References

5.   *The Civil Engineer & Architect's Journal*, March 1839, pp 93-96.

I   The background to the steam engine

The 'power of steam'

While earlier writers usually referred to the use of steam in various inventions, it was not until the nineteenth century, when inventors and writers began to appreciate how steam under pressure could be safely employed that the phrase 'the power of steam' truly came into being. Unfortunately, it was applied retrospectively to engines that did not use 'the power of steam' in their operation. In particular, accounts about the achievements of Newcomen and Watt, who were the first to devise engines that we would recognise, never claimed that they were using steam as a powerful force. In his early days Watt talked about exerting the pressure of steam on a piston but avoided actually doing it; and it is doubtful if it even occurred to Newcomen. It may come as a surprise to some readers to know that the steam employed in the engines designed by Newcomen and Watt only became useful when it was cooled, condensed and returned to water, then atmospheric pressure could be used. In 1797 Matthew Boulton, Watt's partner, wrote to his agent in Truro complaining about Trevithick, saying that he,

> … continue to erect his Atmospher Engines & most strenuously asserted that he could work them cheaper than ours under the terms required by us.[6]

The early inventors spoke of 'fire' engines and knew better than many of the writers who followed that they were using 'the power of the atmosphere' to work their engines. Steam was not being used, as it would be in post-Trevithick days, as a means to transfer power but to create a vacuum. It was only with the arrival of Trevithick with a boiler that could successfully and safely produce high-pressure steam that we can sensibly employ the phrase, 'the power of steam'. Then, as Trevithick prophesied, 'everything becomes possible'.

In order that we may better understand the stories of success and failure in steam engine design it will be necessary to explain what we commonly refer to as 'steam'. Steam is an invisible gas that only exists at or above 100° Celsius and usually under pressure. What we see coming out of a kettle or steam locomotive is condensed steam, or 'water vapour'. Steam has remarkable properties that were little understood a couple of centuries ago. It was well known that water could be boiled to produce something that could 'do work' and, if it were out of control, it could have very damaging consequences, even causing death.

Before Trevithick showed how this amazing gas could be controlled it appeared to have a will of its own, something that God-fearing people viewed with foreboding. In many cases the mysterious activities within a vessel and pipework designed to hold steam would frighten the public as they saw the gas escaping in an ethereal cloud. It is no coincidence that the vessels were believed to hold the Devil and that Trevithick's first steam locomotive was described by a woman in Camborne as a 'Puffing Devil'. Steam was developed against a background of public suspicion where daring steam engineers practised the black arts of their alchemy and were known as philosophers.

There is the apocryphal story[7] frequently told of Trevithick and his cousin Andrew Vivian arriving at a toll gate one night. The toll-keeper, when asked how much they would have to pay is reputed to have said, "Na-noth-nothing to pay! My de-dear Mr Devil, do drive on as fast as you can! Nothing to pay". A doubtful story but it would not exist if it were not for the superstitions prevalent at the time.

Because the Chinese invented gunpowder and paper in the distant past, there have been some inevitable suggestions that they also invented the steam engine. Joseph Needham, CH, FRS, who went to extreme lengths to prove Chinese originality in all things,[8] has failed to find any conclusive proof of this and although he alluded to "that strange episode when Jesuit mechanicians put a model steam turbine locomotive through its paces in the palace gardens of the Khang-Si emperor about 1671,"[9] he only adds another model or drawing to the multitude of inventors' dreams that have littered engineering history. Although one might be forgiven for thinking that he was short on evidence, Needham was prepared to suggest in a diagram that the 'Chinese double-acting single-cylinder piston-pump' directly influenced Trevithick. It would have required a series of practical applications en route for the steam engine to travel westwards and to arrive in Europe before the time we are studying.[10] There is every indication that it was late in the 18th Century that the Chinese learnt about practical European steam engines.

Steam was used in Egypt and Greece to drive toys or items of curiosity. It was from about 1600 AD that it began to have any real purpose. Most ideas were European and the descriptions or illustrations, even the patent drawings that are available frequently describe a dream; there were few actual applications. Giambattista della Porta, 1538-1615, a philosopher in Naples demonstrated atmospheric pressure in a laboratory by drawing water into a flask after first filling it with steam and then allowing it to condense.[11]

Dr Dionysius (Denys) Papin 1647 – 1712
It is said that by watching the pressure release valve on his cooker rhythmically move up and down, he conceived of the steam engine.

As with many inventions, the steam engine came at the end of a long line of contributory developments, each one opened people's mind a little further. One was the Magdeburg hemi-spheres invented by Otto von Guericke 1602-1686, a German, in 1650. His vacuum pump and two hemispheres demonstrated the power of a vacuum. Denys Papin, a French

17

Denys Papin.

Huguenot who fled to England in 1658 and was made a Fellow of the Royal Society in 1680, together with Robert Boyle, FRS, 1627-1691, who worked with him, were amongst the first to put the pressure developed by steam to some practical use. Papin, who had previously used compressed air, steam and explosives to pump water from nines, invented his steam digester, or pressure cooker, in 1679. After some serious mishaps, he wisely invented the safety valve. Boyle's work on the pressure of gas is known by the law named after him. It was Guericke and Papin who provided us with the fundamentals of the earliest steam engines: vacuum and pressure. In 1648 Bishop John Wilkins of Chester was the first Englishman to mention the possibility that a machine might be moved by the elastic pressure of steam. The bishop was half-brother to Walter Pope, the astronomer, a remarkable man who also wrote of submarines and aeroplanes in his *Mathematical Magick*. Being a Bishop he was seen as having connections with a Higher Being so his thoughts were not for general discussion.[12] There was much fundamental work to be done and the description by Edward Somerset, the Marquis of Worcester, of an alleged frightful explosion did much to stimulate fear of the Devil existing in boiling water.

Papin's 'steam digester'. *Wikipedia.*

The Marquis of Worcester, 1601-1667,
The flamboyant Marquis is frequently overlooked although there is the belief that he conceived the engine frequently attributed to Savery. He clearly understood the power of steam under pressure and remarked on the necessity for vessels to be strongly built. He must also have built some kind of engine to his design as he refers to water being pumped forty feet in the air.

The Marquis wrote in his, *A century of the names and scantlings of such inventions as at present I can call to mind to have tried and perfected which (my former notes being lost) I have, at the instance of a powerful friend, endeavored now, in the year 1655, to set these down in such a way, as may sufficiently instruct me to put any of them to practice.* A snappy title, published in 1663,

I have invented an admirable and forcible way to draw up water by fire; not by drawing or sucking it upwards, for that must be, as the philosopher terms it, *infra sphoeram activitatis,* which is but at such a distance; but this way hath no bounder, if the vessel is strong enough. For I have taken a piece of a whole cannon, whereof the end was burst, and filled it three quarters full of water, stopping and screwing up the broken end, as also the touch-hole, and making a constant fire under it: within twenty-fours hours it burst, and made a great crack.

So that having a way to make my vessels, so that they are strengthened by the force within them, and the one to fill after the other, I have seen the water run like a constant stream forty feet high.

One vessel of water rarefied by fire, driveth up forty of cold water; and a man that tends the work has but to turn two cocks; that one vessel of water being consumed, another begins to force and refill with cold water, and so successively; the fire being tended and kept constant, which the self same person may likewise abundantly perform in the interim between the necessity of turning said cocks.[13]

Tradition has preserved nothing on this subject, but there is an anecdote that described the Marquis's attention having been drawn to steam causing the lid of a vessel to rise when he was confined in the Tower of London.[14] This story is frequently attributed to James Watt. Historian Robinson Buchanan even described it as apocryphal when attributed to the Marquis.[15] D. P. Miller of the University of New South Wales overlooks the above and explores the myth at length having found a reference to it in Watt's notes.[16]

The inventors who sought to employ the little understood property of contained steam frequently put themselves in danger. Many who knew of the Marquis's experiment considered that there was something else in the cannon alongside the water to cause such destruction. Little was known of the pressures created by the Marquis in his cannon but it was clear that if a small quantity of steam could burst the thick iron sides of a cannon, the possibilities of building a boiler with iron walls thick enough to contain sufficient steam under pressure to drive an engine was considered virtually impossible.

This dangerous situation was well appreciated by Watt who is certain to have heard of the Marquis and others. He explored high-pressure steam and his adventures with an iron bound boiler made of wooden staves probably frightened him. It must have been at this stage that Watt, a timid man who sought to avoid trouble, thought that high-pressure steam was beyond the reach of man and vowed never to use it. Throughout his working life and in the following years, the company associated with his name did not build even moderately pressurised steam engines until long after his death. This was in spite of the influence of his engineer, William Murdoch, who clearly felt comfortable with the force.

Sir Isaac Newton, 1642 – 1727

Many people had dreams of using steam to power industry and transport. One was a design by Sir Isaac Newton who demonstrated his Third Law of Motion, 'that for every action there is an equal and opposite reaction' by designing a steam jet car in 1680. Of course, he did not have the materials or expertise to successfully construct such a vehicle but this illustrates how the cleverest in the land were foiled in their attempts to produce a self-propelled carriage.

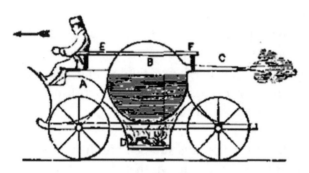

Newton's steam jet car.

Thomas Savery, 1650 – 1715

Captain Thomas Savery, FRS, was a military engineer and trench master. We see him as a prolific, forceful inventor from Modbury, near Plymouth, Devon who, in 1698, took out a patent on an engine 'for Raiseing of Water and … Drayning Mines'.[17] Known as *The Miners' Friend* it is interesting to note how many inventions were applied to mining. It was a difficult contrivance that was intended to work on both atmospheric and steam pressure without the use of a piston. While a small model may have worked very well in a demonstration to King William III at Hampton Court, the prospect of raising any quantity of water to a significant height was clearly out of the question.

To pump water from a mine it was necessary to install the Savery engine, boiler and furnace at some depth below ground where the operation would have been both difficult and dangerous. It would have been impossible in a coal mine. John Farey said that he used a boiler made of wooden staves .[18]

One of its failings was the requirement for steam under pressure but the lack of a suitable boiler or steam tight joints between the pipes was a distinct drawback. Savery is understood to be the first to install a Papin-type 'steelyard' safety valve on the boiler of a steam engine. An attempt to drain a large pond in Staffordshire revealed the engine's shortcomings.

> The engine thus erected could not be brought to perfection, as the old pond of water was very great; ... and the steam when too strong tore it to pieces; so that after much time, labour and expense, Mr Savery was forced to give up the undertaking, and the engine was laid aside as useless.[19]

The Rev. John Theophilus Desaguliers, 1683-1744, another Huguenot who came to England and was made a FRS, described the problems he witnessed in London,

> I have seen Captain *Savery* at *York*-Buildings make steam eight or ten times stronger than Common Air; and then its heat was so great, that it would melt common soft Solder; and its Strength was so great as to blow open several of the Joints of his Machine: so that he was forced to be at great Pains and Charge to have all his Joints solder'd with Spelter or hard Solder.[20]

Desaguliers also had some fundamental doubts whether Savery had actually invented the engine or whether he had obtained the idea from the Marquis of Worcester.[21]

While Savery's engine is mentioned frequently in books about steam engines, the abundance of excellent drawings and descriptions do more to explain the use of atmospheric pressure than the engine ever did to draw water. The verb *pump* is often used incorrectly nowadays instead of *draw*, there was no mechanical pumping action in the Savery engine although the text frequently creates an impression of the water pump we know today. H. W. Dickinson doubted if a Savery engine was ever installed in a mine although, as mentioned above, one was used to lift water from the River Thames to York Buildings in the Strand. This 'was liable to so many disorders if a single mistake happened in the working of it, that at length it was looked upon as a useless piece of work and rejected'.[22]

Had Savery been content to restrict his engine's operations to the drawing of water and not attempted to raise it further by steam pressure he might have been much more successful. However, his interesting book written in 1702 has provided subsequent authors with possibly over-stated, material which is now found in every steam engine history book. His lack of success with high-pressure steam could well have been a deciding factor for the achievement of Newcomen's atmospheric pumping engine.

The past few pages may have conveyed something of the anguish faced by just a few of those who sought to place the power of steam and atmosphere at the command of Man.

Thomas Newcomen, 1663 - 1729

It would be another Devon man, Thomas Newcomen, 1663--1729, generally recorded as a blacksmith but with one significant description of him as a whitesmith[23] from Dartmouth, one who makes objects from white metal, often tin. The Science Museum calls him an ironmonger. Whatever he was, he had the vision to build the first practical machine that we would recognise and mistakenly describe as a steam engine. Newcomen employed a piston in a cylinder to separate the steam from atmospheric pressure and used a practical pump at the other end of a beam to lift the water. Because of the wide patent taken out by Savery, Newcomen was forced into partnership with him. The use of wide patent protection was subsequently employed by James Watt but it was something on which Trevithick failed to capitalise.

Contemporary illustration of a Newcomen engine.

Although Newcomen's first engine is widely reported as operating at Dudley Castle, Staffordshire in 1712, Joseph Carne, in his paper on the mining of copper in Cornwall[24] tells of one at Wheal Vor, Breage where it worked from 1710 to 1714. Whatever the situation, it is clear from other records that Newcomen's remarkable[25] pumping engines were soon to appear in large quantities performing the essential work of pumping the mines throughout Cornwall. So great was the impact of these pumps and other machinery on the mining industry that, at the time, Cornwall was described as "one of the most advanced engineering centres of the world".[26] Newcomen's engine was not limited to Cornwall. By 1769 ninety-nine were reported to be in use throughout the North of England. The age of the engine had arrived.

Newcomen was a Baptist lay preacher.[27] In 1700, Humphrey Potter built his first Baptist church at Bromsgrove and, on his death, bequeathed the church to its trustees, the first of whom was Thomas Newcomen. It is believed that it was at this church that Newcomen first made the acquaintance of the Potter and Hornblower families who would erect his engines throughout the length of the country with Joseph Hornblower starting as early as 1712.

Newcomen died of fever while on a visit to London and is buried in Finsbury but his grave is unknown. Dickinson suggests that he derived very little pecuniary advantage from his invention.[28]

The operation of the Newcomen engine was remarkably well described by John Hulls in 1736 when he took out a patent to operate a boat by means of a Newcomen steam engine.

> He proposed to employ his steamboat in towing. In 1737 he published a well-written pamphlet, describing this apparatus, which is shown in Fig. 66G, a reduced fac-simile of the plate accompanying his paper. He proposed using the Newcomen engine, fitted with a counterpoise weight and a system of ropes and grooved wheels, which, by a peculiar ratchet-like action, gave a continuons rotary motion. His vessel was to have been used as a tow-boat. He says, in his description: "In some convenient part of the Tow-boat there is placed a Vessel about two-3rds full of water, with the Top closed; and this Vessel being kept Boiling, rarifies the Water into a Steam, this Steam being convey'd thro' a large pipe into a cylindrical Vessel, and there condensed, makes a Vacuum, which causes the weight of the atmosphere to press down on this Vessel and so presses down a Piston that is fitted into this Cylindrical Vessel, in the same manner as in Mr Newcomen's engine, with which he raises Water by Fire".[29]

Note the description of the creation of steam within the boiler vessel, the cylinder, the condensation, the vacuum, the action of the atmospheric pressure to press down the piston within the cylinder and the raising of water by fire. There was no mention of the 'power of steam'. It is not thought that Hulls built this ship but he may have constructed a model.

For over half a century the Newcomen engines made deep mining practical but they were exceptionally expensive to operate. The cooling of the cylinder each time the steam condensed meant it had to be re-heated to boiling point again to hold the next charge of steam. The mighty Newcomen engines surrounded the birthplace of Richard Trevithick in 1771 and they served the Cornish mining industry well, if uneconomically, for half a century.

Nicolas Joseph Cugnot, 1725 -1804

While Trevithick can be credited with having built the world's first successful steam carriages and railway locomotives, it was the French inventor who built two steam traction units in the Paris Arsenal, one in 1769 and another two years later. Their performance was limited by their weight and design and they barely travelled any distance. They were the first self-propelled steam carriages. Lord Montagu provides us with an extensive account of the vehicle's engineering, questions whether the exhibited boiler is the original and states that the stories of Cugnot's *fardier à vapour* being confiscated and its owner imprisoned 'are flights of the purest fancy'.[30]

James Watt, 1736 - 1819

While James Watt invented a number of things, he only claimed to have improved the Newcomen engine. He did this by condensing the steam elsewhere. In the Watt engine the condensation occurred in a separate cylinder separated by valves from the main engine. The saving was dramatic but the cost to the mine owners was expensive. While they could then operate their mines more efficiently the engines were expensive and Watt charged a premium on their savings; it would never be an amicable situation. James Watt introduced his first engine to Cornwall in 1777 when Trevithick was six years old.

There is a significant difference between the Watt engine and Trevithick's that followed it. Watt did not use the high-pressure steam we associate with the steam engine. He said,

> It is never advisable to work with a strong steam when it can be avoided as it increases the leakages of the boiler and joints of the steam case and answers no good end.[31]

Watt is supposed to have avoided overseas sales because of the lack of patent protection. However, we will see his years of work in Holland and several instances like this one in France.

There is the excellent but unrewarded work of nobleman Claude-François-Dorothée, Marquis de Jouffroy d'Abbaus, 1751 – 1832, who built a model steam boat in 1776 and, after visiting the demonstration of a Watt engine in Paris, a full-sized 140′ boat of 150 tons displacement that he successfully demonstrated on the Sâone at Lyons in 1783. Although the boat ran successfully for eighteen months, he was refused financial support from the L'Académie Française. He retired in 1831 to Hôtel des Invalides, a home for old soldiers where he died of cholera, a poor, disappointed man. The detail in reports varies but Claude-François-Dorothée is credited with successfully building and operating the first steam boat and a statue was erected to him at Besançon in 1884.

Richard Trevithick, 1771 – 1833

While the inventions of Richard Trevithick appear later in these pages, it would be wise to explain the important differences between his engine and those that preceded it; the technology was very different.

Trevithick's contribution to the advance of Man was the design of a successful, high-pressure steam boiler and the creation of an engine that depended on it. His did this, not as two separate components but in a compact, single unit. As this had not been previously achieved, it had been regarded as impossible. Trevithick cut through the convoluted thinking of Hornblower to produce an essentially simple engine that depended solely on high-pressure steam and did away with a second cylinder and condenser. The arrival of this entirely fresh, effective machine was due in great part to the craftsmanship of his father-in-law, John Harvey who created the boiler, the product of Trevithick's optimistically febrile mind, in cast iron. Watt could only see disaster and he responded accordingly.

The significant heart of this engine is not the piston within a cylinder, which had been done before, but the boiler. Today we take the cylindrical boiler for granted, we expect all steam engine boilers to be round but, before Trevithick, they were not. By designing a cylindrical boiler to retain the high-pressure steam and then inserting the cylinder and piston within the boiler, Trevithick created a compact, self-contained engine that avoided leaking pipework. This radical change in engine design necessitated a number of innovations to make it work satisfactorily. The furnace, which had always been placed beneath the flat base of the atmospheric boiler, had to be inserted within it. The water level in the boiler would fall as the steam was consumed and a high pressure pump with a non-return valve had to be incorporated into the action of the engine to maintain the water level. Trevithick included a number of other features to his engine such as a pre-heater for boiler water, a blast pipe and, later, a fusible plug. These items enabled the engine to operate independently of peripheral equipment, making it suitable for transport use.

We see throughout history that many people receive the credit for something that should really be that of another whose hard work and perseverance deserved better treatment.

Model of steamship, built in 1784 by Claude de Jouffroy *(see opposite). Wikimedia.*

References

6.   *Boulton &Watt Papers* 6 December 1797

7.   *The Mining Almanac for 1849* Hyde Clarke pp304-5

8.   *Science and Civilisation in China* J. Needham

9.   *Forbidden City* conversazione of 1671 J. B. du Halde

10. *The Pre-Natal history of the steam engine* J. Needham. Transactions of the Newcomen Society, Volume 35, pp3-58 (1962) and *Mechanical engineering.* Part 2 of *Physics and physical technology*, 1965 and Volume 4 of *Science, and civilisation in China*

11. *A Short History of the Steam Engine* H. W. Dickinson, 1938, p4

12. *Bishop Wilkins on Submarines & Aeroplanes, 1648.* J. F. Fuller, 1917

13. *Century of Inventions,* 1683 p12

14. *A Treatise on Propelling Vessels by Steam* Robertson Buchanan, CE, Glasgow 1816, p16

15. *Stuart's descriptive history of the steam engine.* Robinson Buchanan p17

16. *True Myths, James Watt ... his chemistry.* D. P. Miller p333-347

17. *A Short History of the Steam Engine.* H. W. Dickinson, 1938, p20

18. *A Treatise on the Steam Engine,* Volume 2. John Farey p5

19. *History & Antiquities of Staffordshire,* Volume 2, p85

20. *A Course of Experimental Philosophy,* Volume II J. T. Desaguliers pp467, 1743

21. *Links in the history of engineering and technology from Tudor times* Rhys Jenkins, published by the Newcomen Society

22. *Ten Practical Discoveries Concerning Earth & Water'* Richard Bradley, 1727, p33

23. *Lloyds Steamboat Directory,* 1856 p13

24. *Thomas Newcomen,* L. T. C. Rolt p58-9

25. *Power from Steam* R. L. Hills p23

26. *The age of manufactures 1700–1820* M. Berg, 1994, p112

27. *The End of Oil: on the edge of a perilous new world* Paul Roberts, 2005, p21

28. *A Short History of the Steam Engine* Dickinson 1938 p51

29. *A History of the Growth of the Steam Engine, 1800-1850, Chap 5.* R. H. Thurston Lectures of 1878

30. *Steam Cars 1770-1970,* Lord Montagu and Anthony Bird p18

31. *A treatise on the Cornish pumping engine,* Part 1. Wm Pole , p49

II   Boulton & Watt, their families and friends

'There are two names which beyond all questioning have become – and to the end of time will remain – identified with the development of steam power and its practical application. Those names are Matthew Boulton and James Watt.'[32]

So read the opening lines of a review in 1865 of Samuel Smiles' book about the famous couple. No mention is made in the several columns of text how steam engine design had moved on since Boulton & Watt released their stranglehold on its development sixty-five years earlier. However, in the same book there is an elaborate description of the Merryweather fire engine working at 120 lbs per sq inch and winning orders from authorities all over Europe.[33]

Stories of Boulton & Watt's work in the field of steam have been told many times over the years. Here we consider who Watt was and his effect on Trevithick. Was he the thorn in his side that accounted for Trevithick not being recognised in the world of steam power? Did the two men cross swords as many writers would have us believe and was Watt's sojourn in Cornwall to stunt Trevithick's progress? Was the relationship between Watt and Boulton something that Trevithick should have tried to emulate? Two other men of significance in this story were Watt's engineer, William Murdoch, and Jonathan Hornblower, Junior.

Matthew Boulton, 1728 – 1809

Many of those who study the evolution of the steam engine see the partnership of Boulton & Watt as the ideal base upon which industrial power was built. Watt is frequently perceived as the remarkable inventor while Boulton is the necessary, financially astute, solid foundation that enabled Watt's designs to reach fruition; they are shown working as a team, creating an unassailable regime that did nothing but make money. Little could be further from the truth. Boulton's nature and attitude were much closer to those of Trevithick. His responses to challenges and his wayward financial decisions were sheltered from disaster by the good fortune of being born into a circle where his associations brought him favours. He had a financial base that provided his initial cash and enabled him to borrow even more money. The fact that Boulton's struggling partnerships eventually ended in success is often seen as a vindication of his business methods. That view does not take into account how haphazard his administration was and how close he had come to destroying the whole enterprise throughout his life. It could be said that Boulton enjoyed good fortune and spent a great deal of it unwisely.

Boulton's life is well documented and several books refer to the way in which his company led large scale manufacturing in Birmingham. Here we are only concerned with Boulton's effect on Watt, the inventor's subsequent state of mind and how it may have affected his relationship with Trevithick, the Cornish mine owners and other inventors. J. E. Cule carefully examined the commercial operation of Boulton's enterprises and wrote in 1940,

> In short, the overall manufacturing operations at Soho were run in what can only be described as a spectacularly disorganised manner. Insufficient attention was given to overseeing the workforce, to ensure that products were priced at a level which would make them profitable, to monitoring and controlling stock, and to recovering payments owed from sales – particularly from customers abroad.
>
> Matthew Boulton's frequent absences from Soho to court prospective customers, and his propensity to veer off into launching new business enterprises, also both caused and exacerbated the failings of the manufacturing operations. Above all, the partners were saddled with huge debts arising from the building of the Soho Manufactory, which forced them to borrow heavily to keep their enterprise going. By 1773 Fothergill considered their financial situation to be serious enough for him to suggest that they should cease trading.
>
> For Boulton, a man with huge ambition and unswerving determination, such a course of action was unthinkable; his response was to raise further loans to keep the toy business afloat, support his diversion into manufacturing silver and ormolu* wares, and allow investment in a new commercial venture, namely the steam-engine enterprise with Watt.[34]

Matthew Boulton had been born in 1728 into the long-established, landed and respected Anglican family of Matthew Boulton senior, a reputable manufacturer of small personal accessories known at the time as 'Brummagem toys'. He joined his father in business at the age of fourteen. By 1749, at the age of 21 he had married Mary Robinson, the elder daughter of a wealthy mercer in the year of her father's death. She died in 1759 shortly before Boulton's father and he inherited substantial estates from both of them.

He was now in charge of a prosperous business and controversially married his deceased wife's wealthy sister within the year. She also inherited another share of their father's fortune when her brother Luke died barely four years later. Prior to the passing of the Married Women's Property Act in 1870-82, a woman's possessions became those of her husband on marriage. Boulton's financial position was now secure and he was able to raise further capital.

---

* Ormolu is an attractive alloy of copper, zinc and tin used in the manufacture of lower cost ornaments.

He sold most of his father's property and the Patkington estate that had come to him from his first wife for a further £15,000. By raising another £3,000 on mortgages, he was able to tackle a considerable expansion of the family business. In 1761 he leased thirteen acres of land at Soho, Birmingham and, driven by his 'boundless energy and ambition', commenced an extensive building programme that would include a Mint for the striking of coin. At that time Birmingham employed 20,000 people in the manufacture of inexpensive items such as buttons and buckles. Its turnover of £600,000 a year included £500,000 from export sales. Boulton set his sights on higher things and went into partnership with John Fothergill who invested a further £5,000 into the enterprise and travelled extensively, selling their wares on the Continent.

Boulton was anxious to improve the quality of the company's products and developed extensive ranges of silver and ormolu that sold well. Boulton and Fothergill became the largest producers of expensive ormolu in the country but, in spite of the remarkable increase in sales, an examination of its records reveals the company failed to be profitable. Fothergill, who had suggested that the business should close, ceased to be a trouble to Boulton when he died in 1782 and Boulton found another partner in John Scale. Matters continued much as before with Boulton entertaining his aristocratic clients and providing them with an ever-widening product range of high quality, fashionable ware paying little attention to manufacturing costs.[35] There is a record of Boulton having obtained £2,000 from Elliot & Praed, bankers in Truro.[36]

In order to understand fully how Watt's position within the partnership affected his attitude, it is necessary to read what he wrote to Boulton in March 1782 after Fothergill had died insolvent and he worried about meeting their debts. Watt considered selling his share and returning to a simpler, less worrisome way of life.

> The want of the superfluities of life is a trifle compared with continual anxiety. I do not see how you can pay Lowe, Vere and Williams £1,000 per quarter. I am sure it cannot be from the engine business unless we can reduce the amount of our general expenses to 0 and live upon air ourselves. Though you and I should entirely lose this business and all its profits you will get quit of a burdensome debt and as both of us lived before it had a being so we may do afterwards. Therefore consider what can be done and do it without reluctance or with as little as you can and depend upon it that I am sincerely your friend and shall push you to nothing that I do not think to be for our advantage.

A couple of days later he was still worried and had to say some more,

A hundred hours of melancholy will not pay one farthing of debt. Summon up your fortitute and try to turn your attention to business and to correct the abuses at Soho. All the idlers should be told that in case they persevere in want of attention then dismission must ensue. The Soho part of the business has been somehow a perpetual drain to us and if it cannot be put on a better footing must be cut off altogether by giving out the work to be done by others.[37]

Boulton was a very complicated man who provided for the wife and children of Fothergill but was unable to turn down what he saw as a commercial enterprise. In this he was similar to Trevithick, who could not walk away from an opportunity to demonstrate the ability of his steam engine. While Boulton was away from Soho on business administration fell to the poorly-paid James Keir who said, 'To understand the character of Mr Boulton's mind, it is necessary to recollect that whatever he did or attempted, his successes and his failures were all on a grand scale'.[38] Keir was partly recompensed by being made a partner in Watt's company to exploit his letter-copying machine in 1780.[39]

One of the features of the Soho manufactory and Mint was the hospitality afforded to visitors and, at different times, Gilbert and Trevithick would be amongst the crowds that benefited as they joined the organised tours to examine the company's superb products. On a visit to Soho, Josiah Wedgwood described the factory as 'the first or most complete manufactory in England in metal'.[40]

Boulton's interesting circle of philosophical friends included Erasmus Darwin and broadened to form the Lunar Society, an influential luncheon club that contained many of the powerful people mentioned in these pages. Boulton & Watt were both made Fellows of the Royal Society on the same day in 1785.

Watt, with his steam engines and his strict Calvinist upbringing[41] was a difficult fit into this exotic world of precious metals. From 1761 Boulton had sought a steady supply of water for his manufactory and was developing his own engine with Dr William Small, another of his Lunar Society members, when, in 1768 Small introduced him to Watt.

At that time Watt was being funded by Dr John Roebuck, an English chemist in considerable financial difficulty. When Roebuck became bankrupt in 1773,[42] Boulton took over his position and moved the nervous Watt to Birmingham where they went into partnership the following year.

Boulton saw the potential in Watt's engine and that it required a more accurately made cylinder. He brought in John Wilkinson, 1728 – 1808, an armaments supplier who had developed a cylinder-boring machine for cannon at his Broseley Ironworks in Shropshire.[43]

It would be Watt's name that would go down in history for his work on the improvement of the atmospheric steam engine but it was Boulton's ability to fund the development that made this possible. He saw an opportunity in the beginning and it must have been a relief to them both when the engine was accepted by industry.

James Watt, 1736 – 1819

James Watt's parents, James Watt, Senior and Agnes Muirheid (Muirhead) had five children of whom the three eldest, two sons and a daughter, died in infancy or early childhood. James was the fourth child and his brother John, born in 1739, died on a voyage to America in 1762 leaving James, the remaining child, reported as having an extremely delicate constitution and incapable of taking part in the common sport of boys, and little prepared for those struggles with difficulties which afterwards marked his career.[44]

James Patrick Muirhead, author of *The Life of James Watt with Selections from his Correspondence,* describes himself as a kinsman of the inventor. His maternal grandmother was a first cousin of James Watt. Muirhead married Katherine Elizabeth Boulton, the daughter of Matthew Boulton[45] and he spent a great deal of time with James Watt Junior, becoming the executor of his Will. This gave him an intimate knowledge of the Watt and Boulton families. Muirhead had a hand in a number of publications concerning Watt's story but there appeared to be no reference to Trevithick in any of them. Maybe Trevithick was not the thorn in Watt's side that many would have us believe or his presence and achievements were simply ignored as being of no consequence.

Muirhead reported that, as a young man, Watt was sickly, 'The agony he suffered from continued and violent headaches often affected his nervous system, and left him for days – even weeks – languid, depressed, and fanciful; at those times there was a roughness and asperity in his manner that softened with returning health.'[46]

Cornwall appears frequently in Muirhead's writings but there are no signs that Watt enjoyed his years on the peninsula. He wrote variously to Soho seeking his 'peace of mind and delivery from Cornwall' in 1782 and, later, how he considered 'the districts of Cornwall – a poor exchange, in his opinion, for the intellectual pleasures and hospitable sociality of the neighbourhood of Soho.'[47]

The Muirheids were a proud Scottish family that can be traced back before the reign of David the First of Scotland in 1172 and had the fatal honour of forming the bodyguard to King James IV of Scotland at the bloody Battle of Flodden Field.[48] This stirring story could have sparked Sir Walter Scott's interest in the Watt cause as he became a frequent commentator and supporter. In his *Minstrelsy of the Scottish Border* he preserved the activities of the fallen in his ballad of *The Laird of Muirhead.*

Scott's literary genius has shaped much of what we understand today as Scotland and the Scottish. He could have been described as one of Watt's most ardent fans and he used his skills to describe the engineer's achievements. Here is an example of his work.

In the *Life of James Watt* by Argo, Brougham & Vaux, 1839, Scott, who had died seven years previously, is quoted as saying,

> Amidst this company stood Mr. Watt, the man whose genius discovered the means of multiplying our national resources to a degree, perhaps, even beyond his own stupendous powers of calculation and combination; bringing the treasures of the abyss to the summit of the earth, – giving to the feeble arm of man the momentum of an Afrite*. – commanding manufactures to arise, – affording means of dispensing with that time and tide that waits for no man, – and of sailing without that wind that defied the commands and threats of Xerxes himself. This potent commander of the elements, – this abridger of time and space, – this magician whose cloudy machinery has produced a change in the world, the effects of which, extraordinary as they are, are perhaps only beginning to be felt, was not only the most profound man of sciences, the most successful combiner of powers, and calculator of numbers, – as adapted to practical purposes, – was not only one of the most generally well-informed, but one of the best and kindest of human beings.

Such was the impact of the steam engine when this passage was being written that any observant correspondent would have felt the desire to congratulate whoever was responsible for such a change in the fortunes of mankind. All around Scott there were examples of the profitable use of steam, but he had made one fundamental error. In his phrase, the 'cloudy machinery' he aptly and poetically described the cloudy atmosphere that surrounded steam engines. It is very unlikely that a man of Scott's literary standing would have been referring to the haze of coal smoke that permanently hung over all industrial areas, but to that temporary white cloud of water vapour that identified the operation of a steam engine. Of course, they would not have been Watt's engines; all his worked on the principle of the steam being absorbed into the condenser to create a vacuum. Watt's engines were never 'cloudy'; Scott was mistakenly praising the high-pressure engines developed by Trevithick.[49] The nickname of 'Puffing Jamie' sometimes applied to Watt was a misnomer.

There is a strange link between the fortunes of Scott and the debt crises in Peru.[50] Scott had invested heavily in his printers and publisher. Their failure during the first Latin American debt crises in 1825, that included Peru, left him with debts between £117,000 and £130,000.[51]

* A powerful evil jinnee, demon, or monstrous giant. *Webster's Revised Abridged Dictionary, 1913.*

Watt married his cousin, Margaret Miller in 1764 and theirs was a very happy relationship that encouraged Watt in his work. In 1773, Margaret died whilst expecting their fifth child, leaving Watt with two surviving children, a son and daughter. The boy was James Watt, Junior who would later take his father's place in the engineering company for a few years. Watt, Senior was devastated by the loss of his wife and companion just when his inventive work was showing signs of success.

He worked with a partner called John Craig in the business of making, retailing and repairing small mechanical items such as mathematical and musical instruments, burning glasses, and toys, small metal ornaments made in Birmingham. A particular invention of his was the perspective machine that caught the attention of Dr Erasmus Darwin in 1767. Darwin was the poet and visionary who was grandfather of Charles and foresaw the coming of steam carriages as 'fiery chariots...' Darwin also hoped that Watt was 'well and less hypochondriacal'.[52] It was during this time that Watt was working as a mathematical instrument maker at Glasgow College and famously received a model Newcomen engine for repair from the Professor of Natural Philosophy.[53] He saw the flaw in its design and devised a method to substantially improve its economy and speed of operation. Who had made the legendary Newcomen model engine?

Watt is credited with having created some significant improvements to the long-established but grossly inefficient engines designed by Thomas Newcomen. In 1768 he built a model of his improved engine. The engines of Newcomen and Watt were operated, not by steam, but by atmospheric pressure. For this reason, their power was limited to that of the pressure of the atmosphere and the only way to increase their power was to increase the size of the engine, the condenser and reserves of water coolant. This meant that engines of a reasonable power had to be substantial in size, weight and cost. That Watt should be frequently credited with the construction of compact engines capable of powering railway trains is an example of conjecture based on historical ignorance.

There were those who said that, 'Watt had invented the steam engine thanks to Humphrey Gainsborough'.[54] The Reverend Humphrey Gainsborough, 1718 – 1776, a brother of the famous artist Thomas, was born in Suffolk and became a non-conformist minister and an engineer who invented a sun dial and a tide mill. There are claims that he built a model steam engine with a separate condenser in 1760 and showed it to a man called Watt.[55]

There was an alternative suggestion that Watt showed it to Richard Lovell Edgeworth, 1744 – 1817, engineer, educationist and inventor who was born in Bath and educated at Oxford and Dublin. Both he and Watt were members the Lunar Society and writers probably jumped to a conclusion. It is unlikely that he would have known Watt before the Society's inception in 1765 and, as Watt claimed to have made his improvements to the Newcomen engine in 1763, we must leave it to others to decide whether there were grounds for suggesting that Edgeworth was the source of knowledge.

This leaves Gainsborough improving the Newcomen engine 'upon a construction much more useful to the public than the common [Newcomen] steam engine, by having much greater power and velocity,'[56] and advising Watt. He is reported to be been saddened all his life by the action of Watt in taking out a patent on his idea of a separate condenser. Although Gainsborough's family and friends claimed he was wronged throughout his life,[57] it is difficult to find proof of this.

However, Watt's devotion to the atmospheric engine did not mean that he never considered the construction of an engine that would be operated by the expansive power of steam, or did not dream of some form of turbine. In his *Improvements on the Steam Engine* he made no claim to have invented the steam engine as many historians would have us believe but to have improved the existing engine. He described what we recognise are his improvements to Newcomen's engine; he goes on,

> My method of lessening the consumption of steam, and consequently fuel in fire-engines, consists in the following principles: - First, that the vessel in which the powers of steam are to be employed to work the engine, which is called the cylinder in common fire-engines, and which I call the steam vessel, must, during the whole time the engine is at work, be kept as hot as the steam that enters it; …

After explaining more of the operation of his engine, he goes on to describe a high-pressure engine exhausting to air and a turbine. The italics are by Robert Stuart from his *Stuart's descriptive history of the Steam Engine,* 1824.

> Fourthly, I intend in many cases to employ the *expansive force of steam to press on the pistons*, or whatever may be used instead of them, in the same manner as the pressure of the atmosphere is now employed in common fire-engines. In cases where cold water cannot be had in plenty, the engines may be wrought by this *force of steam only* by discharging the steam into *the open air* after it has done its office.[58]

> Fifthly, where motions round an axis are required, I make *the steam vessels in form of hollow rings, or circular channels, with proper inlets and outlets for the steam, mounted on horizontal axles like the wheels of a water-mill.*[59]

These glances into Watt's earlier thinking show that, in his dreams, he was as advanced as Trevithick but must have wondered when he looked about him at the available materials and engineering of the day, whether he would ever achieve what he saw as the future. Making such an engine must have seemed as unlikely as travel to the moon. It was not surprising he was annoyed when young Trevithick achieved what he had failed to do thirty-odd years previously.

Boulton took Watt under his wing and conceived ways in which a patented improvement to Newcomen's fire engine could be put to profitable use. They had the opportunity to create their own demand by offering engines to do a variety of work that was only achieved by manual labour. As the earlier engines were only capable of a vertical motion their obvious market was pumping the mines.

As 'any Cornish mine engine of magnitude consumed £3,000 worth of coal every year'[60] it was essential that every opportunity should be taken to achieve fuel economy. Cornwall represented an excellent market for Watt's improved engine. Boulton provided Watt with financial and some engineering facilities to exploit the mine owners and demand from them a premium for the use of his patent.

In his early years at Soho, Boulton did not have the facilities to make more than a few of the smaller parts for Watt's engines. For what many considered as an exorbitant fee, customers received the right to construct their own engines and be provided with instructions how this could be achieved. These expensive purchases would have been fractionally more tolerable to Cornish mine owners had Boulton and Watt not charged an additional premium of one third of the purchaser's savings, payable annually on the mine's accounts. The mine owners were anxious to avoid this premium and encouraged other engineers to provide machines that would be cheaper to operate.

This entailed Watt having to live in Cornwall and ask for money from people who were averse to parting with it. This was a task he could barely face and Boulton had to make numerous journeys to Cornwall to deal with the mine owners. This was not a happy situation for the sensitive Scot who was well aware of the poor financial situation back at Soho and he frequently wrote to Boulton imploring him to do something about the size of their outstanding debts.

Many of the coalmine owners also objected to the prices demanded by Boulton & Watt for their monopolistic engines but, as they had all the coal they could burn, they were happy to keep to the Newcomen engines or even buy new ones. Cornwall, where the cost of importing coal from Wales was exorbitant, was an obvious place for Boulton & Watt to exploit. Within six years of the first Watt engine being erected in Cornwall, there were twenty-one single acting Watt pumping engines and only one Newcomen engine left. In addition, Murdoch erected some engines on his own account so the total number of replacement engines is not known.[61]

Boulton invested in the manufacture of a number of unrelated products, many of which were uneconomical. One that proved worthwhile was Watt's invention of the letter-copying machine he patented in 1780.

Like Trevithick, Watt had an inventor's mind. In addition to the letterpress, we hear of his steam carriages and a machine for copying sculptures. Watt said that he had unsuccessfully tried high-pressure steam and his results were not something he and Bolton wished to contemplate. Watt gave us his own account of his experiments, his reasons for not continuing with his design and his methods of ensuring that no one else did.

Farey said of all this, 'It is certain that, although high pressure engines were known, and frequently mentioned, during a long course of years, as mere projects, no such engines were brought into efficient use until Mr. Trevithick took up the subject'.[62]

'But in his own lifetime and again in the mid-nineteenth century just how Watt was depicted was of considerable commercial importance.'[63] In other words, it was important to Boulton and the appearance of his business that, irrespective of his troubles, Watt should be seen as a genius.

Young Trevithick was just six years old when James Watt introduced his first condensing atmospheric steam engine to Cornwall. Although Samuel Smiles says that the first Watt engine was erected at Ting Tang Mine near St Day in Cornwall[64] it had not been possible to ship some vital parts to Ting Tang so Wheal Busy, near Chacewater and between Truro and Redruth became the site for the first engine. Watt arrived with his wife to supervise the installation. After a four-day journey Watt was not in the best of moods. Having advised Boulton not to take the ferry at Saltash, he sent his first report on the Cornish:

> The people here … have the most ungracious manners of any people I was ever among – In general the Engines here are clumsy and nasty, the [engine] houses crackt & everything dripping with water from the [engine] house cisterns[65]

It was clear that the easily deflated Watt preferred the lush green pastures of Smethwick to the barren wastelands of industrial Cornwall.

Progress was made and within a few days there was a change of mood,

> 'Wheal Bussy is in considerable forwardness, and what iron work has been made there is little inferior to our own if any – all the world is agape to see its performance'.[66]

36

William Pole in his *Treatise on the Cornish Pumping Engine* suggests that the Wheal Busy engine was first erected for a few months at the nearby Creegbraws Mine.[67]

The Watts could find no accommodation to rent close to Chacewater and initially stayed nearby with their agent, Thomas Wilson. Wilson is frequently referred to as residing in Truro but that was a generalisation. Ashley Rowe gives his life span as 1748 – 1820 and describes him as superintendent of Chacewater Mine.[68] If this was his job in 1777 it is unlikely that he travelled the five miles daily from Truro and Daniell says the accommodation he offered his employer was in the village of Chacewater.[69] Watt's second wife, Ann described the village after their arrival and spoke of her husband's adoption of religion in a letter of the 1st September 1777 to Boulton's second wife, also Ann,

> I scarcely know what to say to you of this country. The spot we are at is the most disagreeable in the whole country. The face of the earth is broken up in ten thousand heaps of rubbish, and there is scarce a tree to be seen. But don't think that all Cornwall is like Chacewater. I have been at some places that are very pleasant, nay beautiful. The sea-coast to me is charming, but not easy to get at. In some cases my poor husband has been obliged to mount me behind him to go to some of the places we have been at. At one of our jaunts we were only charged twopence a piece for our dinner. You may guess what our fare may be from the cost of it; but I assure you, I never eat a dinner with more relish in my life, nor was I ever happier at a feast than I was that day at Portreath. One thing I must tell you of is, to take care of Mr Boulton's principles are well fixed before you trust him here. Poor Mr Watt is turned Anabaptist and daily attends their meetings: he is, indeed, and goes to chapel most devoutly.

It is likely that Mrs Watt made a common mistake when she mentioned Anabaptist instead of Baptist; there are considerable differences between the two beliefs. According to reports, Watt appeared to be catholic in his religious values. Jason Foster and others claimed him as a Calvinist although he was accused of the heinous crime of breaking the Sabbath[70] and Dickinson and Titley suggest he is a chapel going Presbyterian,[71] a condition described elsewhere as 'lapsed'. There was the little publicised friendship between the Baptist Hornblowers and Watt that Susan W. Howard[72] claims was amicable. Thomas Newcomen was a Baptist lay preacher who employed another Baptist, Joseph Hornblower, c1692-1761 and born in Staffordshire, to erect his engines. In 1745 Hornblower was sent to Cornwall to build an engine at Wheal Rose, near Redruth.[73]

Boulton sent a number of erectors to assist Watt with a degree of mixed success. These men presented Watt with a variety of drunkenness and blundering to add to his fears of bankruptcy. Watt wrote to Boulton in July 1778, 'On the subject of Mr Hall I should not have been so earnest had I not been urged on by the prospect of impending ruin, which may be much accelerated by a wicked or careless servant in his place'.

It must have cheered Watt immeasurably to find in the Hornblowers family people in that blasted landscape who understood the concept of steam engineering. Jonathan's eldest brother was the much travelled Jabez. He was already known to Boulton & Watt as a skilled engine erector but he was seen as a threat to their business interests because of his activities in Holland where the partnership had no patent protection. Watt's ploy was to find Jabez work in Birmingham and the following year he was working for Boulton & Watt in Shropshire. Jabez was often the cause of trouble and Boulton sent him back to Cornwall. The Hornblower family was a substantial force in mine engineering in the area and Watt was happy with their relationship until he discovered in 1781 that Jonathan Hornblower had designed and patented a steam engine in competition with his own.

Watt was furious with the family of Hornblowers; he wrote to Boulton saying, ". . . I am much vexed by this affair, Jabez does not want abilities, the rest are fools . . ."[74]

Watt returned to Soho in September 1777 after having seen Wheal Busy and Ting Tang engines put to work[75] (Ashley Rowe says Ting Tang was put to work in 1778)[76] and came back to Cornwall the following year to rent a property at Plain an Gwary in Redruth[77] sometimes known as Chylowen, Cornish for Happy House. He lived there until the family with their two younger children moved to more comfortable accommodation in Cusgarne in 1781. Although he was frequently reported as being in poor health, life in Cornwall had some rewards and there were brighter periods; Mrs Watt wrote,

> James's spirits are surprising since his arrival. This is a most delightful place, a neat roomy house with sash windows double breadth, the front to the south covered with vines loaded with young grapes, the walled garden has excellent peaches and plums, plenty of currants, two orchards, a lawn before the door. The whole surrounded with elm trees. It stands in a valley safe from the north and south winds, but the east and west can get at us. The worst thing about the house is the bad roads which lead to it in every direction, however they are ridable.

Watt's engines were sold on the claim of their greater efficiency over that of their predecessors, the Newcomen engines. Each stroke of the engine would lift no more than a Newcomen engine of the same size but, because the engines were more thermally efficient they had a higher stroke rate for the same amount of fuel. This increase in efficiency was the basis for a charging system, hated by the Cornish mine owners. Disputes always arose over the claims and the subsequent charges. These were often

The house at Plain an Gwary, Redruth, occupied by James Watt.

resolved by a test in which the performance, known as 'duty', of an engine was measured; it the relationship between the water raised and the fuel consumed. Each side would accuse the other of cheating so the following contemporary account serves to compare Watt's claims with the actual performance of his engines. While it is fairly boring and the reader will be excused for skipping it, the results collected by John Smeaton, 1724-1792, are straightforward and clarify the controversy surrounding the Watt engines. Smeaton, who built his own engines by improving those of Newcomen, does not take the opportunity to inflate their reported performance figures. Justice is a rare commodity and seldom found where there are other interests, especially the opportunity of monetary reward. The following snappy title says it all,

Improvements made in the duty performed by the Steam Engines in Cornwall, compiled at the request of the British Association for the Improvement of Science.

> *Mr Taylor,* in his *Records of Mining* says:
>
> The facts which I have collected are as follows, and I place them according to their dates, as best calculated to exhibit the progress that has been made.

1769. Mr. Smeaton computed the effects of 15 engines (atmospheric) working at Newcastle and according to the data he furnished, the average duty was 5,590,000. Note, the best was 7,440,000; the worst was 3,220,000.

Smeaton began his alterations in the steam engine, and succeeded in performing 9,450,000.

1776. Mr. Watt stated in a letter to Mr. Smeaton that his engine at Soho raised between 20,000 and 30,000 cubic feet of water 20 feet high, with 120lbs of coal; which would be equal to 21,600,000.

This was more, however, than Boulton & Watt would engage that their engines should perform; as, in a letter written by Mr. Boulton to the Carron Company in this year, which contained proposals for erecting an engine, he stated the performance at equal to about 19,000,000.

Mr. Smeaton about this time, after many experiments, laid it down as a rule, that Watt's engines would do double as much as his own; which as we see above, was 9.45 millions, consequently 18,900,000.

1778, 1779. Mr. Watt, having stated that his engines should do 23,400,000, Mr. Smeaton made trial of two (one on the Birmingham Canal, and one at the Hull Water works) and found the duty of one equal to 18,000,000, and the other 18,500,000.

1778. Boulton & Watt erected an engine at Hawkesbury Colliery, near Coventry, cylinder 58 inches diameter, stroke 8 feet, load 26,064 lbs, which was found to do nearly 19,000,000.

Mr. Watt introduced the improvement of working steam expansively, and he calculated that engines which would previously do 19 or 20 millions would thus perform 26,600,000; but I do not find any record of this duty being performed in practice.

1798. On account of a suit respecting their patent, which was carrying on by Boulton & Watt, an account of the duty of all the engines in Cornwall was taken by Davies Gilbert, Esq. and the late Captain Jenkin of Treworgie, and they found the average to be about 17,000,000.

An engine at Herland was found to be best in the county, and was doing 27 millions, but being so much above all others, some error as apprehended … it was under the care of Mr. Murdock, their agent in the county.

Watt's mind was still on his disputes with Hornblower many years later when he wrote to his son in 1808 concerning Hornblower's arguments over his patents. Watt illustrated the normal progress associated with the development of groundbreaking machinery when he said that, 'Hornblower's arguments … that the first [Watt] engines erected in Cornwall were not so perfect … which is perfectly true … it has been in a course of improvement even unto this day. I was ignorant of many things … neither do I pretend that I ever possessed an eminently inventive genius … my forte seems to have been reflection and judgement … He finds fault … in my patents … it was my business not only to describe the things I preferred but also those by which it could be evaded'.[78]

Watt's improvements to Newcomen's engine had started with the inspirational addition of the steam condenser. Modifications and improvements continued for a further quarter a century and during that time other inventors saw shortcomings and gaps in Watt's patent on which they aimed to capitalise; the result was a lot of argument and expensive litigation. Trevithick's attitude to invention was very different. He thought through all the components necessary to make his engine work satisfactorily and, although he varied its layout, he did very little to develop the engine. Instead, he pursued opportunities to use the engine and left its development to manufacturers who created their own power units and took little notice of the patents Trevithick held.

When Watt died in 1819, there was a general appreciation of his services to industry among the close-knit community of academic scientists. They seemed oblivious to the fact that, at the time, the country's industrialists were turning away from Watt's designs to replace them with high-pressure steam engines as quickly as the manufacturers could build them. However, the magical five-letter word was 'steam' and it was associated with Watt. Steam was driving the industries and transport of the country and the industrialists were establishing Britain throughout the world. From a political point of view, it was expedient to be associated with the development of steam and that meant Watt.

The Hornblowers
For three generations the Hornblower family was instrumental in the innovation, development and erection of steam, or more correctly, atmospheric fire engines. Their contribution is not so well known as some others but their dedication was sincere and enthusiastic. It matched their family life and religious conviction as Baptists.

Our story of the Hornblowers starts with Joseph, 1696 – 1762, who was born at Broseley in Shropshire and came to Cornwall from Staffordshire in about 1725 to supervise the erection of a Newcomen engine at Wheal Rose, the second engine in Cornwall. He followed this with engines at Wheal Busy and Polgooth. Joseph was appointed engineer at several mines including Ting Tang[79] and, seeing the prospects for engine building in the area, he brought his family to settle at Chacewater in 1745, calling the little community he created, Salem. By 1768, he lived in a cottage and built the adjoining Salem Baptist Chapel. His children were born in one of the richest mining areas then known in the world and, like Trevithick after him, grew up in a family committed to mining and steam. Two of Joseph's sons, Jonathan, 1717 – 1780, and Josiah, 1729 – 1809, joined him in Cornwall. Jonathan had married Ann Carter and the first of their thirteen children, Jabez Carter Hornblower, 1744 – 1814 was born in Broseley and their only child to bear the middle name Carter. Jethro, 1746 – 1820, Jonathan Junior, 1753 – 1815, and his subsequent siblings were all born in Chacewater. Jonathan Senior died at Whitehall, Scorrier in 1780.[80] By 1777, the 24-year-old Jonathan junior, to whom we will refer just as 'Jonathan' from here, was an accomplished engine erector living close to Wheal Busy, sometimes identified on maps as the Great Works, where he assisted the forlorn Watt by raising his first engine in Cornwall.

Joseph and Newcomen had a common interest in their Baptist devotions and this was exemplified by the Hornblowers naming all their numerous children with first names that started with the letter J. Not surprisingly, this caused considerable confusion over the years.

Jabez was employed in the erection of Newcomen engines as far away as Holland and Sweden. His uncle Josiah travelled even further afield. William Nelson, the Recording Secretary of the New Jersey Historical Society delivered his paper entitled, *The First Steam Engine in America,* to the Society in May 1883 and published it later that year. This takes us away from the Trevithick narrative for a moment but this story might be of interest to American readers.

Nelson speaks highly of Josiah and his quest for knowledge. At the age of just 20 he was erecting an engine in Anglesey when a call came to him from the agent of Colonel John Schuyler of New Jersey. It was a request to erect a steam engine at Schuyler's copper mine in America.

At that time each engine was made to order and details would have been required from America before the engine could be designed. The time taken for correspondence to cross the Atlantic contributed to the delay of more than four years before the engine was ready. Newcomen engines were substantial engineering achievements for their day. They were usually made as close as possible to the point of use or wherever there were good transport links.

Josiah and his engine left Falmouth for London in May 1753 where he trans-shipped to the snow* *Irene* under the command of Captain Nicholas Garrison. So gruelling was the three month voyage that Josiah would never cross the Atlantic again.

This was the seventh voyage of the *Irene,* built to carry Moravian immigrants from Central Europe to America. Hornblower's engine is mentioned in the details of the voyage.[81]

It would take another two weeks for the engine to reach the mine. Josiah then had to face the fact, recounted by Nelson, that 'There was, perhaps, scarcely another mechanic in all America who had the slightest idea of the construction of a steam engine'.[82] Josiah had to see to everything. Stone had to be quarried and dressed, timber hewn and shaped, clay burnt to brick, and then all set up as an engine house. Accidents happened and parts were broken. Fortunately, Josiah had brought a number of spare parts, 'for it

* A square sailed vessel similar to a bark [barque].

Drawing of the *Irene* by Benjamin Garrison son of Captain Nicholas Garrison.

is safe to say there was not a shop in America where the necessary castings could have been made'.[83] Nelson provided full details from Josiah's cash book and records that the engine was put to work in early 1755. A few pages explain the operation of the engine and the excitement as it came to life, pumping at the rate of 10 – 12 strokes a minute. It was estimated to have cost a total of three thousand pounds Sterling and was capable of pumping eight hogsheads* a minute.

At the time Nelson was writing, parts of the engine were on display at D. M. Meeker & Son's foundry in Clay Street, Newark, N. J. Nelson gives the actual dimensions of the engine to reveal the cylinder would have been nearly eight feet in length and three feet in diameter with a stroke of six feet. The cylinder of the pump was about ten inches in diameter and he calculated that it would lift 134 gallons a minute or a trifle less than 200,000 gallons daily. He commented that the engine could have worked a larger pump.

Nelson went on to explain Josiah's life, his marriage in 1755, the building of a church, the war with the French and the outstanding contributions made by the Hornblower family to the communities in New Jersey.

As a step towards the universal acceptance of the steam engine, it is reassuring to note that the first steam engine in America was designed and constructed in Cornwall, the

* A hogshead is slightly larger than a 45 gallon drum.

homeland of engine development, and shipped from there to the New World when Watt was a youth of just seventeen years. It was into this environment that Trevithick would be born eighteen years later.

Jonathan Hornblower, Junior, 1753-1815

Men everywhere were striving to find a way in which the properties of steam could be used to supply greater power than muscle and sinew. While many of their ideas were ill-fated some showed promise that could not be brought to fruition due to the lack of suitable materials or skill. In 1765 Dr Erasmus Darwin[84] described a twin cylinder steam engine that used steam pressure and a vacuum.[85]

Looking back to those who struggled to bring their inventions to fruition, we see in the development of the steam engine how designs would lack significant factors and fail. Many designs were quite revolutionary. For instance, in 1781, Jonathan Hornblower, an inventive Cornish-born engineer, built and patented a complicated engine. His engine had been designed to pump the Cornish mines and could not be easily adapted to other needs; it also required a satisfactory boiler to safely produce high-pressure steam, something that eluded its designer.[86] Like Erasmus Darwin's vision, it was a twin-cylinder compound engine using steam under pressure in the first cylinder and condensing it in the second. Many years later Arthur Woolf claimed a similar design as his own. This twin-cylinder engine was some twenty years before Trevithick's simpler but more effective single-cylinder version.

Watt took exception to Hornblower's engine and its newly acquired patent and, in July 1781 he added in his letter to Boulton,

> They have laboured to evade our act, have long had a copy of our specification ... they pretend to condense the steam in the cylinder, but I have heard they do it in a separate vessel. It is no less than our double cylinder engine worked upon our principle of expansion.

James Watt, junior was a forceful character and he would pursue unmercifully those he thought were infringing his father's patents. In two letters to Wilson during a period of litigious war, we have,

> Four of these Affidavits are by the Hornblowers, viz Jonathan, Jethro, Jesse & Jabez and the remainder by Bramah, David Watson, Rowntree, Strode & Wolffe, who are all pirates themselves. They are in matter & form contemptible and ridiculous in the highest degree.[87]

The unusual name Bramah is mentioned and, in the following letter we have,

We are fully prepared to over throw the Affidavits of these Water Closet Engineers and Organizers of Stinktraps, and although they may gain another trial and another defeat, there is little chance of their getting the Injunction dissolved.

This is curious until you trace Joseph Bramah, 1748 – 1814, as the Yorkshire cabinetmaker who set up in London, had little time for Watt, was a defence witness for Jabez Hornblower and Maberley and taught Arthur Woolf. He patented the hydraulic press and in 1784 he patented an improved water closet. Why he should owe dues to Boulton & Watt we do not know. That may be connected to Woolf and his early engines, but we know why he was referred to as an organiser of stinktraps.

Hornblower continued to rile Watt by claiming in 1788 that his design for a separate condenser was already 50 years old and that Watt had no right to burden the Cornish mine owners with demands for premiums. It is doubtful that Watt's regular attendance at the Baptist chapel absolved him from the wrath of others at the same place of worship; it is very likely that he stopped attending. No court had declared Watt's patent as being valid, yet the establishment supported his invention as the one engine upon which the industry of the British Empire was being built.

Although Hornblower had sold nine (some say seven) of his engines and developed some aspects of steam power beyond the designs of Watt, he was losing heart and adopted an alternative lifestyle. Many things coursed through his mind, leaving him lonely with his thoughts and he told self-appointed mentor Davies Gilbert,

> I have lately had a Slight Rage again for the consideration of it. I have before told you that I am so insulated as to society of my own that I can make appeals to no one but yourself in cares that are abstruse i.e. Philosophy etc.[88]

In his last letter to Davies Gilbert, 9 July 1814, he appealed for assistance with the design of a reflecting telescope. There is no trace of a reply or correspondence. His interest turned to the stars and he would study them with the assistance of his telescope.

The loss of Hornblower and his fighting spirit from the Cornish engineering scene was a disappointment for Gilbert and many of the local mine owners. Gilbert was still willing to help him and, as he set out from Marazion on a lengthy journey by horseback to consult Beddoes in Bristol about his health, he called in and found Hornblower's last engine in 'a state of advanced dilapidation'. When Gilbert heard of Hornblower's death on the 23 February 1815, he wrote to his two unmarried daughters and asked if he might recover whatever letters he had written to their father; they agreed.

Unlike many true inventors of the period, Hornblower was to die a relatively wealthy man and he is buried in St Gluvias churchyard on the outskirts of Penryn. His occupation was described in his will as Jonathan Hornblower, Plumber and Civil Engineer. Other members of the Hornblower family were still resident in Chacewater at the 1841 Census.

An examination of contemporary books on the subject of early steam engines such as John Farey's *Treatise on the Steam Engine,* Volume One, published in 1827 and Volume Two, published in 1971, reveals that there were many inventors and builders of steam engines, all vying with Watt for a share of the industrial power cake. Their engines came in a variety of designs with single and twin cylinders, high-pressure steam and condenser formed vacuums. Many of them were seeking to create rotary motion before Watt. Most were unsuccessful but their designs surely contravened Watt's view of his patent protection. A few designers were threatened with litigation and the Hornblowers were unfortunate in this, being so close to Boulton and Watt and working as their engineers and erectors. In the Hornblowers' position, both in Cornwall and Birmingham, their every move was likely to attract the attention of the partners and engender their wrath.

Irrespective of what the British establishment did to comfort him, life in Cornwall was going to be hard for Watt. This was the first substantial opposition that he and Boulton had come across and Jonathan Hornblower appreciated the strength of his position when Watt asked Jethro to persuade his brother to sell his patent rights. Being stubborn, Jonathan refused and Watt realised that he was going to face significant opposition from the mine owners and engineers in Cornwall, something he would have to fight with his extended, but unvalidated, patent rights. It was an indication of how much Boulton and Watt valued their steam engine patents that they would face total legal costs of £78,000 before they made any profit.[89]

No wonder Watt was a worried man.

William Murdoch, 1754 – 1839
A canny Scottish inventor, Murdoch had been born at Bello Mill, his family home rented from James Boswell of *London Journal* and *Life of Johnson* fame. He joined Boulton & Watt in 1777, the year Watt introduced his first condensing engine to Cornwall. As an engineer he was paid 15 shillings a week and worked in Cornwall from 1779 as senior engine erector at 21 shillings a week.[90] By September 1780 Murdoch was asking for two guineas (£2 10) a week. The measly Watt refused the increase but Boulton overruled him.

During his time in Redruth he married a local girl and invented a number of improvements to Watt's engine such as the famous sun-and-planet gearing. His employers were apt to claim the credit for much of Murdoch's work. In 1782 Boulton wrote highly of Murdoch saying,

> We want more Murdocks, for of all others he is the most active man and best engine erector I ever saw...When I look at the work done it astonishes me & is entirely owing to the spirit and activity of Murdoch who hath not gone to bed 3 of the nights.

There is a story that Murdoch fought a duel with Richard Trevithick, senior, over an alleged insult to Watt. Whatever the truth was behind this story it was clearly something that did not improve relationships between the engine designers in Smethwick and the Cornish miners, especially the Trevithicks.

There is another reference to the difficulties that Murdoch experienced in the course of his work in Cornwall.

> Edward Bull prepared drawings of a large double engine for Poldice mine. He left them in the counting house where they were found & copied by Wm Murdock. He sent the copy to Boulton & Watt who applied to the Lord Chancellor for an injunction to stop the engine being erected. The upstart of this is the action of the Poldice miners who marched to Redruth & forced him to march to Poldice. There they received his promise that he would never again set foot on the mine, so they let him escape unhurt[91]

Murdoch's locomotive and the Vicar of Redruth
A great deal of the profit made by Boulton & Watt in Cornwall was due to the attention of Murdoch to his responsibilities. Nevertheless, he found time in 1784[92] or 1786[93] to build a three-wheeled steam-propelled model locomotive that clearly revealed the power embodied in a steam boiler could be harnessed to propel a vehicle. This was believed to be the first example of steam propulsion in England. One of the models that Murdoch built is in the *Thinktank* Science Museum at Birmingham but because he wrote little or nothing about this little carriage we have a problem that various authors have been all too ready to solve. Their explanations have been seized upon by those wishing to prove one thing or another. Murdoch's father was still living at Bello Mill in September 1792 when Boswell records in his journal that he twice called on Murdoch in Cross Street, Redruth and was shown a number of things. There is no mention of either gas lighting or a steam carriage.[94] This is an example of how Murdoch kept matters close to his chest. Thomas Wilson was frustrated by Murdoch's attitude and, in a letter about his intended pneumatic pumps says, 'the Deuce have I heard from Murdoch of late about his new improvement. But I hear from others he is still sanguine about it.'[95]

Many have claimed that Murdoch taught Trevithick all he knew about high-pressure steam; Francis Trevithick went out of his way to refute the suggestions. He wrote in a derogatory manner about Murdoch's 'liliputian'[96] locomotives and ended with, 'There was no similarity between those proposed locomotives and Trevithick's reality'.[97] Murdoch worked secretly on his own projects when advised not to do so, he did not tell James Boswell, a lifelong Scottish friend about his inventions and he travelled to London to patent his steam engine in contravention of his employer's patent. This, together with Wilson's clear frustration about Murdoch's closeness and the lack of any notes regarding his inventions does not indicate someone who would be willing to share precious, unpatented secrets with young Trevithick, an unruly upstart he had little time for and his employer's avowed competitor. Anyway, Trevithick would have been just thirteen years old in 1784. Whether Trevithick subsequently discovered what Murdoch had been doing is another matter but his model locomotives of 1797 onwards appeared unique and to borrow nothing from Murdoch's design. In another twist of the story, Boulton & Watt claimed Murdoch showed his engine to Andrew Vivian.[98]

Murdoch left us very little about himself. Griffiths says, 'There are no diaries, no recorded speeches, and only a tiny handful of letters and mechanical drawings'[99] and, 'Only one item, a letter from Murdoch to Watt, May 1782, concerning engine design survives in the extensive Boulton & Watt archive'.[100]

Murdoch was so concerned that his invention should not be displayed for all to copy and criticise that he is reputed to have experimented with it one dark night in Church Lane, Redruth. It must be remembered that this was a time when people shut out the night air to guard themselves against the evil spirits it might contain; not many would be abroad at that time. However, William Buckle tells us that Murdoch had not reckoned with the local parson who probably had a guiding hand by his side as he walked in darkness down the lane. His belief was sorely tried as he saw what he was alleged to have graphically described as the Devil leaping about and spitting fire.

This description of the event in the lane by Daniel Kinnear Clark,[101] an author who followed the development of early locomotives and railways in some detail. Clark attributed the Murdoch story to *Proceedings of the Institute of Mechanical Engineers*, Oct 1850 that contained *The Biographical Notice of William Murdoch* by Mr Buckle of Soho.[102] It was a good tale and Samuel Smiles repeated it in 1860[103] and again in 1884.[104]

Mr Buckle is the source of the often told story about Murdoch, but, who was Mr Buckle? Griffiths says Buckle worked at the Foundry as a young man while Murdoch was still alive.[105]

There is an obituary to William Buckle in the *Gentleman's Magazine* recording him as being the Vice President of the Society [sic] of Mechanical Engineers. It says he built the Rocket locomotive that killed William Huskisson, MP at the Rainhill Trials. A friend of Stephenson and Watt, Buckle joined the latter's Soho Works after arranging the visit of George IV to Ireland in 1821.[106] He held a responsible post at Soho and moved to the Royal Mint in 1851, dying there in September 1863.[107] Is this the William Buckle who demonstrated Murdoch's 66-year-old locomotive to the Institute and recorded his address in their *Proceedings* of October 1850?[108] He would have been at least 27 years of age before he was associated with the Soho Works. By then Murdoch was in his dotage and we have to wonder whether Buckle would have been privy to his elderly employer's anecdotes; perhaps it was a story that circulated in the works at Soho.

The Institution of Mechanical Engineers (IMechE) can find only one William Buckle becoming a member, and that was not until 1880; membership was surely a pre-requisite for Vice-Presidency. That was William H. R. Buckle of the locomotive builders, R. & W. Hawthorn, Limited, located next to Robert Stephenson & Company at Newcastle-upon-Tyne, and a company that was amalgamated in 1880 with shipbuilders to become Hawthorn, Leslie & Company.

No one offers dates for the incident in the lane so we are unable to pinpoint Murdoch's model locomotive or the name of the rector. However, various accounts speak of the rector facing a fiery monster, one that spat fire and sparks. These could all be in the imagination of the writers but there is a reference to a locomotive having a 'fire Shovel, poker & tongs'.[109] Again, if we search beyond the original writer's imagination this may indicate that, unlike earlier spirit lamp engines, the locomotive was large enough to be coal-fired, able to scatter glowing embers and so was probably a substantial weight to carry any distance. Looking further at D. K. Clark's writing we see he confused Trevithick's 1801 and 1803 locomotives in the same page that he talks about Murdoch's use of high-pressure steam in his 1784 model locomotive so we may have a writer who develops stories to explain doubtful facts.

Buckle said that the church was a mile from the centre of town where Murdoch lived, and it still is; a prodigious distance to carry a coal fired model locomotive. It has been suggested that he could have driven it that distance but, if the purpose of the exercise was to ascertain whether the locomotive worked, a few yards outside his house would have been sufficient to prove that.

In his address to the IMechE, Buckle claimed that Murdoch arrived in Cornwall in May 1779 to erect Watt's first engine there. It is well known that Watt's first engines were erected in 1777. Buckle also says that Murdoch was present at the commissioning of several engines including that at Chelsea. Boulton's letter to Watt of 17th May 1779[110] mentions the Chelsea engine having just been set to work.

Myths, like verdant bushes, grow from the smallest of seeds when they are nurtured by creative writers. Chapter XI of *Our Iron Roads,* first published in 1852, provided a truly alarming tale.

> One dark night in the year 1784 the Venerable Vicar of Redruth, in Cornwall, was taking a quiet walk in a lonely lane leading to his church. Suddenly he heard an unearthly noise, and to his horror, he saw approaching him an indescribable creature of legs, arms, and wheels, whose body appeared to be glowing with internal fire, and whose rapid gasps for breath seemed to donate a fierce struggle for existence. The vicar's cries for help brought to his assistance a gentlemen of the name of Murdoch, who was able to assure him that this terrible apparition was not an incarnation or a messenger of the Evil One, but only a runaway engine that had escaped from control.

Supposing this account had appeared in the first edition of the book in 1852 and not been added to the subsequent editions published in the 1880s, it appeared just two years after Mr Buckle had informed the IMechE. It is noticeable that the creative author does not refer to the venerable vicar's wife or daughter.

Whatever was the truth behind the tale of Murdoch in the lane it attracted Francis Trevithick who said that he had lived nearby for years but knew nothing of the story until he heard it from the lecture to the IMechE in 1850. It did not matter to Francis whether the story was true or not, it was clearly a good one that people would believe. Francis used Clark's 71-year-old account of Mr Buckle's story published in 1855[111] to build a scenario, not found elsewhere, to include two additional characters in the story. In order to authenticate his account of events Francis was fortunate, as he was so many times when writing his book, to find someone of great antiquity who had a memory as sharp as a knife.

Neither Buckle nor Clark made any mention of the rector being accompanied by either his wife or young daughter as Francis Trevithick suggested. Had he been, they must have been made of stouter stuff than the man of the cloth as no mention is made of their screams or reactions to the Evil One coming towards them.

Whatever were the truths in this famous story of the clergyman, Francis was alone when he claimed that the rector's daughter, subsequently to become Mrs Rogers, and able to recall the events as they were witnessed by both her parents. She was also reputed to have remembered that Mr Murdoch had expressed the wish that the experiment be kept a secret.[112] Francis was indeed lucky to have found the vicar's daughter eighty-five years after the frightening incident with a memory that revealed, as he put it, 'all the freshness of a modern event' living near him in Penzance as he was writing the history of his father. Supposing Mrs Rogers had been a girl of just ten, the earliest we can expect her to have recalled anything in partial detail, by the time she met Francis she would have been 95, a prodigious age and one where she may well have remembered her fear but one has to question whether she could remember, in all the excitement, a conversation between Murdoch and her parents. If she had been fifteen at the time, she would have been a centenarian when she met Francis. If she existed at all and if her account was true it would have gone a long way towards exonerating Trevithick from any involvement with Murdoch, something that is frequently repeated in Redruth to this day. We do not know the exact year in which Murdoch was alleged to have frightened the vicar but Trevithick would have been in the region of thirteen years of age, probably too young to have taken advantage of anything he might have seen or heard. We may never know the truth but the story of the vicar is looking suspicious. If Francis Trevithick inherited anything from his father it was imagination.

There is a film made by the Gas Council about the life of Murdoch that shows his model steam locomotive was able to perform its frightening antics in Church Lane. Whether the film makers used the original model or a replica is not known.[113]

Returning to Trevithick, John Murdoch, William's son wrote to James Watt, junior, in 1815 and said that his father had demonstrated his 1792 locomotive several times in Redruth, about two years after having shown it to Trevithick and Vivian.[114] Griffiths also recounts how the thwarted Murdoch gave demonstrations of his carriage in the Great Room at the Kings Head in Truro.[115] Griffiths is clear in his understanding that Trevithick knew about Murdoch's engine.[116]

If Francis's account of Mrs Roger's recollections is to be believed, it is unlikely that the existence of Murdoch's model carriage would have been known at all in Cornwall had it not been for the talkative vicar who probably used his encounter with the Devil to improve his sermon the following Sunday; we find no account of the incident from Murdoch. In recent years, there has been a fruitless study of surviving correspondence in the hope of finding anything pertinent. There is a note in a letter written by Trevithick to Gilbert[117] enquiring after the carriage that was apparently being built by old William Budge in his Tuckingmill workshop. Trevithick asked whether it exhausted its steam or used a condenser. Those seeking references to Murdoch constructing a full-sized steam carriage suggest that they have found the corroborating evidence they were seeking. I have found no indication that Murdoch ever had any interest in, or encouraged, what was going on in Tuckingmill. No evidence has yet been offered of any correspondence between the inventor and the alleged builder or of any return by the inventor to supervise the construction, surely pre-requisites of a project to build such a rare engineering contrivance at the turn of the 19th century.

Trevithick's Tuckingmill enquiry raises more questions that he ever imagined. Murdoch had left Cornwall with his family for Soho in 1798,[118] a full five years earlier than Trevithick's letter. Either Budge was a very slow worker or he was unable to finish the work without the guidance of Murdoch. Was Budge, an able brass founder who had visited Soho Foundry with Richard Trevithick Senior in 1776 to view Watt's new fuel-efficient engine,[119] trying to make a steam vehicle of his own similar to the model for which he had been commissioned to make parts by Murdoch? William Buckle tells us Murdoch made all the parts for his model himself and also paints a picture of Murdoch working through the nights 'completely occupied by his mechanical pursuits'.[120] Murdoch had taken his model(s) with him when he left so, without drawings, Budge had very little reference. A subsequent pamphlet draws attention to an engraving in 1804 of someone riding a similar locomotive. Only the most gullible would attach any credit to an illustration or patent application as an indication that the featured item actually existed or, better still, even performed satisfactorily. Had it been otherwise we would have had to believe in Isaac Newton's jet car and the helicopters of Leonardo del Vinci, known to some as the *Daedalian Mythmaker*.[121]

The engine for Murdoch's model did not use a condenser as was the case of the Boulton & Watt engines but exhausted the used steam to air in a manner similar to the subsequent Trevithick locomotives. However, it would have operated on a very low pressure of steam, much as the Mamod model steam traction engines do today. As can be seen in the well-known illustration of the model by Robert H. Thurston[122] Murdoch's copper boiler was square and an enlarged design was clearly unlikely to safely retain sufficient steam at high pressure to operate a full-sized locomotive. There is also the opinion that '… the boiler was incapable of sustaining even moderately high pressure …'.[123]

Although Murdoch had discussed steam locomotion previously with his employers, the construction of this locomotive was unknown to them until, on a journey to London with the model in order to patent the design in August 1786, Murdoch unfortunately met Boulton near Exeter coming the other way. Boulton wrote to Watt on the 2nd September, telling him of the encounter, how he had persuaded Murdoch to return to Cornwall with his model and resume his employment, working with the company's engines. It is unlikely that Murdoch, who had

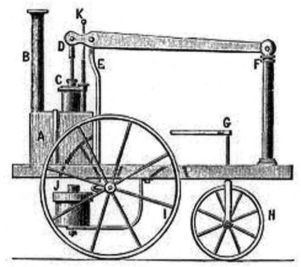

Murdoch's model steam tricycle
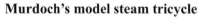

52

been so careful to keep his invention secret whilst working in Cornwall alongside Watt, would either have shared its principles with Trevithick or be building a full-sized steam carriage for all to see without the security of the patent he was going to such lengths to obtain. We hear nothing more of Murdoch's model locomotive until it was demonstrated by Buckle in 1850 and made a surprise appearance at the Great Exhibition the following year.

William Budge was a well-known engineer who, like Jonathan Hornblower, was an engine erector in Cornwall.[124] He was an immediate candidate for the erection of Watt engines and was sent to Soho to appreciate their technology. He was not impressed and it took some time before he eventually accepted the improved efficiency of the Watt engine and built one. Watt commented that he thought Budge was about to retire in 1777 as he was wealthy and had no family. However, he kept going and in 1780 offered Murdoch a partnership and half of his engines. At this time Budge built a boiler with an inclined internal flue, a feature that Murdoch incorporated into his model steam carriage a couple of years later. Budge would have been 73 when Trevithick wrote to Gilbert enquiring if he was building a carriage for Murdoch. He died at the age of 93 after having been confined to his house for several years.[125]

Although Murdoch had married the daughter of a local mine captain he was damned locally by association with Watt. Following his departure his true value was appreciated by the Cornish mine owners. The Murdoch's twin children were frail and one died in November 1787 with the other following three months later. Anne gave birth to William in 1788 and John in 1790, sadly dying herself shortly afterwards.[126] Murdoch was left to bring up the children with the help of his mother-in-law. There were times when Murdoch found it difficult to face the demands of life and those of the mine owners; in August 1797 he wrote to Watt saying, 'I am ther [mine owners'] slave and must take all that comes, Dear sir, if possible you can procure my deliverance from this place will be much oblige, your humble servant, Wm Murdoch'.[127] William and John grew up to take responsible positions in the Boulton & Watt company.[128]

While it is true that Murdoch had built a model steam carriage, there was very little, if any of the technology in his engine that subsequently appeared in the Trevithick locomotives. The mechanical differences are so pronounced that they could have been built by strangers at different ends of the country. A study of Watt's patent of 1769 makes interesting reading; the control it gave Watt over the operation of any steam engine with a form of separate condensation is also worth mentioning. The 1769 patent was followed by the 1775 Steam Engine Act. (Anno Regni Decirno Quinto Georgii III Regis). This was an Act of Parliament which vested in *James Watt,* Engineer, and his Executors, Administrators and Assignees, the sole use of steam engines of his invention throughout the United Kingdom and His Majesty's Dominions for a limited length of time.

Murdoch and coal gas lighting

Murdoch did receive recognition in his own right for developing the use of artificial light from coal gas. In fact, it is remarkable that his work received any recognition at all as the following are just a few of the people known to have previously experimented with vapours from coal and other materials: Thomas Shirley; 1659, Van Helmont Fleming, Dean Clayton; 1688, Stephen Hales; 1726, Sir James Lowther; 1733, George Dixon; 1760, M. Jars; 1764, Spedding; 1765, M. Chaussier; 1776, Diller; 1787, Jan Pieter Minckelers; 1784. In 1785 Minckelers lit his lecture room by means of the inflammable gas obtained from coal.

Substantial claims to the application of gas to lighting were made by Phillippe Lebon in a paper read to the French Academy in 1798 in which he said:

> The gas, produced by heating wood in a closed retort, was first passed through water and...

On 28 September 1799 Lebon took out a patent to include the use of, 'coal, oil, resins, tallow and other combustible materials.' The patent also covered the use of gas for heating, lighting and cooking. By 1820 Paris had adopted gas street lighting.

Lebon was one of the outstanding inventors of the day and also took out a patent in 1801 which anticipated the internal combustion engine in that it detailed the mixing of air and gas under compression in a cylinder and its ignition by an electric spark, yet another example of brilliance that did not leave the drawing board.

Murdoch's arrival on the gas scene was noted by D. Chandler in *Lighting by Gas*,

> In 1792 Murdoch lit his house and offices with gas. Renewed research in 1797 when the Boulton & Watt Soho offices were lit by gas. Murdoch claimed to have devised a way in which gas could be used in a practical manner for the common good of the community.

It was the following recognition by the French that secured Murdoch an honoured place in the history of gas lighting.

René Masse, in his book *Le Gaz, Paris 1914,* believed that Murdoch had been the first to demonstrate gas being burnt at a different place to that where it had been produced (1794) and therefore named Redruth as the birthplace of the gas industry.[129]

According to Thomas Wilson, Mrs Paynter, Murdoch's mother-in-law, doubted that 'gas was conducted a considerable distance'. She 'positively denied that the gas was ever set fire to at a greater distance than the length of a gun barrel from a retort'.[130] Because she was a very elderly woman her remarks were not given much credibility. However, Francis was much more successful with another example of his remarkable luck in finding people who remember exactly what happened almost a century beforehand. He said, 'Those still live who saw the gas-pipes conveying gas from the retort in the little yard to near the ceiling of the room, just over the table. A hole for the pipe was made in the window frame'.[131] Whoever this was, they were very fortunate to be 'still live' with the full faculty of memory in their late 90s.

Speaking for himself in an address to the Royal Society on 25th February 1808, Murdoch said,

> It is now nearly sixteen years, since, in the course of my experiments I was making at Redruth in Cornwall, upon the quantities and qualities of the gases produced by distillation from different mineral and vegetable sources, I was induced by some observations I had previously made upon the burning of coal, to try the combustible property of the gases produced from it, as well as from peat, wood, and other inflammable substances. And being struck with the great quantities of gas which they afforded, as well as the brilliancy of the light, and the facility of its production, I instituted several experiments with a view to ascertaining the cost at which it might be obtained, compared with that of equal quantities of light yield by oils and tallow.[132]

Murdoch received the Royal Society's Rumford Medal in 1806 'For his publication of the employment of Gas from Coal, for the purpose of illumination'.[133]

Murdoch, the declining years
Murdoch eventually returned to the Soho factory from Cornwall in 1798[134] and promptly left the company when his pay was reported to be £100 pa. We can imagine his dissatisfaction as this may have been marginally lower than he was receiving in Cornwall, it was certainly no more. Murdoch returned to Boulton & Watt the following year as manager of the new Soho Foundry. It is almost certain that he negotiated a substantial increase in pay as, a year later, he signed a five year agreement with Boulton & Watt at £300 pa, plus 1% commission.[135]

Murdoch returned to Cornwall occasionally and wrote to Watt, Junior from Redruth in March 1800 to say he was about to be made a beneficial offer to stay in Cornwall.[136] He spent the summer of 1831 in Penzance with his ailing son, William Junior, who died there in June. Murdoch wrote few letters and left very little by way of notes. There is little or no mention on paper of any interest in mine machinery or steam carriages.[137]

William Buckle tells us that, prior to his departure from Cornwall the mine owners were so pleased with his maintenance of the Watt steam engines that they offered him £1,000 a year to remain in the county but he turned down the offer because of his attachment to Soho and his friends there.[138] Dickinson confirms that Murdoch received offers from mine owners to stay in Cornwall but did not quote any figures.[139]

We can imagine Murdoch's returns to Cornwall were much more convivial than his earlier life there had been. Following the end of the Watt patent and the demands for premiums, Murdoch would have been welcomed for his skills with steam engines as mine owners tried to persuade him to stay. It is likely that he even looked up old adversaries like Richard Trevithick who, being much more open than Murdoch, would have willingly shown him his developments in high-pressure steam. Although Murdoch worked for Watt, he had his own desires about the use of high-pressure as the force for the future and Trevithick's work would have enabled him to see that more clearly.

In 1815, Murdoch's leg was crushed in an industrial accident and he was disabled for the rest of his life. He subsequently became a director or partner in the company and, depending upon whose account you read, he accepted £1,000 a year in lieu of a salary and share of the profits. This was a canny move as he could see that the Watt engine had enjoyed its heyday and that profits would fall. By 1830 Watt Junior noticed that Murdoch's income was far greater than that of any of the partners and that, because of his increasing infirmities he did very little work.[140] Murdoch, one of the country's greatest inventive engineers, was retired in 1830 and died in November 1839 at the age of 86; he was buried in Handsworth churchyard, near the remains of Bolton & Watt.

Watt's proposed locomotive
Joseph Bramah said, 'Mr. Watt took out his patent not for what he had invented, but for what he might invent in the future.'[141]

Watt was often reported as saying that he had invented and patented a steam locomotive years before Trevithick but that claim is seldom explored. The features of a proposed self-propelled carriage contained in Watt's designs of 1769 and his subsequent patents of 1781 makes most interesting reading.

> In the patent granted to Mr. Watt in 1784 he gave an account of the adaptation of his mechanism to the propulsion of land-carriages. The boiler of this apparatus he proposed should be made of wooden staves, joined together, and fastened with iron hoops like a cask. The furnace to be of iron*, and placed in the inside of the boiler, so as to be surrounded on every side with water. The boiler was to be placed on a carriage, the wheels of which were to

* Lord Montagu of Beaulieu says in *Steam Cars, 1770 – 1970*, p 16, that the fire-box was made of copper.

56

receive their motion from a piston working in a cylinder, the reciprocating motion being converted into a rotary one by toothed wheels, revolving with a sun-and-planet motion, and producing the required velocity by a common series of wheels and pinions.

By means of two systems of wheel-work, differing in their proportion, he proposed to adapt the power of the machine to the varied resistance it might have to overcome from the state of the road. A carriage for two persons might, he thought, be moved with a cylinder of 7 inches in diameter, when the piston had a stroke of 1 foot, and make sixty strokes a minute. Mr. Watt, however, never built a steam-carriage [being too busily occupied with the perfecting of his condensing engine to proceed further with his proposed locomotive.][142]

Watt said, 'I soon relinquished the idea of constructing an engine upon this principle (high steam), from being sensible that it would be liable to some of the objections against Savery's engine, viz. the danger of bursting the boiler (constructed of wooden staves), and the difficulty of making the joints tight, and also that a great part of the power of the steam would be lost, because no vacuum was formed to assist the descent of the piston. I however described this engine in the fourth article of the specification of my patent on 1769, and again in the specification of another patent in the year 1784, together with a mode of applying it to the moving of wheel-carriages.'[143]

He found the boiler merely a hot-water tank and left it very little better.[144]

Trevithick is unlikely to have considered building a boiler in a wooden barrel and Watt's fears that it might explode were well-founded. The rest of the specification, including the location of the furnace within the boiler but omitting Trevithick's use of a double acting piston instead of Watt's precious vacuum, is very similar to Trevithick's 1801 locomotive. There is no indication that Trevithick knew the details of the road carriage in Watt's patent specification; reading boring documents was not his forte. Gilbert or Davy never referred to Trevithick having acquired ideas from Watt. They surely would have done had they noticed them.

Watt summed up his work on the locomotive by saying, 'I have given such descriptions of engines for wheel carriages as I could do in the time and space I could allow myself; but it is very defective and can only serve to keep other people from similar patents'.[145]

The fact that two inventors arrive at the same conclusion to a problem at about the same time is a co-incidence often found in science, and it usually causes trouble. It occurred with some of the characters in this book. Davy and George Stephenson both claim to have invented a very similar miners' lamp and Trevithick's high-pressure steam engine appeared before Oliver Evans built his engine in 1804,[146] although many Americans would have it that Evans was first!

While there was little significant difference in the designs by Watt and Trevithick, it was Trevithick's determination and the use of cast iron for the construction of his boiler that made him the winner. Trevithick's design of a satisfactory boiler and its creation in John Harvey's foundry was crucial to the subsequent exploitation of high-pressure steam. His ability in this area may have been due to what he had learnt at the Hayle foundry, one of the world's leading resources of engineering excellence in the late eighteenth century. In 1781 Watt probably knew very little about casting iron. Had he the skill and the self-belief of Trevithick together with the resources of the Harvey family, the story of the steam engine might have been different, but he hadn't and it wasn't.

By dismissing both his own and Murdoch's locomotives, Watt reveals something of his myopic vision towards the industrial steam engine. In a way, he was perfectly right to continue exploring how he and Boulton could recover their investment as quickly as possible by exploiting their sure source of revenue. Had he pursued other lines of experiment, as people like Hornblower and Trevithick did at every opportunity, he would have wasted precious time when he should have been making money. His attitude to Henry Bell's enthusiasm to build a steamboat illustrates his feelings about what he saw as peripheral matters. Bell, 1767 – 1830, continued on his quest, building a remarkable engine and installing it in the *Comet*, a little ship on the Clyde that became known as the mother of British steam shipping, but it did little for Bell.

As early as 1824 there were those who were casting doubts about Watt's position in the world of engineering science. Thomas Carlyle wrote to John A. Carlyle, Birmingham on 10 August 1824,

> The name of Watt has become synonymous with the steam engine in the eyes of the world, although some countries have their own claims for its invention. It is heartening to see that, in recent years, the academic world has shown an interest in the adulation shown to Watt. Several have questioned whether he was entitled to the reverence accorded to him in the titles of inventor and philosopher.'[147]

> Watt was undoubtedly a great inventor, as much because of the remarkable range of his eclectic mind and his insistence on checking every speculation by detailed, thorough and carefully recorded experiment as because of his skilful and occasionally unscrupulous plagiarisms.

And, in amplifying the suggestion that the historical records were 'cleaned' by James Watt Junior, he expresses the view that,

> While in many respects James Watt was a modest man, he was also inordinately jealous of his reputation as an inventor and philosopher, and James Junior seems to have been almost psychotically compelled to try to win from Watt's ghost a posthumous affection and approbation he had been denied in his lifetime, by maintaining and enhancing that reputation. This he did more ruthlessly and unscrupulously than the great inventor would have dreamed of doing for himself.[148]

On 18th June 1824, within five years of Watt's death, a public meeting was held at the Freemasons' Tavern, London, to discuss the erection of a monument to commemorate his life and achievements. Transcripts of the proceedings were published later that year.[149]

A committee of some seventy notables was created at the meeting to raise funds for a statue to commemorate Watt. It included The Earl of Liverpool, the current Prime Minister, who pledged £100, and was also empowered to pledge £500 towards the fund on behalf of His Majesty King William IV. Other members of the committee included the Rt. Hon. Robert Peel, MP, FRS, the Rt. Hon William Huskisson, MP, who was to die following a mishap with Stephenson's Rocket at the Rainhill Steam Locomotive Trials five years later, Sir Humphry Davy, PRS, Sir Walter Scott, FRS, Davies Gilbert, MP, FRS, J. H. Tremayne, Richard Arkwright, Matthew Boulton, FRS, William Murdoch, Thomas Telford, FRS, John Vivian, FRS, Josiah Wedgwood, FRS, and James Watt, Junior. FRS. Just over half of those listed in the report on the meeting were Fellows of the Royal Society. A full list is given in Appendix 1.

The members of this committee clearly subscribed sufficient funds to cover the cost of the statue and they produced a fighting fund to provide Watt with everlasting glory. It is almost impossible to believe, although an examination of the transcripts of the meeting has shown it to be true, that not one of the thirty-odd eminent Fellows of the Royal Society knew better, or was willing to raise his voice in the burgeoning Age of Steam against the proposition. It must have been at this time that Watt adoration reached hysterical proportions, something the retiring inventor is likely to have felt uncomfortable with. The transcripts also reveal that, while there were several in the group who knew that Watt was being applauded for something he did not do, no mention was made of advances since Watt's work or the name Trevithick.

After an opening address by the Earl of Liverpool, Davy, who was inclined to assert himself on these occasions, stood to speak of Watt,

I consider it as a duty incumbent on me to endeavour to set forth his peculiar and exalted merits, which live in the recollection of his contemporaries, and will, transmit his name with immortal glory to posterity.

He then continued to describe at length the applications of Watt's engines in powering industry and traversing the world, most of which were more truly attributable to engines built in accordance with Trevithick's principles. Davy was a scientist who had met Trevithick and had known the details of his engine for the previous twenty-two years. The meeting continued with sickening approbation and was summed up as follows,

> A time will come when the science of destruction will bend before the arts of peace; when the genius that multiplies our powers, which creates new products, which diffuses comfort and happiness among the great mass of the people, shall occupy, in the general estimation of mankind, that rank which reason and common sense now assign it.

> Then Watt will appear before the grand jury of the inhabitants of two worlds. Everyone will behold him, with the help of his steam engine, penetrating in a few weeks into the bowels of the earth, to depths which, before his time, could not have been reached without an age of the most toilsome labour, excavating vast mines, clearing them in a few minutes of the immense volume of water which daily inundates them, and extracting from a virgin soil the inexhaustible mineral treasures that nature has there deposited.

> Combining delicacy with power, Watt will twist, with equal success, the huge ropes of the gigantic cable by which the man-of-war rides at anchor in the midst of the raging ocean, and the microscopic filaments of the aerial gauze and lace of which fashionable dresses are so principally formed.

> A few strokes of the same engine will bring vast swamps into cultivation; and fertile countries will thus be spared the periodic returns of pestilential fevers, caused in those places by the heat of the summer sun.

> The great mechanical powers which had formerly to be sought for in mountainous districts, at the foot of rapid cascades, will, thanks to Watt's invention, readily and easily arise in the midst of towns, on any storey of a house.

> The extent of these powers will vary at the will of the mechanician; it will no longer depend, as heretofore, on the most inconstant of natural causes, on atmospheric influences.

The common branches of each manufacture may be carried on in one common place, under the same roof; and their products, as they are perfectioned, will diminish in price.

The population well supplied in food, with clothing, and with fuel, will rapidly increase; it will, by degrees, cover with elegant mansions, every part of the earth; even those which might justly have been termed the Steppes of Europe, and which the barrenness of ages seemed to condemn to be, forever, the exclusive domain of wild beast.

In a few years, hamlets will become great towns; in a few years, boroughs, such as Birmingham, where there could be counted thirty streets, will take their place among the largest; the handsomest, and the richest cities of a mighty kingdom.

Installed in ships, the steam engine will exercise a power a hundredfold greater than the triple and quadruple ranks of rowers, of whom our forefathers were wont to exact a labour which is deemed a punishment for the most atrocious criminals.

By the help of a few bushels of coal, man will vanquish the elements; he will play with calms and contrary winds and storms. The passage from one place to another will be much more speedily accomplished; the moment of arrival of the packets may be known beforehand, like that of public coaches; no one will any longer wander on the shore for whole weeks and months, with a heart tortured with anguish, watching with restless eye the horizon for the dim outline of a vessel, which is to restore a father, a mother, a brother, or a friend.

Lastly: the steam engine, drawing in its train thousands of travellers, will run on railroads with far greater speed than the swiftest racehorse, carrying only his light jockey.

Such is a very brief sketch of the benefits which have been bequeathed to the world by that machine.'

It is possible to detect numerous flaws in this statement and wince whenever Watt is credited with building locomotives that power the railway trains of the world.‡ In fairness to Watt, he never professed to have invented or improved as much as was claimed on his behalf.

It was true that the atmospheric engines produced by Boulton & Watt were the basis for British industry but by the time of the meeting they were outmoded and most had been scrapped or modified to high-pressure steam. It was twenty years since Trevithick had demonstrated his first high-pressure steam railway locomotive at Penydarren and some of the delegates would have arrived in London behind locomotives built on his steam principles. The situation was akin to holding a celebratory meeting about the (very worthy) man who invented the radio valve some years after the arrival of the transistor, and then not mentioning Texas Instruments or the transistor.* This hypocrisy concerning Watt's pre-eminence was being firmly established and it would flourish.†

It must be remembered that this was not the first time that Watt had received Royal patronage. When he sought an extension of his patent of 1769 to relate to any engine that operated by the use of steam, his petition and subsequent extension in 1775 for its renewal would, '…clog engineering enterprise for more than a generation'.‡ It received the Royal Assent.

L. T. C. Rolt summed up the situation concerning Watt,

> For Watt retained his prejudice against high-pressure steam to the last. He had brought about a power revolution in his lifetime, but having come so far he would go no further. He had fought off his rivals so stubbornly because he refused to accept the fact that his engine, like himself, was growing old; that both must inevitably give way to new men and new machines.[150]

Returning to the plan to create a statue to Watt, not everyone was convinced that the admiration accorded to Watt was well merited. When Thomas Carlyle wrote to his brother, he said,

> I do and must call Marcus Brutus a more virtuous man than James Watt of Soho near Brummagem, come of it what will: yet for its utility the steam-engine was worth five hundred deaths of Caesar.' Thomas Carlyle to John A. Carlyle, Birmingham, 10 August 1824,

When the statue was eventually raised, it bore the inscription,

* In 1956 Walter Brattain, John Bardeen and William Shockley shared the Nobel Prize for physics for their invention of the transistor.

† Mistakenly repeated to this day. *Genius of Britain* programme, Channel 4, 31st May 2010

‡ Thomas S. Ashton, 1899-1968, a professor of economic history at the London School of Economics whose best publication is reputed to be *The Industrial Revolution (1760 - 1830),* published in 1961

Not to perpepuate a name which must endure while the peaceful arts flourish but to shew that mankind have learned to honour those who best deserve their gratitude the King his Ministers and many of the nobles and commoners of the realm raised this monument to JAMES WATT who directing the force of an original genius early exercised in philosophic research to the improvement of the steam engine enlarged the resources of his country increased the power of man and rose to an eminent place among the most illustrious followers of science and the real benefactors of the world.

The monument carrying this hyperbole was on a scale baffling and even distressing to later generations.[151]

Nikolaus Pevsner noted that the monument cost £6,234, a very significant sum. When the divided base was dragged into St Paul's Chapel of Westminster Abbey its weight broke through the floor breaking the lid of a medieval tomb and revealing numerous gilded coffins beneath.[152]

> This chapel and everything in the neighbourhood, is utterly dwarfed by an enormous statue of James Watt, who made some improvements in the steam engine; it should be carted off to the Embankment, where it would be in scale with the Shot Tower and the Cecil Hotel.[153]

The gigantic marble statue by Chantrey was eventually removed from the Chapel in December 1960 and replaced by a simple plaster bust presented by the Institute of Engineers. The monument was placed in the Transport Commission Museum, then at Clapham.[154] The statue is currently in the Scottish National Portrait Gallery and is destined for the Heriot-Watt University.

It is clear that the enthusiasm shown in 1824 has eventually been moderated and the outcome of the zeal has proved an embarrassment. Having been shunted from pillar to post the colossal refugee will inevitably reside at an institution that finds it very difficult to refuse it asylum. Watt would have been totally embarrassed by this whole sad affair.

At the time of the meeting in the Freemasons' Hall Trevithick was fighting for his life in the jungles of Central America. He was doing this in the belief that his family was well rewarded from royalties on his plunger pole engine being gathered by William Simms. He was seeking his fortune in the manner of the pure adventurer and inventor. He had little appreciation of man's attraction to greed and status and how, in his absence, it would deprive him of what he considered was rightfully his.

Had Trevithick known about the meeting he would have wondered about those he considered to be his friends and supporters. Why had they not had a good word to say for him? There were many John Vivians, was this the one who had driven his carriage through London in 1803? It was certainly the Davies Gilbert in whom he had implicit faith. Trevithick was being revealed as a sad trusting pawn to Gilbert's scheming bishop.

Although Watt's name will be inextricably, and often erroneously, linked to the invention and development of the steam engine throughout its long history, he and earlier chroniclers would consciously refer to his work as 'improvement'. In a letter to Boulton revealing his frustrations over those who chose to defy his patents, '… if I had not a very distinct recollection of my doing it, their impudent assertions would lead me to doubt whether I was the author of any improvements on the steam-engine …'.[155]

Chantry's marble statue of James Watt.

In these enlightened times it is still seen as politically correct to applaud Watt's contribution to the development of steam power rather than Trevithick's, even in Cornwall where there is something to be gained. The 200-word description of Cornwall's Mining World Heritage Site prepared for the Local Authorities World Heritage Forum in the 2012 Cultural Olympiad Project draws attention to the many Cornish mines and their engines but fails to attribute them to Trevithick's inventiveness. It merely says, 'Great Wheal Busy was reputedly the site where in the 1770s James Watt introduced some of his early improvements to the steam engine'.[156]

Boulton & Watt Partnership

The twenty-five year partnership between Boulton & Watt is usually cited as a perfect example of co-operation between two intelligent men of fundamentally different backgrounds, fortune, culture and attitude who appreciated each other and saw the advantages in a common purpose. Some historians remark on Watt's canny ability to acquire and keep Boulton as a partner so that he might support and finance the development of his improved steam engine. Almost in the same breath they castigate Trevithick for not doing exactly the same thing; it makes agreeable and understandable story-writing. The Boulton and Watt partnership situation may not be as we are often led to believe.

As we have seen, Boulton possessed an entrepreneurial flair that fed on other people's ideas and cash. He drew these together in a flamboyant manner that attracted the attention of those people he chose to impress. The quality and prodigious output of his Soho factory caught the attention of wealthy buyers throughout the world. While the business blossomed it lacked a steady hand on the tiller to control its day-to-day operations. When problems arose Boulton tended to buy his way out of trouble by either increasing the facilities of his factory or borrowing more money, very often both.

An early response from Boulton to an enquiry concerning their terms of trade describes what we would call a set of 'do-it-yourself' instructions,

> As to the price of and Engine whose cylinder is 12 inches, I cannot pretend to say because we only sell the license for erecting our Engines, and the purchacer of such licence erects his Engine at his own expence. However in general I can acquaint you that the price of our Engine is not more but rather less than that of an Old Engine of equal power. It is quite inconsistent with our plan to give a licence for erecting engines when and where you please. We make an agreement for each engine distinctly, and the profit we reserve to ourselves is one third of the savings made by the use of our Engine instead of one of the old construction. The sum therefore to be paid during the working of any Engine is not to be determined by the diameter of the Cylinder, but by the quantity of coals saved & by the price of coals at the place where the Engine is erected.[157]

The standard agreement included some important restrictions, such as the prohibition on the movement of the engine and the 'old construction' is clearly a reference to the Newcomen engine. The arrival of Watt's improved engine did not, as is frequently supposed, seal the death knell of its predecessor, the Newcomen, in other parts of the country. Between 1775 and the end of the patent protection period it is estimated that the total number of Boulton & Watt engines including rebuilds totalled 550 while a thousand Newcomen engines were built in the same period,[158] to be added to those already in use.

Many of the major Watt engine components were made in William Wilkinson's foundry in Denbighshire, North Wales and at his half-brother John's ironworks in Shropshire. From there they would be shipped to Cornwall and elsewhere. The costs of this bespoke manufacture and transport were enormous.

John Wilkinson was enterprising although not altogether honest and, following a family row, William, his younger brother, divulged to Boulton & Watt that John had been making similar engines on his own account. Although this is often suggested as the cause of Boulton establishing his own foundry at Soho, Smethwick, a letter from Watt,

Junior to Wilson stated that Wilkinson had stayed with them in Birmingham as 'an old friend', had paid up all his dues and promised not to make further engines without their consent.[159] This repentance could have been attributed to Boulton having opened his foundry for the manufacture of steam engines in January 1796 with a luncheon for 200 guests[160] earlier that year, so reducing the opportunity for clandestine manufacture.

This move to produce the majority of the engine parts 'in house' at the home of the manufacturer was a major departure from the previous practice of having the work sub-contracted to ironworks that were either the choice of the manufacturer or close to the point of erection.

By 1780 Boulton & Watt had sold forty pumping engines, twenty of them in Cornwall. Watt could do nothing by way of a cash injection to the business but his anticipated steam engine royalties were mortgaged for £7,000. Watt was living a great part of his life in Cornwall where he was burdened by overwhelming debt and the attitude of the local mine owners. He would frequently write to Boulton about his distress caused by 'sickness, headaches, and low spirits; by the pecuniary difficulties of the firm; by the repeated attempts of the Cornish miners to lower their dues; and the threatened invasion of his patent from all quarters'.[161]

Watt was thoroughly sick of Cornwall where he could see the problems of the Cornish miners and spoke of them starving. He imagined they saw him and Boulton as some incarnation of the Devil and wrote to Boulton,

> In short almost the whole county is against us and look upon us as oppressors and tyrants from whose power they believe the horned imps of Satan are to relieve them.[162]

Letters mentioned other troubles, even telling him to wear a waxed linen coat and bring one for himself, 'as there is no going out now for a few miles without getting wet to the skin. When it rains in Cornwall, and it rains often, it rains solid'.[163]

Watt was seldom happy in Cornwall and he must have made Boulton despair at times. After he discovered he had been duped by the Hornblowers, Boulton had to bolster Watt's spirits, dispelling his despondency and visions of doom. Boulton asked him to calculate the potential return on his labours, 'what all the engines we shall have in eighteen months erected in Cornwall will amount to: you will find good for low spirits'.[164]

Watt, a nervous man, continued to worry about the parlous state of his partner's financial dealings as a report stated,

The Soho works speedily became famous all over England. Yet, in 1780, Watt and Boulton were still out of pocket by his inventions, and as late as 1783, when the former was forty-seven years old, they had reaped no profit. But for an Act passed in 1775 to continue the rights of the patentees to the year 1800 … the inventor must have been entirely deprived of the rewards of his labour'.[165]

We can only guess what Boulton thought of his partner, the whining Watt, and how attention to his needs interfered with his chosen lifestyle but the steam engine business, being mainly outside the daily shenanigans at Soho, was to prove substantially lucrative.

Historians frequently suggest that Trevithick would have done well to have found himself someone like Matthew Boulton as a partner but it is doubtful if that thought ever crossed his mind. When anyone made such a suggestion Trevithick turned on his heel and walked out, never to return. He would never have had the patience of Watt to put up with such a fanatical partner: Boulton was too much like himself.

Following the discovery of the 'Great Lode' of copper at Parys Mountain, Anglesey in 1768, the subsequent mining developments presented serious competition for Cornish mine owners. The culture of blame in Cornwall for any financial problems connected to mining was immediately aimed at Watt for his premium charges. It was calculated that the imposition of Boulton & Watt's charge on the benefits gained by the use of their engines added one and a half guineas a ton to the price of Cornish copper and two guineas to the price of tin.[166] A more logical observer would have noticed that, at the time, the copper in Anglesey was won from an open cast pit high on a mountainside where any unwanted water could be channelled away in streams and adits down to sea level. This gave the Welsh miners a considerably lower cost than the Cornish who faced the dreadful expense of pumping water up from hundreds of feet below ground. It was not until a hundred years later that a windmill was erected on Parys Mountain to pump water from the mines.[167] Also, the Anglesey method of mining and refining copper ore with iron in ponds was financially advantageous.

The economic situation provided controversial opportunities for the iron founder and manufacturer of Watt's engines, John Wilkinson along with Boulton, to set up cartels and to force Cornish mine owners into agreements within the Cornish Metal Company and the Birmingham Mining & Copper Company. John Vivian was appointed manager of the Cornish Metal Company. These arrangements aimed to provide the Anglesey miners a fair profit on a smaller output and the Cornish a living by maintaining the price of copper at £80 a ton but deals were done by both the Welsh and Cornish at lower prices outside the cartel[168] and by 1792 the agreements had collapsed.

In spite of the plans of Wilkinson and others, the late 1780s were bad for Cornish mining and Boulton's actions, aimed at providing copper for his ormolu production, and did nothing for the popularity of Watt. The competition from Anglesey caused problems in the operation of Cornish mines and social unrest. Whilst the miners rioted, the owners withheld their payments to Boulton & Watt. The account of the closures, riots and the arrival of the military that were told to fire on the miners but refused, are documented by John Griffiths.[169]

Watt was caught up in the quarrels and wished he was a thousand miles away. It was clear that there would always be disputes between him and those using his engines. The scenario of a grasping Scot trying to get money from a tight-fisted Cornishman does not conjure up a scene of contentment and delight. Until he left Cornwall Watt would be embroiled in many confrontations concerning payments; they all badly affected his health and nerves. The following report was a typical worry for Watt.

> The Adventurers at Tin Croft mine received a demand from Boulton & Watt for £3,684 in respect of using a machine erected by Hornblower. 'A great many proprietors of mines besides those of Tin Croft are attacked in the same manner and it appears to be the universal resolution of the whole of them to resist the demand by every legal means that can be devised.'[170]

This was the situation in Cornwall whilst Trevithick was growing up. While one can understand Watt's uncomfortable position and his anxiety attacks, it did not affect Trevithick, being the cut and thrust of practical business dealings in which there was little or no compromise to be found.

As he saw it, Watt stood little chance of recovering the monies due to him from the wretched Cornish mine owners; this was his future income that Boulton had so glibly mortgaged to their creditors. Isolated in Cornwall, far from his friends and his desired way of life, he took no comfort from Boulton's assurances (very similar to those made by Trevithick to his family) that one day he would receive the just deserts of his labours.

> Although Watt and his partner succeeded in their lawsuits they were nearly ruined by the expense of litigation. During the last four years of their patent alone, these expenses amounted to between five and six thousand pounds.[171]

Boulton's intervention was clearly a great help to Watt who willingly admitted that he could not face the business side of their enterprise. Boulton took their company right to the brink of disaster but his son and James Watt, Junior, managed to turn it round to show a considerable profit. In this, their timing was crucial as the high-pressure engines emerged in hundreds following the expiry of the Boulton & Watt patent in 1800.

Boulton and Watt retired as wealthy men, an indication to casual observers that they had conducted a thriving business during their partnership, taken advantage of the opportunities as they presented themselves, controlled their expenditure and garnered nest eggs for their declining years. Apart from Boulton seizing business opportunities and both men working very hard, their partnership was very different from that perceived by indifferent historians. A great deal of their fortune was due to the intolerant attitude of Watt's son, James Watt Junior, who took on the organisation and running of the Foundry and turned it around to become 'a positive gold mine'.[172] Boulton's son, Matthew Robinson Boulton was admitted as a partner along with Watt, Junior in 1794 but we do not hear of a similar interest in the operation of the company although he was sent to Cornwall to collect outstanding dues, something he successfully achieved. Although neither had the entrepreneurial or inventive skills of their fathers they restructured the accounts and regulated the staff levels and activities; at last the enterprise started to show a profit.

We do not know the details of Boulton and Watt's pension plans so this is mere conjecture. It is interesting to draw comparisons between Boulton and other people who might have been privileged to inherit four fortunes. Most would have carefully invested the money and lived comfortably, maybe quietly, off the proceeds: not Boulton. One wonders whether he retired a wealthier man than he became during life; or, in other words, was all his effort and the heartache experienced by Watt and others worth the trouble. Of course, there was no way that Boulton would have lived a quiet life and, had he done so, he would not have encouraged Watt who, with Newcomen before him, provided the basis for the Industrial Revolution. Their industrial power created the initial demand for cotton and other raw materials, so provided the circumstances that generated wealth and shaped the British Empire.

During the heyday of Newcomen and Boulton & Watt, the industrial world was unaware of high-pressure steam so there was an exciting market for the atmospheric engine, something that would continue to grow as various improvements were judiciously added. Boulton must surely have seen that one day something more efficient would replace it but other than ridiculing Trevithick's high-pressure engine at every opportunity and ensuring that its inventor did not have the exposure enjoyed by Watt and himself, it was not his concern.

Boulton had invested heavily in the technology and he had to ensure that it was protected by patents and brought to the market place in the most expeditious manner. He would choose which ideas to develop; double action and parallel motion, something that grew out of Watt's perspective machine based on the work in 1765 of Mr Hurst in India. The variable valve opening and Murdoch's sun-and-planet gear were vital improvements to be incorporated as soon as they had been commercially developed.

The Dutch connection

It is only natural that the manufacturers of the world's first pumps to lift substantial quantities of water should seek opportunities to sell their machines. So important were their products that the world beat the proverbial path to their door. The Dutch decision to drain their lowlands made them potential customers and a number of Newcomen engines had been built in Holland. Initial contact was made by a Dutchman with an English businessman called John Enslie, a partner in a Dutch business firm who was also acquainted with Watt.

In recent years a considerable correspondence between Watt and the Dutchman, Jan Daniël Huichelbos van Liender, has been examined in connection with the pumping of the lowlands of Holland. This correspondence covers the period from 1769 to 1809, from the very beginning of Watt's first patent, before his partnership with Boulton, to nine years after his official retirement date. This research has been carried out by the late Jan A Verbruggen, a former member of the Trevithick Society, whose work spanned ten years in this country and elsewhere. In addition to the 346 letters he transcribed between Watt and correspondents in Holland, he believed that 187 were known to have been destroyed in the Rotterdam blitz of May 1940 and the innumerable letters and private papers of van Liender were probably destroyed by his family. Nevertheless, the Verbruggen thesis runs to nearly 500 pages.

It is remarkable that very little trace has been found of this activity during forty years of Watt's life and a great deal of Boulton's. There is one small clue to be found in Boulton's letter of 19th May 1779 to Watt in Cornwall that begins, 'Chelsea engine was set to work on the day I set out for Holland'.[173] Both men travelled to Holland and were engaged in sufficient work to have fully employed them without all their business in England and Cornwall. Howard[174] states that Boulton & Watt were reluctant to sell engines to Holland because they could not obtain a Dutch patent. However, they eventually built engines there. A scan of eleven on-line books by Google concerned with the history of the Boulton & Watt partnership has revealed several references to Holland but only in the context of windmills, holidays, trips up the Rhine by James Watt, Junior and examinations of Dutch methods of land reclamation to provide ideas for the drainage of the East Anglian fens. Smiles in his *Lives of Boulton & Watt* refers to an undisclosed number of orders being received from Holland and Watt's fears that the Europeans might ascertain their designs and start manufacturing competitive engines.

The story of Boulton & Watt's connections to Holland is being mentioned because it is more than just an episode and it links to Trevithick's abortive tie with Holland many years later. He received orders for steam engines including a floating pump and made disasters of all these remarkable opportunities. Henry Harvey eventually sold the largest steam engines in the world to the Dutch.

Watt's relationship with Trevithick

There was the strongly held belief that the antagonism between Watt and the Cornish mine owners spilled over into his relationship with Trevithick. One example, from the *Mining Almanack for 1849* clearly illustrated this,

> The Watt party were able to retaliate in time and their northern adherents have exercised a serious retribution for wherever the name of a Cornish engineer comes before them they never fail to decry his claims and to blacken his reputation. This in a great degree accounts for the neglect of Trevithick whose share in the Watt quarrel was never forgiven or forgotten particularly when he became the decided champion of the high pressure system.[175]

While there was the underlying resentment felt by both sides about the financial behaviour of the other and Watt was not happy with Trevithick or the Cornish people in general, Trevithick followed a path he had fashioned for himself and he did not waver, irrespective of what the analysts and academics have said subsequently. Much has been made of the problems and conclusions are often drawn that a great deal of Trevithick's obscurity in the engineering world is credited to Watt's assertion of his supremacy. There is little or no evidence to support this view.

Watt's position was that of an unhappy innovator working to capitalise on the money that his creation was generating for him. In this he was faced by financially astute businessmen who did not want to give it to him. Watt would have preferred to have continued as an inventor and left the monetary matters to others. In this respect he was remarkably like Trevithick and had a similar strong desire to walk away, something he managed, unlike Trevithick, to overcome. When Watt found he was out of his depth in dealing with Cornish mine owners he would call for assistance from Boulton or Thomas Wilson, his agent in Cornwall.

Watt did not stand in the way of Trevithick other than to enforce his patent. Boulton & Watt were in severe financial difficulties and it fell to Watt to recover as much as he could from those people who were using his patented engine. He also had to prevent the development of other engines that would conflict with his patent and undermine their financial position. His actions were nothing more than those expected of any businessman who was working hard to protect his interests.

Watt did not want to be a personal problem to Trevithick. He could barely wait for his patent to expire so he could leave Cornwall. Murdoch had left a couple of years previously and when the day of Watt's release arrived he fled and never returned. Watt's patent expired just when Trevithick was establishing his high-pressure puffer steam engine; the interests of the two men barely overlapped. Apart from Trevithick's impatience in the previous two years, the timing could not have been more opportune for Trevithick.

This was Trevithick's chance. The thorn in his side had gone and the annoying patent had expired. Trevithick's little engine was proven and a whole new world of steam power was at his feet. Engineering works and foundries all over the country were clamouring to build the engines. The next five years, until just after the Penydarren railway triumph, were crucial to Trevithick. It is easy to see now that these were the years when Trevithick could have behaved in a manner similar to Watt and secured his future and his fortune.

He did not do so. Many said that he was he own worst enemy, a phrase that was probably not understood by Trevithick in respect of his personal activities. Instead of consolidating his position in 1804 by refining and developing his engine for the people who were showing increasing interest, Trevithick continued to seek new applications for its power, something his customers would willingly have done for him. Boulton & Watt's denunciations of his high-pressure steam were the ploys of their marketing strategy. While he worried about their effects he would never see the thrust of Brutus was to come from within.

References

32. *The Mechanics' Magazine and Journal of Engineering,* Volume 14, 1865. p341
33. *Ibid* pp 4-5
34. *Finance and Industry in the Eighteenth Century: The Firm of Boulton & Watt* J. E. Cule 1940 pp4-6
35. *Matthew Boulton, Selling what all the world desires* Ed. Shena Mason, p2, 2009
36. *Matthew Boulton* H. W. Dickinson 1936 p97
37. *Lives of the Engineers, with an account of their principal works,* Volume 4 S. Smiles, p314
38. *Matthew Boulton, Selling what all the world desires* p10, 2009
39. *Matthew Boulton* H. W. Dickinson 1936 p108
40. *Matthew Boulton, Selling What all the World Desires.* p3
41. *The Life and Time of Joseph Priestly* http://www.search.revolutionaryplayers.org.uk
42. http://www.electricscotland.com
43. http://www.broseley.org.uk
44. *The Temple Anecdotes* R. & C. Temple, 1865 p 33
45. *The Life of James Watt with Selections from his Correspondence* J. P. Muirhead p vi
46. *Ibid* p 23

47. *Ibid* p 217

48. *Ibid* p 8

49. *The Commercial & Ideological importance of being a philosopher, ... James Watt.* D P Miller, Uni of NSW, p 298

50. *The Ascent of Money* Niall Ferguson, p 167

51. Ibid p197

52. *Darwin to Watt,* 18 Aug 1767

53. *The Pursuit of Knowledge,* G. L. Craik, 1831, p307

54. *Little Journeys to the Homes of the Great* - Volume 06. Elbert Hubbard, p92

55. *Ibid*, p81

56. Abstract from Newcomen Society Volume 76 (1), pp51-86

57. *The Eclectic Magazine of Foreign Literature, Science ...*1856 Volume 39, p540

58. *Stuart's descriptive history of the Steam Engine,* 1824 p112

59. *Ibid*, p113

60. *Life of Trevithick* Francis Trevithick Volume , p115

61. *James Watt,* Dickinson & Titley p 336

62. *Treatise on the Steam Engine* Volume 1 Farey p7

63. *Between Hostile Camps: Sir Humphry Davy's Presidency of the Royal Society of London, 1820-1827* David Philip Miller Uni of NSW

64. *Lives of the Engineers.* S. Smiles 1862 Volume 3 p177

65. *James Watt,* L. T. C. Rolt, p73

66. *Ibid*, p74

67. *Treatise on the Cornish Pumping Engine* William Pole p20

68. *Chacewater's Famous Engines* Ashley Rowe

69. *A Compendium of the History of Cornwall* 1880. John J. Daniell, p248

70. *James Watt* Andrew Carnegie, p131

71. *James Watt & the Steam Engine* Dickinson & Jenkin p78

72. http://www.penrosefam.com Susan Woodland, US

73. *Josiah Hornblower & the First Steam Engine in America* William Nelson, NJ History Society, 1883. p178

74. James Watt to Matthew Boulton, 16 July 1781

75. *Matthew Boulton* HW Dickinson 1936 p96

76. *Around Truro* Ashley Rowe, Susan Howard http://www. horwitzfam.org

77. *Chacewater's Famous Engines* Ashley Rowe *West Briton*

78. James Watt to James Watt Jnr 12 Nov 1808 *James Watt & the Steam Engine* Dickinson & Jenkins p75

79. *James Watt & the Steam Engine* Dickinson & Jenkin p129

80. *Dictionary of National Biography* p354-5

81. *Transactions of The Moravian Historical Society, Moravian Immigration to Pennsylvania 1734-1767* Vol 5 Part 2 printed 1896 compiled by John N .Jordan

82. *The First Steam Engine in America,* New Jersey Historical Society. p191

83. *Ibid*

84. http://en.wikipedia.org/wiki/Erasmus_Darwin#Inventions

85. *The Engineer* 7 December 1866, p436.

86. *The Engines of Our Ingenuity* is Copyright © 1988-2005 by John H. Lienhard

87. James Watt Jnr to Wilson 13.05.1796 CRO AD1583/9/24

88. *John Harvey to Davies Gilbert* RIC 26 June 1813

89. *Elemental treatise on steam & locomotion, based on the principle of connecting science with practice in a popular form*, John Sewell, 1852, p278

90. *Wm Murdoch* J. R. Taylor 1993, p 17

91. *News from Cwll* WJ Richard Phillips 30 July 1795 p 37

92. *Railway Machinery, a treatise on the mechanical engineering of railways* D. K. Clark 1855 XX

93. *Wm Murdoch,* J. R. Taylor p27

94. *Ibid* p31c.

95. *3rd Man* John Griffiths p219

96. *Life of Richard Trevithick.* Francis Trevithick Volume 1 p146

97. *Ibid* Volume 1, p151

98. *The Story of the Vivians.* Stanley Vivian, p 73

99. *3rd Man* John Griffiths, p345

100. *Ibid,* p115

101. *Railway Machinery, a treatise on the mechanical engineering of railways* D. K. Clark, 1855 p2

102. *Life* Volume 1 p147

103. *Life of George Stephenson* S. Smiles, p64

104. *Birmingham Stories,* The Thinktank Trust

105. *The Third Man* John Griffiths 1992, p162

106. *The Eclectic Magazine,* Volume 61, 1864, p133

107. *Gentleman's Magazine* Volume 215, Dec 1863, p792

108. *The Biographical Notice of William Murdoch* IMechE October 1850 p19

109. *The Third Man,* John Griffiths 1992, p161

110. http://www.adam-matthews-publications.co.uk

111. *Life of Richard Trevithick* Volume 1 Francis Trevithick p147

112. *Ibid* Vol 1 p148

113. In the possession of the Trevithick Society

114. *The Third Man* John Griffiths 1992, p164

115. *Ibid,* p161

116. *Ibid,* p165

117. Richard Trevithick to Davies Gilbert 8th October 1803 RIC

118. *William Murdoch* J. R. Taylor p44

119. www.penrosefam.net

120. *The Biographical Notice of William Murdoch* Wm Buckle, Proceedings of the IMechEng Oct 1850. p17

121. Title by Giancarlo Maiorino, pub 1992

122. *The Modern Steam Engine.* John Richardson p153, fig 45

123. *The Third Man* John Griffiths 1992, p155

124. *James Watt & the Steam Engine* Dickinson & Jenkins p308

125. *Ibid* p309

126. *Wm Murdoch*, J. R. Taylor p42

127. *The Third Man* Griffiths p204

128. *Murdoch Flyer Project,* Issue no. 17

129. *The Third Man* John Griffiths, p242

130. *Ibid* p246

131. *Ibid* p247-8

132. *Ibid* p239

133. Royal Society Archives

134. *Wm Murdoch*, J. R. Taylor p44

135. *Ibid* p 44

136. *James Watt & the Steam Engine* Dickinson and Jenkin p296

137. *Wm Murdoch,* J. R. Taylor p50

138. *The Biographical Notice of William Murdoch* Wm Buckle, Proceedings of the IMechE Oct 1850

139. *Matthew Boulton* H. W. Dickinson 1936 p170

140. *James Watt & the Steam Engine* Dickinson and Jenkin p297

141. *The Third Man* John Griffiths p196

142. *Life of George Stephenson.* Samuel Smiles and Robert Stephenson, p63.

143. *A Treatise on the Steam Engine,* Volume 2, p5 John Farey.

144. *Industrial Power in the U.S.* Hunter, Bryant and Mills, p317

145. James Watt to Matthew Boulton 17 Aug 1784,
    http://www.steamreplicas.co.uk/BoultonWattCollection.asp

146. *History and progress of the steam engine,* Galloway and Herbert, 1829, p303

147. *The collected letters of Thomas and Jane Welsh Carlyle*, iii: *1824–25* (Durham, 1970), 120–4, Charles Richard Sanders (ed.), p123

148. (Griffiths, *op. cit.* (ref. 21), 345, 348). *Between Hostile Camps* David Philip Miller, University of New South Wales, p21

149. Pamphlet, Cornwall Studies Library, Redruth c/621.1092

150. *Great Engineers,* L. T. C. Rolt p129

151. *The buildings of England. London 1* p245 Nikolaus Pevsner

152. *Westminster Abbey website*

153. *The buildings of England. London 1* Nikolaus Pevsner p246

154. See: *Westminster Abbey* (London, 1987) Edward Carpenter and David Gentleman.

155. *Life of James Watt* Arago, Brougham & Vaux, p57

156. http://www.lawhf.gov.uk

157. *AoS ref.MS 3147/3/81/44* Verbruggen p17

158. *Matthew Boulton, Selling what all the world desires,* p69, 2009

159. James Watt, Jnr. to Wilson, 9.08.1796, CRO

160. *Wm Murdock* J. R. Taylor 1992 p43

161. *Lives of Boulton & Watt* Smiles p311

162. James Watt to Matthew Boulton 27 March 1782

163. *Lives of Boulton & Watt,* Smiles p260

164. *James Watt and the Steam Engine* Dickinson and Jenkin. p53

165. *Ibid* p88

166. *The Third Man* John Griffiths p170

167. http://www.anglesey-history.co.uk/windmills/ParysMountain/index.html

168. http://www.oldcopper.org/Wilkinson

169. *The Third Man,* John Griffiths. Chapter Eight

170. *News from Cornwall,* William Jenkin to George Wilbraham 2 Oct 1799, p73.

171. *Temple Anecdotes.* p105

172. *Matthew Boulton* H. W. Dickinson 1936 p172

173. http://www.adam-matthews-publications.co.uk

174. http://www.penrosefam.org Susan Woodland, US

175. *The Mining Almanack for 1849* Henry English, p304

III   Davies (Giddy) Gilbert, MP, PRS, 1767-1839, family and friends

Davies Giddy, St Erth

A story of Richard Trevithick cannot be told without the inclusion of Davies Gilbert, a formidable Cornishman who began life as Davies Giddy. Gilbert was just four years older than Trevithick, a very clever man who is described by numerous writers as Trevithick's lifelong friend, mentor and patron. Trevithick wrote to Gilbert from the early days in the development of high-pressure steam and Gilbert answered his questions. While they sometimes differed in their opinions we do not find them quarrelling. Gilbert had the ability and opportunities to promote Trevithick in the highest places in the land; how well did he do that? This is Gilbert's life as it related to Trevithick and some of the people he knew.

Davies Giddy was born the son of an impoverished country curate at St Erth in Cornwall. Today the village is a haven of tranquillity but in the late eighteenth century, it was a hive of noisy activity with a copper rolling mill driven by a water wheel next to the bridge and close to the church. We find Davies Giddy, one day to become the President of the Royal Society, growing up in surroundings similar to those we associate with Trevithick.

His father Edward Giddy, 1734 - 1814, was born at Calenick near Truro and attended Truro Grammar School before going to Oxford University. Unable to find other suitable employment he was ordained curate of St Erth parish in 1757 and received a stipend of just £35 a year. Davies Gilbert's family lived at Tredrea, a manor farm house that had been rebuilt in about 1750 and was listed as a gentleman's seat in *Magna Britannica Vol 3, 1814*. It was here that his mother and grandmother scraped a living. Gilbert recalls a hard life in which he and the family would, 'sit on Winter Evenings round a very small Fire and without a candle'.[176] His mother, Catherine Davies, was born in 1728, and inherited the fine house. She was described in *Huguenot Pedigrees* as co-heir of the barony of Sandys-by-the-Vine of Tredrea.[177] Although she was subsequently, and rather grandly, frequently referred to as an heiress, the property brought in a meagre £40 a year, barely enough to cover the cost of its upkeep. Catherine also brought the Manor of Amyll an Tryll and the moiety of Chiverton into the partnership but these were held in trust by Samuel Stephens of St Ives from the time of her marriage, probably in respect of the dowry she raised.[178] There is a record of Rev. Edward Giddy of St Erth being in receipt of arms on the 8th June 1770[179] although we will see other sources suggest that he was a wealthy man by this time.

Before we go any further, the confusion about Davies Gilbert's name should be explained. Although he sometimes signed his first name in the more common Cornish form without the 'e', (notice how Humphry Davy is correctly spelt) he uses his given name, his mother's maiden name, in most official documents such as his last great publication, the four volumes of *The Parochial History of Cornwall* and on the coat of arms in his 1801 journal. The latter bears the motto *Mallem Mori Quam Mutare*; Latin for 'Death before compromise' and *Teg Tw Hedwch* meaning 'Peace is beautiful' (although linguists agree that *Hedwch* would be *Heddwch* in Welsh). So prevalent had his use of the Cornish form of his first name become that, in one published list of Fellows of the Royal Society, his name is spelt in both forms in the one paragraph, once as a Fellow and then as the Treasurer.

Prior to her marriage, Giddy's future wife Mary-Ann Gilbert and her widowed mother had become dependent on her uncle, the wealthy unmarried lawyer Charles Gilbert. He made it a condition in his will that she and her future husband should change their names to Gilbert to ensure Gilbert ownership of the extensive Eastbourne estate on his death and, hopefully a line of male succession. He passed away in 1814. In December 1817, after fifty years as Davies Giddy, Mary-Ann's husband changed his name to Gilbert by royal sign manual and the family names of his children were changed the following month[180] along, we presume, with that of his wife who became Mary-Ann Gilbert again. Davies Giddy also obtained a licence on 1st January 1817.[181] to take and use the arms of Davies Gilbert.

Although he had used the name Davies Giddy for most of his life, for simplicity and clarity we will use Davies Gilbert throughout these pages.[182]

It may not have suited Gilbert to be associated with the industrial village of St Erth. He described his home as being near to the better-known historical, coastal fishing village of Marazion, although that is about five miles away. In time, Gilbert and his sister Mary Phillipa Davies Giddy would inherit Tredrea and live there together. Educated at home and in Penzance and Bristol, Gilbert became a gentleman commoner at Pembroke College, Oxford in 1785 where he exhibited a marked ability with mathematics and studied all manner of subjects including medicine and astronomy. He was rightly known as 'the Cornish Philosopher'[183] and took an interest in a number of marginally obscure subjects including the Cornish language. In 1827, he considered he was sufficiently competent to edit *The creation of the world, with Noah's flood,* written in Cornish in 1611 by William Jordan. However, his work found little appreciation from Peter Berrisford Ellis in his *Cornish Language and its Literature*. He suggested that Gilbert did not understand the Cornish language and had gloried in its decline. Gilbert was elected a Fellow of the Royal Society and the Linnaean Society after coming down from Oxford in 1791.[184]

Gilbert's financial background

Edward Giddy had resigned his curacy in 1775 after being overlooked for the position of parish vicar. By then he had found his forte in life as his cash books revealed that his wise judgements in the sale of tin had apparently made him profits of some £6,000 a year between 1766 and 1774, a total of no less than £48,000[185] (about £2.4 million in present day values). We will find that at some time Gilbert or his father apparently invested heavily in Cornish property as Gilbert mortgaged a great deal of land in order to raise sufficient capital for his marriage settlement. Having inherited a fortune from his father and married into another, Gilbert was to go through life knowing that he was detached from the pain of making a living and would not have to do anything as menial as work.

Gilbert despised the acquisition of wealth but nonetheless made a number of decisions that ensured that he would enjoy its benefits. We will see how he obtained the wherewithal to fund his extensive further education and support his lifestyle until his wife became substantially endowed on the death of her uncle in February 1816.[186] While he apparently shunned such mundane matters as work, trade and the accumulation of wealth, he may well have received a substantial inheritance and income from his father's shrewd commodity speculation. Gilbert would refer to such unseemly practices as 'dabbling in tin'[187] but it did enable him to pursue his chosen course in life. His father's influence had extended to being taught by him and advised as to his moral conduct. Gilbert recorded that, pinned to his father's study door the instructions from the Book of Ecclesiastes, 4:8 urged him, 'let it not grieve thee to bow down thine ear to the Poor, and give them a friendly answer with meekness'.[188] We will see just how those words would influence Gilbert during his lifetime.

Gilbert was born into a time of artistic and engineering progress. Chippendale had set standards by producing his catalogue of superior furniture in 1754 and Johnson had published his Dictionary of the English Language the following year. The Royal Academy of Arts had opened its doors in 1768 with Joshua Reynolds as its first President.

At the age of eighteen Gilbert had slithered down the slippery ladders of the great Dolcoath Mine in the company of Richard Trevithick's father to stay underground, often up to his knees in water, for eight hours. Two years later, whilst studying at Oxford, he visited the showroom of Matthew Boulton's manufactory in Soho, Birmingham. These brushes with mining and steam were to ensure Gilbert's interest in the industry and the people connected to it. They led to an involvement in the inevitable squabbles, court cases and legislation attached to Cornwall's prime source of income.

A. C. Todd, when recalling the nature of Gilbert, says[189] that he had the experience and ability to attempt the sorting of the fundamental truths of religion in the light of the new scientific discoveries. He saw the meaning of life as somewhere between God the Teacher and Man discovering the marvels of the Universe. Gilbert clearly saw himself as some sort of disciple in this scenario, adopting a position that was not appreciated by the more practical engineers who invented things and made them work. They were unlikely to understand his approach and probably wished him further, especially when he set himself as some sort of higher being and claimed their work was merely an extension of his thought processes.

Gilbert's relationship to his 'pupils'
From an early age Gilbert took an interest in the activities of people he thought showed promise but were unable, or unwilling, to capitalise on their skills. He had a secret Pygmalion view and, for his own satisfaction and entertainment, he would take partially educated people from the lower classes and try to mould them in his own image, in physics or classics. Without any formal agreement, he chose to be their patron, teacher and the source of much of their received wisdom and influence; although his interest invariably stopped before he made any financial contribution, he must clearly have seen something distasteful in that. Chroniclers often referred to Gilbert's approach as that of a patron, a title he did not apparently use but was unlikely to have rejected.

Educated as a scientist who attended lectures on botany and geology, Gilbert had excellent connections. He wrote a number of books including *A Cornish Cantata,* a book of Cornish carols and undertook the substantial editing of the *Parochial History of Cornwall*, founded on the manuscripts and histories of William Hals and Thomas Tonkin. This work runs into four volumes and covers many aspects of Cornwall and its people. As an example of the wide breadth of his learning and interest, the contents include Latin, heraldry, the lengthy *Scawen Dissertation on the Cornish Tongue* and the first written evidence of the flag of St Piran, the patron saint of Cornish miners. The re-edited edition of the latter was published in 1838, a year before his demise. Whilst editing the *Parochial History,* Gilbert had the opportunity to include something of the advances in steam technology that took place in the various parishes of Cornwall. We will see later how he treated this opportunity to describe Trevithick's achievements.

Gilbert developed a strange mixture of philosophies in which it appeared that he had a destiny for the lower social order in his professional life. Although he had considerable intellectual power, he recognised that his application was weak and he feared the illiterate democratic masses and 'lower orders'.[190] He had a terror of an uprising, no matter how small, that would upset the fine balance of the world as he saw it. He passionately believed the masses should not have the benefits of the Poor Laws and neither should they be encouraged to rise above their station unless they achieved this unaided by their own endeavours, and yet he had his own circle of special people upon whom he showered endless attention. In this he appeared to be quite inflexible, a situation that was unlikely to have been appreciated by Trevithick and Hornblower and, had they understood his position, would have wished he had not interfered with their lives.

Many of those who examined the life of Gilbert have been impressed by his contribution to the philosophy of his age and mystified by his presence among the country's hierarchy. With a background that included his education, his mother's inherited countryseat address, his father's fruitful investment in the Cornish mining industry and his frequent elections as a Member of Parliament, Gilbert was able to combine his remarkable intellectual talents with sufficient funds to establish himself among the country's upper echelons.

In this position, Gilbert turned his attention wherever his fancy took him, choosing to meet those he wished and introducing such people as he thought would favour his objectives and his personal gain. Many people in such privileged positions see their lot in life as a duty to those less fortunate than themselves. Gilbert had a similar philosophy and thought that once men had reached a certain stage in life, when they had sufficient time and money not to wonder where it would come from in the future, it would be their obligation, if not pleasure, to offer support to others. On these occasions, he would admit it was tainted with strong feelings about the place of the "lower classes" in society and his concerns about their behaviour and entitlement to advancement.

While Gilbert did not invest financially in the lives and projects of those to whom he offered the advantages of his learning, neither did he seek, unlike venture capitalists of today, any reward from their joint endeavours. We will see that his significance was frequently one of control where he ensured others would know that his interest had been asserted. Sometimes, if the achievements of his pupils were significant he would seek to claim them as his own. He was encouraged in this attitude by Humphry Davy who was occasionally accused of the same fault.

Gilbert's fascinating friends

Dr Thomas Beddoes, 1760 - 1808
While Gilbert was at Oxford that he met the formidable but caring Dr Thomas Beddoes, the University Reader in Chemistry. Beddoes was a linguist, radical physician and philosopher who, in 1789, was reported as becoming 'violently tainted with democritical mania' when he supported the French Revolution, something that obliged him to resign his readership and leave Oxford for Bristol, soiled with a reputation for sedition.[191] Gilbert was reported to 'have abhorred Beddoes's violent democratic principles'.[192] They were clearly too controversial for his liking.

Dr Beddoes, an enlightened doctor who took the pain and suffering of his patients as his own burden was easy meat in the hands of Gilbert. In a manner similar to the way in which Trevithick sought out Gilbert, Todd believed that Gilbert was the 'stone on which Beddoes sharpened many of his ideas'[193] and, when Beddoes was stunned by the deaths of his father and mother Gilbert would reason with him that no system of metaphysics, religion or abstract science could guarantee happiness in this world.[194] Gilbert was becoming accustomed to manipulating those about him so that he might achieve what he saw as the correct order of human development and existence.

Gilbert understood much of what was then known about medical science and, at the age of twenty-eight suggested 'heavy inflammable air' to be 'used before painful operations'[195] so anticipating the work of Humphry Davy by five years. Many of Beddoes' interests concerned pneumatic medicine, a subject that had interested him in France and included the study and search for a cure for tuberculosis, the killer disease of the time. With the financial assistance of Josiah Wedgwood and other patrons concerned about finding a cure for consumption, in particular for their own children, he had set up the well-patronised but generally unsuccessful Pneumatic Institution for Inhalation Gas Therapy at Clifton, near Bristol. The following year he completed his *Contributions to physical and medical knowledge, principally from the West of England* and included a mention of Humphry Davy's work as,

> Every fundamental difcovery neceffitates a revifion of facts and it is to be hoped that Mr Davy himfelf will find leifure for a train of experiments on oxydation and phofoxydation'

The book is interesting reading for anyone not of a squeamish nature and prepared to examine the advantages of a nitrous acid bath as a treatment for *fyphilis*. It was a busy year for Gilbert as that summer he had suspicions that he was suffering from consumption and rode to Clifton seeking Beddoes' medical advice. Beddoes' and Gilbert's influences on each other and the sexual advances of Beddoes' wife, Anna, together with Gilbert's claim to have discovered Humphry Davy are best read in full in *Beyond the Blaze.*

Jonathan Hornblower, Junior, 1753-1815,

In Jonathan Hornblower junior, Gilbert saw a man fourteen years his senior who had both vision and mechanical ability. Hornblower continued to seek Gilbert's advice on a number of matters and demanded his secrecy as Gilbert was associating with James Watt's consumptive son, Gregory. Hornblower was not prepared to take life as it came and thought he should not have received special treatment in respect of a test in the performance of his engine at the Wherry Mine while he believed that he should have received greater sympathy for his endeavours elsewhere. He particularly detested the denigration of those who professed to have theoretical knowledge but clearly lacked the necessary practical experience required to make the science of the day work.

Hornblower was an accomplished engineer with a mind of his own who disappointed both Gilbert and Watt. Gilbert thought he should have more fully developed his engine and Watt thought he should not. Part of Hornblower's relationship with these two men was contained in the section on Boulton & Watt.

In his twenties Gilbert was associated with a number of people in West Cornwall and it is interesting to see just how these various characters are woven into his life to reappear whenever it suited him. The combination of science, mining and controversy excited Gilbert and he frequently visited Jonathan Hornblower at his works in Penryn. He purchased a model of the Hornblower engine and calculated that its efficiency exceeded that of the Watt engine, something that was inevitably disputed by other engineers. These deliberations encouraged mine owners to purchase Hornblower's twin cylinder compound engine, the design of which was an example of very advanced thinking. His work revealed how steam engine design would have advanced in small steps had it not been for Trevithick's remarkable leap forward that produced the satisfactory high-pressure steam engine at a stroke. While Gilbert's calculations on the model of the Hornblower engine correctly proved the efficiency of the design, the lack of knowledge and suitable materials to scale the model up to a practical size frequently stymied its use. Another disadvantage of the Hornblower engine was that it had been designed to pump the Cornish mines and was not capable of easily being adapted to other uses; it also required a satisfactory boiler to generate high-pressure steam safely, something that eluded its designer.[196]

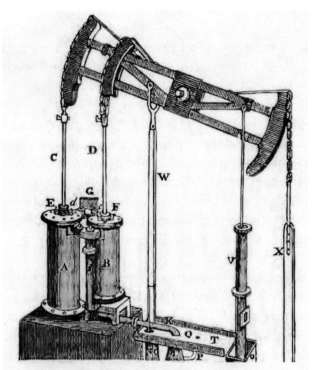

Hornblower's twin-cylinder compound engine.

In 1792, Richard Trevithick (may have been Senior) and Richard Moreau were instructed to carry out tests on engines at Seal Hole Mine, St Agnes. The report announced, "Watt's engine at Seal Hole, St Agnes 9,923,232 foot pounds … Tin Croft compound engine (Hornblower's) 14,663,472".[197] The proof that Hornblower's engine was better than Watt's encouraged Watt to pursue his case against the Hornblowers.

Watt eventually obtained a court ruling in his favour against Jabez, Jonathan Hornblower's elder brother in 1799, just a year before Watt's patent expired. While court battles raged, Hornblower was enthusiastically building his engines and installing them in Cornwall. The young Gilbert did something he would never do later in connection with Trevithick's engines, he spoke of their greater efficiency in Parliament. He stated,

> I have taken much pains to investigate the principles and strength of Mr. H's Engine as compared with Mr. Watt's, as well as to confirm my theoretical conclusions by observing their powers in practice. And on the whole can venture to give it as my decided opinion that Mr. Hr. is superior nearly to the proportion of 15.10 with an equal consumption of coals.[198]

To his surprise and in spite of evidence to the contrary, the Conservative party found Watt's engine to be superior to that of Hornblower. Gilbert, not one to stand his political ground, withdrew the petition, allowing Watt to gain the moral victory, something he was swift to exploit.

Dr Beddoes could not resist intervening, as a man of principle his natural support for the underdog reappeared. As in the case of the French Revolution that lost him his position at Oxford University, he sensed the unfairness of the situation and wanted to come to the aid of Hornblower. He suggested an open letter to all members of Parliament but Gilbert, unwilling to be seen as the advocate of failure, counselled against the idea declaring that the integrity of the engine would speak for itself. Here, in respect of the Hornblower engine, we have seen two examples of Gilbert preferring to step down rather than face confrontation. We will also see in these pages how this reveals Gilbert's preference, in spite of his comprehensive knowledge of both sides of an argument, to side with the establishment rather than take the option of supporting the more radical forces that were at his disposal.

Nevertheless, the mine owners could see the benefits of the Hornblower engine, supported in Cornwall by Gilbert's accreditation, and the orders continued to pour in. By the early 1800s and with the demise of the Watt patents, Boulton & Watt had lost their trump card and effectively abandoned the Cornish mining scene. Having withdrawn their engineer William Murdoch in 1798, the earlier Watt engines were deteriorating from a lack of maintenance and Hornblower claimed that no new ones were being built.

Encouraged by his technical ability and the rewards from the sale of his engines,

Hornblower embarked on the design of a turbine to provide rotary motion. This work did not go well and Gilbert was called in. He assured Hornblower that his theory was right but he might achieve more by adapting his reciprocating engine to rotary motion. Hornblower was fond of his turbine and his persistence became an obstacle.

The relationship between Gilbert and Hornblower deteriorated as the latter developed a persecution complex, worried that even his own compatriots were against him. Gilbert continued to work on Hornblower's engine but he found his calculations placed him further from Hornblower's beliefs. Gilbert sought other advice and received the opinion that the rotary engine was better in theory than it was likely to prove in practice. He tried to explain this situation to Hornblower and then wrote to him in the strongest terms in order to defend his own position and that of his mathematical calculations.

While the following quotation gives the impression that his guidance was positive and helpful, we know that the advice he offered was to tell Hornblower very bluntly that his engine would not work.

> The scientist Davies Gilbert (or Giddy), for example, provided Jonathan Hornblower, the practical engineer, with a great deal of advice in regard to the latter's attempts to develop his compound and 'rotary' (turbine) engines. Similarly, he rendered valuable assistance to Richard Trevithick, inventor of the high-pressure, non-condensing steam engine.[199]

Hornblower was shaken and paraphrased Jesus at Nazareth, saying that it is, 'True that a prophet has no honour in his own country'.[200] Hornblower was wise enough to know that Gilbert would tell the story in his own way and would seek to benefit from the situation.

Although Hornblower had sold nine (some say seven) of his engines and developed some aspects of steam power beyond the designs of Watt, he was losing heart and adopted an alternative lifestyle. Many things coursed through his mind, leaving him lonely with his thoughts; he told Gilbert,

> I have lately had a Slight Rage again for the consideration of it. I have before told you that I am so insulated as to society of my own that I can make appeals to no one but yourself in cares that are abstruse *i.e.* Philosophy etc.[201]

Gilbert took him to task and dealt firmly with him on these issues, writing to him, explaining the situation and saying,

... I would strongly recommend your letting the whole affair die away; since depend upon it, any publicity given to the evidence delivered ... will be unfavourable to your Interest.[202]

In his last letter to Gilbert, 9th July 1814, he appealed for assistance with the design of a reflecting telescope; I could find no trace of a reply or correspondence. His interest turned to the stars and he would study them with his telescope.

The confusion caused by naming all Jonathan's brothers with biblical names beginning with 'J' has caused a little trouble in historic accounts. The author, T. R. Harris quotes Matthew Loam's description of Hornblower in his book on Arthur Woolf.

> [Matthew] Loam considered that but for the fact that Joe Hornblower made it a habitual practice of taking 'a glass of Brandy the first thing in the morning to kill the worms and then a glass of Gin to drown them, with as much Toddy as he could get in the afternoon', he would have been, 'from his high qualifications as a mechanic as well as learning and philosophy', a person of outstanding importance in the development of steam engineering.

Although he appeared to be talking about Joseph, he was more likely to have been recounting the habits of his brother Jonathan.

Hornblower turned to inventions that pleased him, no matter how dangerous they were. A letter published in *The Mechanics' Magazine* of 1825 reveals the scope of his thinking, if not its rationality.

> In 1807, Mr. Hornblower, with whose talents the world is well acquainted, constructed a fire-engine which stood in the compass of fourteen inches square and two feet high, and could be carried from one room to another with ease. He found, by experiment, that the four side of a bed-room, all on fire, could be extinguished in a minute with a little more than a pail of water. (signed) Navarchus

Having fun like this did not stop Hornblower writing to Gilbert in April 1808, worrying him by saying,

> We are doing nothing with the Rotary, nor do I think we ever shall ... I can do no more ... I must begin to employ my Witts about something else or believe I shall soon die. If you have any wonder from the great world to tell me, it will be very acceptable to receive this information.[203]

One has to consider whether Hornblower is getting his own back on Gilbert for past encounters that did not benefit Hornblower.

During Hornblower's lifetime, and frequently after his demise, Gilbert would frequently allude to his support of the inventor in his early days, claiming that it was his philosophy that had brought about the inventor's success. Nine years after his death, Hornblower's opinion on the subject of intellectual intervention was quoted on page 5 of the Preface of the *Descriptive History of the Steam Engine* by Robert Stuart and published in 1824.

> that the most vulgar stoker may turn up his nose at the acutest mathematician in the world, for, (in the action and construction of Steam Engines,) there are cases in which the high powers of the human mind must bend to mere mechanical instinct.

In addition, on page 88 of the same book, Hornblower's disappointment is quoted again in connection with the theorists.

> Such is the degeneracy of man that while the Academy of Sciences at Paris, and the delegates of the States-general in Holland, were pluming him with the gaudiest expressions of their approbation, not one instance can be found where he received the encouragement he was led to expect.

It is certain that Hornblower, whose sentiments on the subject were quite robust, would have made his feelings about 'those who counted themselves men of science' very clear to Gilbert. Hornblower was surely not a suitable candidate for Gilbert's beliefs concerning the rise of man by the greater application of his mind. Nevertheless, Gilbert continued to call on Hornblower and believed that he could still convert him in the ways of his cerebral enlightenment. When all else had failed, Gilbert continued to believe that he had influenced Hornblower's achievements and took the credit he felt was due to him.

Robert Stuart expanded Hornblower's feelings with his own firmly held opinions. Stuart's use of language was marginally stronger than that usually found in publications of this type and it reveals the sense of indignation felt by someone who was clearly aware of the positions adopted by those to whom he refers. The passage does something to balance the sycophantic reporting on the contribution made by theorists against the practical aspects of designing a steam engine. He avoided naming any one philosopher but by quoting one sentence exactly; he presumably knows the identity of the person he claims is anonymous to him, was it Gilbert? It is difficult to think of anyone else.

'We know not ... what "philosopher" first claimed for theoretic men any part of the honour of being instrumental, even indirectly, in the perfecting of the Steam Engine; or gave currency to the phrase of its "invention being one of the noblest gifts that *science* ever made to mankind!!" The fact is, that science, or scientific men, never had anything to do with the matter ... Indeed, there is no machine or mechanism in which the little that theorists have done is more than useless. The honour of bringing it to its present state of perfection, therefore, belongs to a different and more useful class. It arose was improved and perfected by working mechanics and by them only; for tradition has preserved to us the fact that Savery having begun life as a working miner; – Newcomen was a blacksmith, and his partner Cawley, a glazier; – Don Ricardo Trevithick was an operative mechanic; and so was the illustrious Watt, when he began, and after he had made his grand improvements.'

It is clear that Stuart, a contemporary writer who had done his research well, spoke for the engineering fraternity of the day. He knew that Trevithick, who was still in South America whilst he wrote, had received the title of Don Ricardo in Peru. A review of Stuart's book in *The Mechanics' Magazine,* speaks highly of the publication, its comprehensive content and its price. It quotes the above passage and several others related to it, more strongly.

We can derive something about Trevithick from the above lines. It is clear that either Trevithick or someone close to him in South America was in contact with writers in this country as the title Don Ricardo was not generally known here in 1824. Trevithick did not return until 1827. If Trevithick was not in touch with his family whilst he was abroad, he was willingly sharing his experiences elsewhere.

The loss of Hornblower and his fighting spirit from the Cornish engineering scene was a disappointment for his mentor and many of the local mine owners.

Original Hornblower cottages with a meeting room, which was subsequently extended to two floors, built on the end.

Gilbert was still willing to help Hornblower but was worried that he might be suffering from tuberculosis himself. He set out from Marazion on a lengthy journey by horseback to consult Dr Beddoes in Bristol. He called in on the way and found Hornblower's last engine in a state of advanced dilapidation. This was to be the first of Gilbert's disappointments and while he blamed Hornblower for not having taken his advice, it did leave the way open for him to spend time with the mercurial, rising star of high-pressure steam, Richard Trevithick. Burton believes they met when Trevithick appeared along with Gilbert as a witness in favour of Hornblower against Boulton & Watt.[204] Closer examination shows that Gilbert evaded giving evidence, an early example of his tendency to avoid confrontation. Gilbert usually appeared in books about Trevithick as a friendly scientific authority in the background but an examination of his letters and his interest in scientific matters may reveal his influence was a little more disturbing.

When Hornblower died on the 23rd February 1815 it was the loss of a capable Cornish-born designer and engineer who adopted melancholia and a persecution complex. Just how much this could have been attributed to Gilbert's intervention in his life as a visiting academic we will never know but it is clear that

A later chapel has since been renovated as a fine residence.

Hornblower developed a dislike for philosophers, one so strong that it turned him away from his chosen and successful life in the development of steam engines. On Hornblower's death, Gilbert wrote to his two unmarried daughters and asked if he might recover whatever letters he had written to their father; they agreed.

Unlike many true inventors of the period, Hornblower was to die a relatively wealthy man and he is buried in St Gluvias churchyard on the outskirts of Penryn. His occupation was described in his will as Jonathan Hornblower, Plumber and Civil Engineer. Some later authors credit Jonathan with the middle name of Carter, his mother's maiden name, but early indexes of his name in his second marriage, his burial and a trade directory of 1795 omit it or an initial. His eldest brother Jabez does have Carter as a middle name. Other members of the Hornblower family were still resident at Chacewater in the 1841 Census and a fine new Baptist chapel was built. That eventually fell into

Humphry Davy by Henry Howard. National Portrait Gallery.

disuse, became a barn that was subsequently abandoned and has now been renovated to be a comfortable residence.

Davies Gilbert with his other charges

Young Richard Trevithick called at Tredrea with queries concerning his steam engines and the studious Thomasin Dennis dropped in for lessons in Latin and Greek. Through her cousin, John Dennis, Gilbert claimed he met the young Humphry Davy in Penzance. He saw potential that required encouragement in such people. Dr Thomas Beddoes also sent two of his patients, the consumptive Gregory Watt, son of James Watt, and Josiah Wedgwood Junior to Cornwall for the air; they all entered the world of Gilbert's influence.

This description of his contribution to the operation Parliament provides us with a man who was ideally placed to assist Trevithick in any way that he could.

> As a senator Mr Gilbert was considered one of the most assiduous that ever sat in the House of Commons and was probably unequalled for his important services on committees. The numerous parliamentary investigations more especially such as were connected with arts or science in which he took a prominent part form lasting memorials of his profound learning and indefatigable perseverance and the application of his knowledge to practical purposes was attested by the active interest he took in most of our great national works in the ancient usages and customs of the mines of Cornwall the Plymouth Breakwater and the Pevensey Level.[205]

Gilbert's communication skills were not limited to his prodigious letter writing but included excellent and convincing conversation. Sir John Barrow said,

That his most endearing talent was his power of conversation It was not brilliant it was something infinitely beyond and better than mere display it was a continued stream of learning and philosophy adapted with excellent taste to the capacity of his auditory and enlivened with anecdotes to which the most listless could not but listen.[206]

Sir Humphry Davy, 1778 - 1829

Dr John Ayrton Paris, MD, FRS, 1785-1856, one of Sir Humphry Davy's contemporary biographers, refers to the correspondence between Gilbert and Beddoes on the subject of Davy. He clearly places Gilbert's intervention in Davy's early life as a factor in his appointment to assist Beddoes. Releasing Davy from his indentures of 1795 – 1824[207] with Dr John Bingham Borlase in Penzance was not a simple matter and Paris says, 'Mr Gilbert kindly undertook the negotiation (of a *genteel maintenance*) and completed it to the satisfaction …'.[208] This 'easing away' was confirmed by the Oxford Dictionary of National Biography, 1888.

Although Gilbert certainly set Davy's initial course, Thomas Beddoes readily nurtured and introduced him to influential people on his arrival at Bristol. The more open-minded chemist encouraged his interest in poetry and launched him in a literary circle. This gave the youngster from Penzance considerable confidence and he was soon outstripping Gilbert in popularity, scientific achievement and social standing.

Nevertheless, Davy carried on a considerable correspondence with Gilbert whilst he worked at Clifton. When Davy's life changed and he left Beddoes to pursue a career in London as an assistant professor at the Royal Institution, he wrote to Gilbert on 8th March 1801,

> 'You, my dear Sir, have behaved to me with great kindness, and the little ability I possess you have very much contributed to develop; I should therefore accuse myself of ingratitude, were I to neglect to ask your approbation of the measures I have adopted with regard to the change in my situation, and the enlargement of my views on life.' The lengthy letter continued about chemistry and Davy's future, closing with, 'I am, my dear friend, with respect and affection, Yours, Humphry Davy'.[209]

Davy resigned his professorship at the Royal Institution in 1813.

The Royal Society published details of a conference held during December 2008 to commemorate the bicentenary of Dr Thomas Beddoes' death, a man whom they describe as 'a Doctor of Enlightenment'. The details mention his work with the 'then unknown' Humphry Davy but omitted any reference to the work of a man who would also become the President of the Royal Society, Davies Gilbert. The Royal Society also mentioned that Samuel Taylor Coleridge of Devon was one of Beddoes's friends and patients, probably caused by his lifelong suffering from neuralgic and rheumatic pains, something that drove him to become addicted to opium. Research shows Davy as having been born in poverty but at the age of only nineteen he was appointed superintendent of Beddoes's institution at Clifton, again without any clear reference to Gilbert's influence.

Beddoes was more philosophical in his approach to life than Gilbert. His deathbed note to Davy of Christmas Eve 1808 reads,

> Greetings from Dr Beddoes, one who has scattered abroad the *Avena Fatua* [wild oats] of knowledge, from which neither branch nor blossom nor fruit has resulted.

While Beddoes was known for his work in the field of pneumatic medicine, subsequent surveys show that his well-intended research did not produce any improvement in the cure for tuberculosis. Better food and living conditions were found to treat the condition of many patients and, then in the late 1940s, work on streptomycin produced a cure for the disease, one that this author was grateful to receive.

Living with Gilbert

Richard Trevithick and others
Gilbert was a man of considerable intellect who must have possessed even greater tolerance. In his editorship of *Some Ancient Christmas Carols* he says,

> The Editor is desirous of preserving them in their actual forms, however distorted by false grammar or by obscurities, as specimens of times now passed away, and of religious feelings superseded by others of a different cast. He is anxious also to preserve them on account of the delight they afforded him in his childhood; when the festivities of Christmas Eve were anticipated by many days of preparation, and prolonged through several weeks by repetitions and remembrances.

In this, we see him thinking of the carols of his childhood but concerned about their preservation intact and acknowledging their source, 'by others of a different cast'. 'Cast(e)' is a word we find Gilbert fond of using in its racist form, setting himself apart from people of other origins. The word is in his valedictory address to the Royal Geological Society of Cornwall (RGSC).

Gilbert had a desire for further education and the development of science. His lightly applied catholic virtues made him a strange friend of Trevithick whose interest was singular and passionate. Gilbert's attention was drawn to Trevithick's physical attributes and he found a person whose advanced work fascinated him. His instinct was to aid such a man while keeping a watchful eye on the latest developments in steam technology. Gilbert's interest and scientific knowledge were to prove useful to Trevithick over the years as his inventiveness soon outstripped his education.

Trevithick's relationship with Gilbert was probably longer than with anyone so we must consider that Gilbert had as much an influence on Trevithick as anyone. Although Gilbert spent many years writing letters on engineering matters, there is little sign that he actually influenced Trevithick's attitude to life. Trevithick's letters to Gilbert do not include any references to his wife, family or other personal subjects, probably because these seldom occurred to him. On the other hand, they did not seem to matter to Gilbert either.

Did Gilbert consider Trevithick as a friend? For that matter, although Trevithick trusted Gilbert, did he ever think of Gilbert as his friend? Did either man actually have friends? We will have to see whether they both used the other. They tended to keep their liaison between themselves. Gilbert admitted that his relationships with his pupils were his private interests, things that amused him and an opportunity to pursue his favourite pastime of encouraging people to develop their talents and so better their lives.

Gilbert's relationship with the opposite sex was not a comfortable one. We only hear about the sisterly relationship with Phillipa, Thomasin Dennis with whom he had a distant pupil – teacher association, Anna Beddoes from whom he fled and his wife, Mary-Anne of whom he said very little.

At the age of thirty-nine Gilbert's private life was in turmoil. He did not approve of his sister's intended marriage to John Lewis Guillemard, from another former Huguenot family who already had a mistress and a family. As is often the case with siblings, Gilbert was deeply attached to Phillipa, and her loss would bring chaos to his personal life. He was so distraught over this that he turned to Gibbon and wrote in his notebook,

> The relation of a Brother and Sister, especially if they do not marry, appears to me to be a very singular nature. It is a familiar and tender friendship with a female, much about our own age, and affection perhaps softened by the secret influences of sex, but pure from any mixture of sexual desire, the sole species of Platonic love can be indulged with truth and without danger.

The circumstances with Thomas Beddoes' wife Anna were very unsettling and he was quite unprepared. Following years with the comfort of a nonsexual affair with his sister, Gilbert was thrust into a situation where a passionate woman was sending him poetry[210] and begging to be his mistress. She said,

We have known each other so long, so intimately, and now we are placed in circumstances so new that everything is changed. Though you have proved that there is nothing you would not do for me, yet you do not.[211]

This attention by Anna was probably more than Gilbert could tolerate. He was clearly at his wits' end and, for once, out of his depth. There was no scientific reasoning or a way that his soft persuasive tone could extricate him from this situation. Gilbert frequently revealed that his human relationships were handled at arm's length through books and learning, he found any other approach to be very unsettling. He was at a loss handling sexual relationships and, when the opportunity of marriage with the attachment of a colossal fortune arose, he grabbed it.

Mary-Ann Gilbert

One feels that this move into matrimony may have been decided after he had resorted to guidance from the great philosophers of the past who were inclined to advocate such remedies. The solution appeared with the opportunity of marriage and in 1807, he proposed to the thirty-two-year-old Mary-Ann Gilbert. Anna Beddoes quickly revealed her dislike of the idea.

His bride was the daughter of the late Thomas Gilbert, younger brother of Charles and a former grocer in Lewes. He had died leaving his widow and daughter in a parlous state but Mary-Ann would be entitled to a substantial inheritance on the death of her childless wealthy uncle.[212] As Gilbert embarked on the painful process of courting, he clearly had his eye on the inheritance that would come to him on marriage and provide him with an impressive, wealthy estate in East Sussex upon which much of Eastbourne would eventually be built.[213] This would provide him with an honourable name and the style of living he had always desired since his birth in the home of an impecunious Cornish curate. Of course, he would have to marry the woman but he saw that as no obstacle when faced by the opportunity of such extraordinary riches and prestige. We come across several instances of man's greed on these pages; none turns out as intended. After their marriage in 1808 at Northiam, Rye the couple apparently lived with her uncle, some 30 miles away at the Manor House, Eastbourne in Sussex.

While this is no place to discover what happened in the three years between the death of the uncle and the change of Giddy's name, it is interesting to assume that Charles Gilbert had clearly instructed his fellow solicitors how he wished the estate to be run in the future and just what would be the responsibilities and duties of his niece's husband. At a time when the law decreed that a married woman's property became that of her husband it is clear that the solicitors managed to draw up a civil contract so that the couple entered into what would later be called a 'pre nuptial' agreement. One part entailed both parties placing a considerable sum of money into a marriage settlement fund. Gilbert's financial standing was less than his wife's and he was only able to raise £10,000 against her £12,000. Her contribution was sufficiently in excess of his to enable her to exert control without completely embarrassing him. These financial arrangements did not fit well into Gilbert's chosen lifestyle. His usual relationships were ones where he had control over his partners through his superior knowledge of just about everything. His social position was usually superior. His marriage to Mary-Ann was none of these. For a start, she was heir to a large estate in which he was permitted to make his home.

Living with Gilbert
An indication of Gilbert's determination to marry the prospective heiress is revealed by him raising the £10,000 settlement funds by mortgaging all his family's lands at the Manor of Amyll-an-Tryll, an-Tryll, and all his lands in Sennen, Ludgvan, Zennor, Towednack and Lelant to John Hawkins.[214] At the time of Gilbert's marriage his father was still alive and, as we have no indication that Gilbert ever actually worked to raise substantial funds, we must suppose it was his parent's inheritance and investments in property that were mortgaged. Again, we must say that it is remarkable what a man will do when faced by the opportunity of a fortune, many have murdered for less. Historians frequently refer to Gilbert's parsimonious attitude to parting with money; this could well be due to his having to pay considerable sums of interest to John Hawkins over the years. It has not been possible to find where he would have obtained the necessary monies to pay this interest or his other considerable expenses of life unless he was in receipt of some settlement or allowance from his wife's estate.

Their varying financial contributions to the marriage and Mary-Ann's control were illustrated when, as MP for Bodmin, Gilbert was required to make a loan for the repair of the lunatic asylum roof. This was beyond whatever his allowance may have been and his wife permitted him to draw from their marriage settlement. The exchange of letters with the authorities in support of her husband clearly indicated that she had sanctioned this use of the funds. The slates used in the repair of the roof reappear in this story when they are re-cycled in the twenty-first century to hang on the renovated Hornblower chapel at Chacewater.

Without looking further into the relationship or marriage arrangements, it is certain that the solicitors were well paid. Gilbert wrote copiously but barely mentioned his wife. On being asked of his marriage he once made the remark that; on the whole, he thought it had been successful.[215]

The Gilberts used funds from the estate to extend their property at Eastbourne and purchase Trelissick, near Truro as their main seat in Cornwall.[216]

Thomas Beddoes died just nine months after Gilbert's wedding to Mary-Ann Gilbert, leaving the woman who loved Gilbert to distraction free to have married him; he may have breathed a sigh of relief. As a condition of Beddoes's will, Gilbert took on the responsibility of raising Anna's two boys in addition to his own children.

Of Gilbert's own family, his first-born was a daughter called Mary. She was completely incapacitated and Gilbert described her as one who attained her seventeenth birthday without giving indications of sensations or motion from birth.[217] Just how Gilbert took this situation is not recorded but he must have found difficulty aligning his views on humanity with his family life and, in accordance with the beliefs of the time, may have seen his daughter's condition as some form of retribution for a loveless marriage. Gilbert was to bury four of his eight children before he died in 1839.

Like her uncle who had made abundant provision for the poor, Mary-Ann was passionate about creating a living for the poor agricultural workers in Sussex, an attitude that Gilbert probably did not appreciate but was wise enough to keep his mouth shut. Her method was to provide land on which they could work and so provide for themselves.[218] The couple also held different views on the new Poor Laws, the distribution of allotments and the encouragement of the menial classes.

Here we see in the philosophy of the time the difference between the deserving poor and their counterparts, the undeserving. Mary-Ann clearly saw she had a mission to encourage the deserving whilst her husband was inclined to group them all together as useless unless they could make their way in life by their own endeavours. Opinions would be severely divided as the country showed its first signs of community relief. A few years later in 1843 Charles Dickens depicted Ebenezer Scrooge in *A Christmas Carol* as a man who had no time for the undeserving but paid his dues to the workhouse.

Gilbert had an inexhaustible ability to reply promptly and at length to letters, a quality he may have acquired from the quotation pinned on his father's study door. His association with Trevithick very often dragged him into matters that were on the very edge of their relationship. We find him in correspondence with Gregory and James Watt Junior, Arthur Woolf, the Cornish engineer, and Mr M. MacGregor, Consul at Panama. Other letters are written on behalf of Jane Trevithick to mine owner John Williams at Scorrier and he endorses her letters to Pedro Abadia in attempts to tidy-up some of Trevithick's troubles in Peru. In one previously mentioned letter to John S. Enys, his son-in-law at Penryn in 1839, he composed four closely written foolscap pages and included the following dismissive lines after Trevithick's death.

> I will give you as good on an account as I can of Richard Trevithick. … he
> was very frequently in the habit of calling at Tredrea to ask my opinion on

various Projects that occur'd to his mind, some of them very ingenious, and others so wild as not to rest on any foundation at all ... He died I think in the Autumn of 1833.

Although he was writing to his son-in-law and could have written a little more about Trevithick, we must question if he did not really know when he had died. Was this an example of how he was dismissing him from his mind, some form of retribution for never having achieved what he desired or, at the age of seventy-two, an instance of forgetfulness? He continued about his own health. Here we should spare him some personal space because his work for others over the years had clearly been enormous.

> I am becoming quite skin and bones having fallen off Fifty pounds from what I was, a few years since. I have not any particular complaint. The chief incumberance of my ... in, that it prevents my lying down with any comfort in bed, as the Bones ... and ... my skin.[219]

It is difficult to read the original manuscript but Todd reports the following similar entry from Gilbert's diary,

> ... the chief inconvenience from this reduction in the Muscles and the Integuments is that I feel inconvenience from lying in bed, or according to the usual expression, my Bones seem to be coming through my skin.[220]

Gilbert revealed what he saw as his life's frustration in a letter of 1830 to Charles Babbage that 'My most earnest endeavour through the whole of my life has been to please and gratify everyone—a fruitless endeavour as I have found in numerous circumstances'.[221]

In his declining years, Gilbert was involved in the affairs of the newly founded British Association for the Advancement of Science. Just before the 1833 meeting at Cambridge the university gave him an honorary doctorate of laws. He was considered as a possible president at the Bristol meeting in 1836; the leaders of the association thought him still a potentially useful government lobbyist.[222]

Some historians note that he died in 1839, the year that he relinquished presidency of the RGSC and conclude that he died in office. This is a final disservice to a man who chose to spend his life in the service of others. He was clearly aware that he was dying and made the fearfully uncomfortable annual journey, probably by a mixture of train if it was available, horseback and horse drawn carriage over appalling roads from Eastbourne to Penzance to see his beloved homeland for the last time. One can barely imagine what that jolting journey was like for an old man who was unable to find comfort lying in his own bed. Gilbert died on Christmas Eve that year leaving a widow, three daughters and a son.

He resigned his presidency of the Society and passed it to Sir Charles Lemon of Carclew, Cornwall, 1784 – 1868, a friend, MP and a Fellow of the Royal Society who, in 1838 had funded education for Cornish miners. That charitable beginning would eventually become the Camborne School of Mines. Lemon was also president of the Royal Cornwall Polytechnic Society from its foundation.

After his death Dr Buckland said of Gilbert:

> His manners were most unaffected, childlike, gentle, and natural. As a friend, he was kind, considerate, forbearing, patient, and generous; and when the grave was closed over him, not one man, woman, or child, who was honoured with his acquaintance, but felt that he had a friend less in the world. Enemies, he cannot have left a single one.[223]

Thomasin(e) Dennis, 1771 – 1809

Thomasin was born at Sawah, just three miles from Land's End, the daughter of Alexander Dennis, a Cornishman variously described as a respectable yeoman, farmer and miller. He lived at Lower Trembarth Farm, Madron, near to Penzance. Claimed as one of Gilbert's discoveries, she was just three years younger than he was, the same age as Richard Trevithick, and he showered his learning on her, teaching her Latin, Greek and philosophy.

Thomasin was the jewel of Gilbert's academic eye. He saw in her an opportunity to mould a young woman from Penzance into what he believed were the finer ways of living.

Gilbert would share many of his innermost philosophical thoughts with Thomasin, acknowledging her as someone he considered would understand and benefit by the exchange and he frequently used her as an outlet for his feelings. We perceive from their discussions a great deal of Gilbert's thinking about the nature of Mankind and the place of individuals within it. He saw education and the understanding of matters beyond those of the humble man as the sole means by which these movements could be achieved. He clearly abhorred the rise in social standing of those who had bought status by the creation of wealth, an interesting thought as he secured the benefits of wealth without actually working for them. He once wrote to Thomasin, 'Nor am I willing to acknowledge any Rank beyond the reach of Abilities, Application and Virtue'.[224]

Gilbert's relationship with Thomasin was very much that of teacher and pupil and, while we do not know Thomasin's feelings for the very clever, intense young man who had befriended her we see no sign of sexual attraction being admitted by Gilbert. In the three years between 1801 and 1804, Gilbert lived within just seven miles of Thomasin but they barely saw each other a dozen times, continuing their association by letter. In addition to the ancient languages, it is to Thomasin's credit that she also absorbed the literature of both the ancient and modern worlds, argued metaphysics and explored mathematics, chemistry and geography.

Gilbert's ambition for Thomasin had been very similar to that of Henry Higgins in George Bernard Shaw's play, *Pygmalion,* written in 1913. Higgins, a fictitious Professor of Phonetics and a Fellow of the Royal Society, was convinced that he could improve the speech of Eliza Doolittle, a Cockney flower girl, to a standard where she could be passed off as a lady. As with Higgins we detect that Gilbert, having achieved his ambition and amused himself with his research into human behaviour, cannot truly accept his pupil as being any more than the flower girl she really was.

Having explored Thomasin's mind we have no indication that Gilbert paid similar attention to her body. We do not suppose that he ever gave any thought to marrying her. Apart from her mind, she was inanimate in Gilbert's sight and not for his circle of acquaintances.

His attitude is illustrated by his abject refusal to assist her secure the post of surgeon for her brother in the East India Company. He responded to her request by being frugal with the truth concerning the situation and explaining what he saw as an important political position,

> I have not the smallest private connection with any individual possessing Influence in the Government Office; and whatever I may be able to obtain of Patronage, I hold myself most religiously bound to employ for the extensive benefit of those who have placed me in that situation.[225]

Gilbert's adoption of this arrogant stance to a young woman who had so generously given her life in the pursuit of his philosophy on human improvement can be compared with Todd's account of Gilbert's dedicated support of the (Grand Old) Duke of York in 1809 against cash for honours corruption charges. In the ensuing debates Gilbert showed how he saw power, money and political influence being bound inextricably together and the disasters that would befall all if that were not so. He said, 'Property and power should invariably be connected together, for without that connection, no peace could be maintained in society,' and, 'Property must necessarily give a person influence, and the latter would naturally tend to procure returns of members of Parliament'.[226]

In a similar manner to the way he had written to Thomasin, Gilbert also wrote to Henry Trengrouse, the inventor of the life-saving rocket apparatus for distressed sailors, in 1815 advising him that he was unlikely to be able to help him in Parliament. Gilbert would frequently petition Parliament on behalf of his friends; it was a favour that was common among those who had the status and opportunity to grant it.

In these instances, we can see Gilbert's similar attitude to Trevithick. Keeping him at a distance and communicating by erudite correspondence, he did nothing to bring Trevithick into his life or to promote his interests.

In one of the remarkable coincidences that brought characters together in this story, Beddoes prescribed the healing powers of Cornwall's fresh air for Josiah Wedgwood the younger and sent him and his family to Cornwall. In 1797, Wedgwood sought Gilbert's advice for a tutor for his two children and Gilbert proposed Thomasin.

Thomasin was clearly a bright, intelligent young woman who had responded well to tuition. Gilbert saw an opportunity and influenced her in such a way that they agreed to her becoming a governess to Josiah Wedgwood's grandchildren and she left with them. For a while, the Wedgwoods stayed at Upcot House, Taunton where Thomasin would occasionally meet Davy who was living at Clifton, Bristol. Davy apparently found her to be a good listener and she is reported to have read the works of Lavoisier to better understand his work.

Thomasin then accompanied the Wedgwoods to Cobham in Surrey. Gilbert thought her continued association with the family and visitors such as Samuel Taylor Coleridge, who was just a year younger than Thomasin and had a profound effect on Catherine Wedgewood and other young ladies,[227] would provide Thomasin with a degree of culture she was unlikely to acquire in Penzance; but it did not work.

The experiment, for that is what it was to Gilbert, ended in failure. This was partly because the Wedgwood society would not accept a tutor, irrespective of her ability and education, as their equal. The position of governess in a household such as the Wedgwoods left Thomasin in a twilight world, suspended between the family on one side and the servants on the other; she was unlikely to have friends in either. Thomasin was never accepted at the level that Gilbert had intended and the situation was not helped by her temperament, a problem that seemed to plague all Gilbert's pupils.

Thomasin wrote to Gilbert from the Wedgwoods 'that she really did not belong in this world to which she had given herself'.[228]

Being homesick, Thomasin returned to Cornwall, neither a lady nor a member of her previous family.[229] On arrival in Cornwall in 1800 Thomasin found herself more closely allied to her books than to her family, leaving her lonelier than she had been in Surrey.

She wrote a novel, *Sophia St Clare or the Visionary,* in which she tells the thinly veiled story of herself and her dreams of a relationship with the cold Gilbert. She depicts a character, which was clearly Gilbert who has the line, 'Marriage I have always regarded with dislike. My sentiments on the subject are so delicate that it would not be easy to find qualities in a wife that afford me tolerable satisfaction … since I met Mademoiselle St Clare it is otherwise, I feel for her the tenderness of a brother to a deserving sister …'.[230] The full story of how Thomasin tragically unfolds her unrequited feelings along with the reported utterances of Gilbert can be found in *Beyond the Blaze.*

While Gilbert had given her something in the form of studies, a life that she was able to understand and appreciate, Todd recalls that she was a mystery to her family who tended to leave her alone. Thomasin took to nursing her only sister who had contracted tuberculosis. Tuberculosis was the scourge of humankind and accounted for some twenty-five per cent of all deaths in Europe during this period. Her family must have been both relieved and worried that Thomasin had volunteered to undertake this perilous job. The germs are transferred by air-borne bacteria in water droplets from an infected person. At Gilbert's behest, she had studied the great philosophers for several years. Their words must have coursed through her head as she wondered if there was anything left in life for her. She had become a stranger to her family, had failed to secure the better status that Gilbert had intended for her and was subsequently used by him to receive long letters about his problems.

Thomasin must have known the perils of being too close to a consumptive patient; yet one report speaks of her sleeping with her sister; we have to wonder what her motives were. Her sister died having inevitably passed the disease to Thomasin who passed away from her family and life in 1809 at the age of thirty-eight.

As the end drew near, Thomasin wrote to Gilbert:

> I owe it to you, a great original obligation which no circumstance can weaken, but will be felt by me to the last hour of my life.

Gilbert records Thomasin calling him 'Sir' near the end of her life. If she did, this would have immediately put both parties back in their places. Prior to this Gilbert had made Thomasin his confidant, writing letters about steam engines, patents and Greek literature although we can only speculate whether these letters were more an outlet for

Gilbert than an education for Thomasin.

Although Gilbert visited Thomasin the night before her death, he was not thought to have attended her funeral. However, he remembered her twenty years later during his troubles at the Royal Society and erected memorial in Latin to her in St. Leven church.

Thomasin Dennis, de Trembath,
ingenio, suavitate, virtute insignis, doctrina insignissima.
Nata xxix die Septembris, 1771,

vae! lenta sed praematura morte erepta

obiit xxx die Augusti 1809,
anno aetatis xxxviii.

Todd sums up Gilbert's view of her death as a tragedy 'because reason had failed to overcome melancholy and introspection',[231] something that Gilbert could have said of Hornblower.

Sadly, for Thomasin, Gilbert, in whom she trusted and may even have loved, only saw the logical qualities of reason, melancholy and introspection, measured and weighed in the balance of philosophy. He was clearly unable or unwilling to see that there may well have been reasons not covered by his theoretical conjecturing that took the life of this intelligent, sensitive young woman. When we look at Gilbert's fuller life, and into his nature, we must wonder if, like Higgins, it was also one of misogyny.

Lake's Parochial History of St Levan, 1868, suggests that Thomasin already knew French prior to her association with Gilbert and was also the pupil of the Vicar of St Hilary, the Rev. Malachi Hitchens and other ['more or less', *Gilbert's edit*] scholars of the day.[232]

Todd said that Gilbert's view of society was moulded by the lines of the hymn written by Mrs Francis Alexander, although she did not write her 'Hymns for little children' until 1848.[233] Nevertheless, the familiar lines probably encapsulate Gilbert's philosophy on human status better than any other.

The rich man in his castle,
The poor man at his gate,
He made them, high or lowly,
And ordered their estate.

Josiah Wedgwood junior, Gregory Watt and his sister Janet all died of tuberculosis.

We will come across the scourge of tuberculosis many times on these pages, also the several unsuccessful attempts of various parents to cure their children by sending them to breathe in the gaseous unctions concocted by Dr Beddoes, Davy and others. Many of the same children and Murdoch's son were despatched to take the finer airs found in West Cornwall. Tehidy, the country estate of Lord de Dunstanville enters the story as mining and steam activities unfold. In 1919, the allegedly haunted Tehidy mansion and its grounds became a sanatorium for tubercular patients until 1986.

Humphry Davy, 1778-1829

Gilbert claims young Humphry as one of his discoveries and that he heard of him from John Dennis, a cousin of Thomasin Dennis. Humphry's father died in 1794. He had been a woodcarver in Ludgvan and one report suggests he left Humphry's mother with debts of £1,500. She sold millinery in Penzance with a French woman and successfully repaid the debts. Gilbert said he attributed his discovery to Thomasin Dennis,

> I was first introduced to his acquaintance by Mr. John Dennis and never felt myself more surprised on discovering a young man situated in all respects so disadvantageously as Mr. Davy prosecuting experiments and investigations worthy of Doctor Priestly. I could not be the more astonished, perfectly remembering his late father.[234]

There is an anecdote about the early life of Davy that is confirmed by the Oxford Dictionary of National Biography, 1888 edition. John Davy had a completely different account of how the first meeting occurred, but as his brother rose to prominence many people claimed to have discovered him,

> Mr. Davies Gilbert, walking with a friend, observed a boy, with comely countenance, carelessly swinging on a gate, and took notice of his intelligent expression.[235]

A great deal has been written about Davy over the years. Here we are only interested in his demeanour, the treatment he receives from Gilbert and his attention to Trevithick. Examination of the way in which Gilbert records his contribution to Davy's success may also provide us with a clearer picture of his influence on Trevithick.

Two of the many biographies of Davy stand out for examination. Both are by Fellows of the Royal Society, one is by Dr John Ayrton Paris, a much-quoted biography that warmly compliments Davy on his achievements but balances that with criticism of his character and behaviour. It is the latter feature of Paris's work that has received most attention and although it is even-handed, Sir Walter Scott criticised it saying, "I am not pleased with the book, it is not kindly or gentlemanly written." The book is also criticised by Davy's brother John who writes his own *Memoirs of the Life of Sir Humphry Davy*. These are probably the two most widely placed biographies, one being by someone who apparently was trying to write objectively about the great chemist and the other by his brother with all the protection that one can expect of a sibling. In addition, there is the account of Gilbert's acquaintance with Davy and, in the light of the two biographies, we will wonder whether the latter is a fair representation of that relationship. With such disputes possible, the reader will have to judge whether Trevithick got a reasonable deal from those involved in such relationships, most of whom were unknown to him.

Humphry Davy at Bristol

A fair, tactful biography of Davy's life and nature appears on the Notable Names Data Base (NNDB) web page.[236] The Retired Professional Engineers' Club of Bristol also gives a full account of Davy's life[237] and attributes his early discovery and tuition to the patronage of the Penzance apothecary, Dr John Tonkin. It also mentions the scientific assistance he received from Robert Dunkin while Gilbert is mentioned in the former biography just for having introduced Davy to Beddoes. Biographies usually indicate that Davy was inclined to refute or reject those about him, in Dunkin's case he directed an anti-Quaker tract against his published poem 'On God'.[238] Dunkin's response reveals something more of Davy's attitude and approach when he says, "I tell thee what, Humphry, thou art the most quibbling hand at a dispute I ever met with in my life."[239]

The biography of Davy by John Davy, MD, FRS, etc., his 'adoring younger'[240] brother, is written in two volumes. John was an army doctor who was to have a lengthy correspondence with Charles Darwin, but we know Darwin wrote to nearly two thousand people. To avoid confusion between the two Davys and other Johns we shall have to call Humphry's brother 'John Davy'.

As an eight-year-old child Davy was reported as having a love for ballads and verse and he tells us he was a 'tale-teller', a quality he probably inherited from his grandmother who was described as having a fervid mind stored with traditions and ancient legends.[241] One source credits him with inventing unbalanced, unpolished four line verse that eventually achieved respectability as the clerihew. The ODNB credits this to Edward Clerihew Bentley, 1875 – 1956, who, at the age of sixteen invented the verse and later wrote the following well known few lines about Davy.

> Sir Humphrey Davy
> Abominated gravy.
> He lived in the odium
> Of having discovered Sodium.

Gilbert recorded that he had been amazed by the interest Humphry showed in chemistry and would describe him as 'a very wonderful young man'.[242] Always one to manoeuvre situations Gilbert tells us he found a way of housing Gregory Watt, son of James Watt, in the Davys' humble home during the winter of 1797. Watt had just come down from university in Glasgow where he had been studying chemistry and Gilbert encouraged him and Davy to use the libraries at Tredrea and elsewhere.

John Davy has his own version of Davy's early life and his encounter with Gregory Watt.

> The manner in which they became acquainted requires to be mentioned, as it, too, has been misrepresented and placed in a ludicrous point of view by Dr. Paris. It was briefly thus:- My brother, at this time, when prosecuting his chemical inquiries, begged of Mr. John, a gentleman of great respectability, and one of the oldest inhabitants of Penzance (who is my authority), to witness some experiment. He … said that the experiment should be shown to a friend. This was Mr. Gilbert, to whom Mr. John took the opportunity of introducing my brother.

Davy's demeanour was reported to have included some of the characteristics found in Richard Trevithick's personality. The various biographies found in books on the Google books website summed up Davy's attitude as,

> An exuberant, affectionate, and popular lad, of quick wit and lively imagination, he was fond of composing verses, sketching, making fireworks, fishing, shooting, and collecting minerals. He loved to wander, one pocket filled with fishing tackle and the other with rock specimens; he never lost his intense love of nature and, particularly, of mountain and water scenery.[243]

> Davy's style in the laboratory was to work quickly and intensely, pursuing one new idea after another. He aimed at originality and creativity, rather

than tediously repeating tests and confirming results.[244]

and,

> Without entering a special plea for slow wits in early life as a sign of [Trevithick's] genius, it may be said that another famous Cornishman, Sir Humphry Davy, bore the same character as a boy.[245]

Paris described Davy as a lad and tells of his ability to change his demeanour, something we will see that he did later in life. He also reveals how generous artists have been to the great man when he says,

> Davy, it may be remarked, when a boy, possessed a countenance which, even in its natural state, was very far from comely, while his round shoulders, inharmonious voice, and insignificant manner, were calculated to produce anything rather than a favourable impression: in riper years he was what one might be called 'good looking', although as a wit of the day observed, his aspect was certainly of a 'Bucolic' character. The change which his person underwent, after his promotion to the Royal Institution, was so rapid that, in the days of Herodotus, it would have been attributed to nothing less than the miraculous interposition of the Princess of Helen.[246.]

John Davy came back with,

> This is as foolish as it is unfounded and unworthy of remark. No authority is given for the ridiculous assertion; … Such we have seen, is Mr. Poole's notice of him …

> Poole's barbed compliment was, 'You will excuse my making two or three remarks. I do not think you have done justice to Sir Humphry's appearance and manners in early life. Though his manners were retreating and modest, he was generally thought naturally graceful; and the upper part of his face was beautiful.'

Beauty is always in the eye of the beholder. Maybe Davy was not the one-eyed monster depicted by Paris, but there must have been something about his appearance and manner that excited these worthy gentlemen to exchange such dialogue. Poole refers to the beauty of his upper face in early life. This was probably marred by the subsequent loss of an eye and Poole omits to describe his lower face so we can only suppose that such artists as Howard and Linnell have been sympathetic to the extent of generosity and we are left with the painting by Jackson in T. E. Thorpe's biography of Davy, 1896 in which Davy has a pronounced lower jaw, but we will never be sure.

Allowing biographies to be undertaken by sons or brothers clearly has its dangers; look at the criticisms levelled at Francis Trevithick. While sons and siblings are able to supply information about their relatives that is not available to the general historian, something that Francis sadly failed to do, they are inevitably inclined to protect their subjects from the worse abuses of the objective chronicler.

Biographies are best left to the qualified, impartial writer and, although we might wish to include Paris in this category, a closer examination will have to exclude him as much as we must exclude Davy's brother John. Paris had travelled to Penzance to assume the post vacated by Davy as a prospective doctor in the town and he lived there for a couple of years. He must have heard many opinions of Davy including that of his former tutor Dr Borlase, the eminent surgeon and apothecary to whom Davy had been indentured. There is the overwhelming advantage that both writers have over any comments we may make, they were both contemporary with Davy.

Further indications that his lax attitude to his own comfort, safety and life in general was similar to Trevithick's is revealed when,

> "He nearly lost his own life inhaling water gas, a mixture of hydrogen and carbon monoxide sometimes used as fuel," and he "breathed 16 quarts of the gas in seven minutes" and became "completely intoxicated" with it [nitrous oxide].[247]

L. T. C. Rolt in his book, *James Watt* claims that Gregory Watt was the first to recognise Humphry Davy's outstanding ability. John Davy says of his brother's acquaintance with Gregory Watt, 'This gentleman came to Penzance in the winter of 1797, and … fortunately for my brother, became a lodger in my mother's house, boarding with the family.'

John Davy gave no indication how young Watt became a lodger in the Davy home.

While all claimed to have 'discovered' Davy we must recall that it was Gilbert who was well acquainted with Beddoes, Watt, Senior and Davy. It is very likely that the claim of Gilbert to have lodged him in the Davy household had some validity.

It was about this time that Gilbert's influence over Davy waned. If he ever had the sway over Davy that he claimed, we find little reference to Davy having acknowledged it. Released from his career as a small town doctor, Davy was blossoming into the outer world and 'He became intellectually self-propelled.'[248]

Prior to their days at the Royal Society, the last we see of Gilbert near Davy was in October 1798 when Davy was on his journey to Clifton. The two met for breakfast at Okehampton. Davy kept up a reasonable correspondence with Gilbert and shared his experiences into the early 1800s.

Davy revealed his enthusiasm for chemistry by harmfully ingesting dangerous gases and losing of an eye as the result of a laboratory explosion. These sensational adventures are frequently documented elsewhere.

John Davy, says, '… in the short space of four months, he was in correspondence with Dr. Beddoes, relative to his researches on "Heat and Light," and a new hypothesis on their nature, to which Dr. Beddoes became a convert.'

Todd records that Beddoes was not happy with Davy when he arrived but he soon began to appreciate the young man and wrote to Darwin, saying, 'I think that I have the most extraordinary person That I have seen, for compass, originality and quickness of thought'.[249] The recipient was likely to have been the inventor, poet and visionary Erasmus Darwin, 1731 – 1802; who was a relative of Josiah Wedgwood. He was the grandfather of the more famous Charles Darwin who was not born until 1809.

Davy's life in Bristol was to open his mind considerably and he met a great variety of people including a number of poets who excited his love of poetry. One was Joseph Cottle, 1770 – 1853, the Unitarian printer-publisher, described by June Z. Fullmer, biographer of the *Young Humphry Davy, the making of an experimental chemist,* as 'a ponderously humourless poet. Never one to diminish his own importance.' Cottle saw in Davy,

> … the intellectual character of his face. His eye was piercing, and when not engaged in converse, was remarkably introverted, amounting to absence, as though his mind had been pursuing some severe trains of thought, scarcely to be interrupted by external objects, and from the first interview also, his ingeniousness impressed me as much as his mental superiority.[250]

A great deal of Cottle's writing is available and it includes details of his attempts to make Coleridge forsake his 'sad habit' of opium addiction before his painful death.

Coleridge on 17 February 1803 expressed his pleasure at Davy's progress, and said that he hoped 'more proudly of Davy than of any other man,' but afterwards noticed the

*OED explains this is *overindulgent in sensual pleasures*

danger of dissipation* and flattery, 'two serpents at the cradle of his genius.'[251]

Another in the group was Thomas Poole, a local farmer and tanner with a prerequisite for snuff who was to become one of Davy's lifelong friends. Davy impressed him by,

> … the quickness and truth of his apprehension. It was a power of reasoning so rapid … it must, I think have been felt by him, as it appears to me, pure intuition. I used to say to him, *You understand me before I half understand myself.*[252]

John Davy chose to quote some lines written to him by Poole after his brother's death.

> the more his *whole being* is known, the more the *man* will be esteemed and loved, the more the philosopher thanked and venerated

Some of the poems published by this group fell into the hands of Thomasin Dennis whilst she was in the Wedgwood household. She wrote to Gilbert about 'a strange collection of pieces by Southey, Cottle and a tribe of versifiers dignified with the title of Anthology'. She said of Davy's work,

> … nothing more than a string of epitaphs without fancy or thoughts, but they make a respectable figure in company with the rest of the book … Mr Wedgwood observed that the prevailing character of the book is imbecility.

While Davy is credited with the discovery of nitrous oxide as an anaesthetic, he wrote about its exhilarating effects at some length when recovering from semi-delirium and there is only the following throwaway line at the end of a paper that connects him to the discovery of its anaesthetic properties, something he apparently thought was of little importance.

> As nitrous oxide in its extensive operation appears capable of destroying physical pain, it may probably be used with advantage during surgical operations in which no great effusion of blood takes place.

Davy was happy with the title of 'chemist' for himself; an air of mystery and philosophy surrounded this title. Davy had an appreciation of his own pre-eminence, giving Gilbert no credit for his assistance up the ladder in the world of chemical science or for his achievement in being appointed to the Presidency of the Royal Society.

> Davy says himself: 'I consider it fortunate I was left much to myself as a child, and put upon no particular plan of study. … What I am I made

myself.'[253] (so saving the Lord a great responsibility!)

Davy clearly had a good, if not inflated, opinion of himself when one of his first poems, 'The sons of genius' was written in 1795-6 when he was seventeen and published by Robert Southey. It contained the lines,

> To scan the laws of nature, to explore
> The tranquil reign of mild Philosophy;
> Or on Newtonian wings to soar
> Through the bright regions of the starry sky.

(*Collected Works*, 1.26)[254]

Although many allege in retrospect to have seen genius in the awkwardness of Davy, the Rev. Dr. Cardew, who undertook his final education in Truro was mystified by all the claims. He wrote of Davy,

> I could not discern the faculties by which he was afterwards so much distinguished.

In his turn, Davy claimed to have 'discovered' his famous assistant, Michael Faraday, who was persuaded to adopt the title of valet for passport reasons while England was at war with France and eventually became the more famous and influential scientist. Their relationship was often unhappy with Davy claiming credit for some of Faraday's work and a dispute in which Davy accused Faraday of plagiarism. This caused the latter to abandon his important work on electromagnetism until after Davy's death.[255]

Twice Davy refused to admit Faraday as a Fellow of the Royal Society, objecting to honouring him for achieving the liquefaction of chlorine, claiming that he himself deserved credit for the achievement. John Davy gives an account of his brother's involvement in his Memoir, and asserts, 'It was not in my brother's nature to assume to himself another man's merit; he was infinitely above such meanness of conduct; …'.[256] Faraday was eventually elected to the Royal Society in 1824 and approached to be President in 1858, a position that he declined.

Davy became known as a popular, leading chemist of world renown and his entertaining lectures turned into social events. We pick him up after his baronetcy and election as a Fellow of the Royal Society. Even Dr Paris, who is usually accused of only being critical of Davy in his biography, records the events of 1803,

> The enthusiastic audience which his lectures obtained is at this period scarcely to be imagined. Men of the first rank and talent, the literary and

scientific, the practical, the theoretical, blue stockings, and women of fashion, the old, the young, all crowded eagerly into the lecture-room.

Home in Penzance in the autumn of 1821, Davy enjoyed the hospitality of the mayor in a blaze of local publicity for the town's illustrious son. On the other hand, the Cornwall Guide[257] claims that he hated the town and was very glad to leave.

Davy made a similar remark about his schooling and revealed his opinion of the Rev Dr. Cardrew when he wrote a letter in 1802, "I recollect I was rejoiced when I first went to school in Truro; but I was much more rejoiced when I left it for ever."

Among his letters is one to his wife dated September 1827 in which he makes a bequest to Penzance Grammar School. This is repeated nearer his death in a letter dated March 1829.

Davy's personal notebooks do not appear to contain any reference to his meeting with Trevithick and Vivian when seeking a patent for their steam engine in 1802.

The books do contain much poetry and descriptions of chemical experiments. His writings are prodigious and extensive, covering all manner of scientific matters. Davy had been accused of not continuing his pure research for which he had become renowned. However, it is clear that he found greater satisfaction and benefit for others in the extension of his research into further fields. He discusses his activities widely and sometimes he succeeds, sometimes he fails. Little seems to have escaped his attention.

Humphry and Anna?

Apparently, the emotional Anna did not reserve her attentions entirely for Gilbert; there were many references to her in Davy's notes. This was exceptional for Davy, who was clearly infatuated when he wrote in his notebook,

> Anna thou art lovely ever
> lovely in tears
> In tears of sorrow bright
> Brighter in joy.

He also copied some of her poems and in January 1799 he wrote to his mother to the effect that, "Anna was the best & and most amiable woman in the world".[258]

Davy's possible relationship with Beddoes' wife Anna attracted attention from authors seeking sensationalism. In a radio dramatisation of Davy's arrival at the Beddoes household in Clifton his early adventures included a number of barely known chemicals to create an atmosphere of exotic discovery before cutting to the most interesting one, 'laughing gas'. It told how the gas affected Davy's various friends and acquaintances and then Anna Beddoes, the wife of his host came into the scene as Beddoes assistant. The story continued amid much giggling and hilarity until Davy and Anna spent the night together. In another part of the broadcast story, Davy murdered an apparently incurable tubercular male patient with an overdose of opium.[259]

While Todd was certain that Anna was willing to drop anything for Gilbert, even without the influence of nitrous oxide, he never suggested she looked elsewhere. This account of her association with Davy is contrary to anything contained in the biographies of Davy by Paris or John Davy. Davy was associated with Beddoes for three years and June Z. Fullmer suggests that Davy was an unsophisticated, vigorous young man who was attracted to Anna's charms.[260] Davy wrote to his mother that he had become 'quite naturalized into the family, & I love them the more, the more I known them' There are reports of Anna accompanying Davy on walks in the countryside as her husband was both busy and too overweight to attempt such activity. The readers will have to draw their own conclusions about the manner in which storytellers and the media produce the more sensational material of their trade. Are they more fortunate than we are in finding the facts they need or do they leave false trails for others to follow?

Opium is seldom, if ever mentioned in the biographies of Davy although we know that he was prepared to try all sorts of drugs and gases on himself. However, his poetic friends, especially Coleridge, appeared to be synonymous with the drug.

All this appears to matter little to the story of Trevithick but the reader will be aware of a number of well-known people whose names crop up frequently in association with one another. It is unlikely that Trevithick would have had time for poems and the sophisticated chitchat that would inevitably have been a feature of such social life but had he been one of this group his place in history would have been as assured as theirs.

Davy, London and marriage
While Davy is seen as a man of science, he had as much interest in steam as Trevithick had in chemistry. An account of Davy's early life, his rise to power, its effect on him, how he is treated by his biographers and his demise is related later. It is sufficient here to say that Davies Gilbert introduced Trevithick to Davy by letter and that, two years later, Davy advised Gilbert to claim the intellectual property of Trevithick's work for himself.

Davy's work had been an example to all of deliberate investigation while he kept to his experiments in chemistry. It had differed from many of the eminent philosophers in the past that had progressed as much by romantic guesswork and metaphysics as by research. It was from about this time that those who sought their answers in scientific reckoning were choosing to be known as scientists. We are looking at a point when reason was swiftly overtaking the ambiguous label of philosophy, leaving those who truly felt happy with the title of philosopher contentedly discussing their subjects in an obscure world amongst themselves.

Paris takes the opportunity, when mentioning the necessity to erect a statue to the great chemist, to break away from his labours and point out what he, and probably many others, saw as a public disgrace: the lack of a statue to James Watt. In its Munk's Roll, the Royal College of Physicians provided a full description of Paris and noted that in 1814 he was the first secretary of the RGSC, of which Gilbert was the President. The RCP actually claims that he founded the Royal Geographical Society of Cornwall, which is likely to be an error, as there is no evidence that this society ever existed. Paris is credited with the invention of the safety bar, used by miners when fixing explosives. Paris said of a need for a statue to Watt,

> … when it is remembered that not a niche has been graced by a statue of Watt, while the giant iron children of his inventive genius are serving mankind in every quarter of the civilised world.[261]

By this time, the steam engines built on Trevithick's principles were quickly replacing those of Watt. Whatever mechanical advantages were embodied in Trevithick's engine, it would have been in the interests of Paris to be associated with the adulation of a national figure such as Watt rather than support the virtually unknown Cornishman. Paris was seeking greater heights in the world of chemistry, working with many of the leading figures of the day including Davy.

While Davy was well known about London for his intellect and his captivating, if not strange manner, his personality had the ability to change and this must have confused those who had dealings with him. Some people, like his friends in the Bristol area and those in his hometown appear to perceive a different person from that seen by many in the Royal Society. We can only point out these variations in approach and note that Trevithick, who might have looked to him for support as a compatriot was unlikely to have received a positive countenance.

In April 1812 Davy was knighted by the Prince Regent and three days later he married Mrs Jane Apreece, daughter and heiress of Charles Kerr and distantly connected to Sir Walter Scott.[262]

Many historians allude to Sir Humphry and Lady Davy as being aloof from each other. When making such statements it is usually wise to draw comparisons. In the case of

* Angling for salmon

Humphry Davy by John Linnell

the Davys we find that Humphry, a prolific letter writer as were many literate people, wrote frequently to his wife, especially when he was abroad. His letters, many of which are in the National Archives, contained matters of science, salmonia* and general interest such as the scenery. During his latter years, the letters frequently referred to the state of his health and showed concern over that of his wife's. We also find that he wrote poetry to Mrs Apreece in their courting days with, 'I do not envy you the world, but I envy the world you.'

The correspondence between the Davys is in marked contrast to that of the Trevithicks where it is likely that Jane would have responded to her husband if he had written or she had even known where he lived. She once claimed to find her unopened letters in his coat pocket.

While Davy made a name for himself as the great chemist of his day, his disposition was to make him an outcast. Although he worked with Gilbert on various matters of Royal Society business and his own position as its president, he was to distance himself from Gilbert when considering his rise to fame. The relationship grew into one where Gilbert, along with many others, lost their influence over Davy and became subservient. This must have greatly hurt Gilbert who fades into the background, even when he followed Davy into the Royal Society's Presidential chair.

A fine statue was erected to Davy outside the former market hall at Penzance in 1872 for about £600. The sculptor had the last laugh by revealing the second button down was missing from Davy's jacket; reputed to be a reference to his wife's lack of industry with a needle.

Gilbert and his torments
Throughout his life, Gilbert would recognize the endeavours of his pupils and pursue a policy dispensing wisdom and advice. However, we do not notice him absorbing

anything of their thinking that would change his mind about their social status. In spite of his theories, he was happy to leave them where they were or allow them to slip back from whence they came. The one remarkable exception is Davy who climbed from being the son of a destitute Cornish wood carver to be President of the Royal Society. Davy always claimed that he achieved this himself; it appears that he was self-motivated and certainly tolerated little interference from Gilbert once he left Cornwall.

Few men generously offered the products of their minds as did Davies Gilbert. He was documented as Davies Gilbert - Patron of Engineers, 1767-1839.[263] His determination to offer theoretical advice on the development of steam was one of the factors in establishing Cornwall as the font of advanced steam technology. The county's place in the story of the steam engine was profound but not acknowledged as it might be. While Gilbert clearly knew better, it was a pity that he chose Watt as the only significant name to be directly associated with the development of steam in Cornwall.

A. C. Todd in *Beyond the Blaze* commented at length from Gilbert's correspondence and from the entries in his journal. He examined Gilbert's conflicting attitudes to what he saw as many of the social matters of the day. If like Trevithick they did not fit

Davy's statue, Market Jew Street, Penzance. Inset: the missing button.

comfortably into the higher stations of life, he would do nothing to make their transit less painful. He objected to instructing the 'lower classes at the public expense'.[264] Nevertheless, he established his own ability to alter opinion when he told Thomasin he devoutly believed, "Men become whatever you persuade them that they are".[265]

Gilbert developed an uncomfortable mixture of philosophies in which he must have fought with the confusion in his mind because, other than his private charges, he saw the 'lower orders' as a separate unit of Mankind, almost an animal species. To him they were a race where poverty was related in some way to the irresponsibility of those who tended to breed up to the level of their food supply, so they were compelled to spend the greater part of their time "in procuring sustenance", and having found it, began to multiply yet again, thus intensifying the search for food.[266] Gilbert's study of the ancient philosophers would surely have included Plato who, according to Wender and others[267] believed human reproduction should be monitored numerically and controlled by the State.

One has to wonder whether Gilbert had dreams of a super race in which he exercised some power: but we may never know. Hammond records a Parliamentary debate in 1807 when the reformer Samuel Whitbread, 1758 – 1815, introduced a Bill for the general provision of elementary schools throughout England. There were two powerful currents of antagonistic opinion. One was William Windham, 1750 – 1810, … and Davies Gilbert … who said, 'However specious in theory the project might be, of giving education to the labouring classes of the poor, it would be prejudicial to their morals and happiness.[268] He continued at some length warning how, amongst other perils, education would enable the servants of agriculture and other laborious employments to read seditious pamphlets, vicious books, and publications against Christianity. The Archbishop of Canterbury also opposed Whitbread's radical Bill, which was 'easily defeated'.[269]

Gilbert's discussions with Thomasin on this subject and her observations of the Wedgwood children are reviewed by Todd.[270] Gilbert was far from alone with his views. In the following years Sir Francis Galton, the half cousin of Charles Darwin, became famous for expressing his opinion that included the enforced sterilisation of the lower classes and those producing offspring with mental disorders. Gilbert must have been very uncomfortable when fate delivered his first born as a subject for such study.

1813 was a bad year for Gilbert. In May, his eldest and precious son, Charles, died aged three. Gilbert was prostrate with grief and returned to Cornwall where he helped to form the RGSC and busied himself looking after his aged father until he died. A short time later, his wife gave birth to their fifth child, a boy who died within five hours. Three deaths within a year sapped his strength and it was not until the autumn of 1814 that he showed something of his former interest in his work. While there may have been something in the correspondence, we have been unable to find anything from Trevithick during the year that contains any condolence. Maybe Gilbert did not share his problems with Trevithick.

Gilbert's pupils could all have been described in today's terminology as having defects of temperament but that is something nearly everyone in these pages seems to suffer from to a greater or lesser extent. In the case of the Gilbert Four one has to wonder whether he was attracted to such people because he felt comfortable in their company or at ease with his superior intellect and so his ability to manipulate them. His interest in eugenics, the science of selective breeding and the exclusion of physical and mental defectives, was a far-reaching subject that attracted the attention of numerous leading philosophers and politicians over the centuries; it has many aspects that are not for these pages.

It is a pity that Gilbert wished to his pupils to evolve as extensions of his own cerebral outflow. He did not allow them to flourish as individual characters. In the end, in spite of his diligent attention to the improvement of their minds, Gilbert's pupils were all, in some way, to disappoint him and die before him. Hornblower, he saw as a capable designer and engineer who adopted a persecution complex and melancholia. Thomasin, the jewel of his academic eye, faded away from her family and life with reading and tuberculosis, while Davy, who made a name for himself as the great chemist of his day, developed a disposition that was to make him an outcast. Trevithick, who could have achieved so much, died of influenza, leaving behind a world full of his engines but barely a trace of himself. In every case, history has not served Gilbert well because, in spite of his attention to his pupils, little is heard of him, but that is often the lot of the teacher.

In spite of Gilbert's gentle manner and natural reticence to step forward into the limelight, he had very strong views on humanity and government as well as a belief in himself. 'He never doubted for one moment that his own contribution to public service was to make this system of government, whatever its defects, work well'.[271]

Gilbert's interest in the development of steam technology in Cornwall and engineering matters elsewhere was so significant that something should be said about that quiet man of letters.

> … he communicated largely to the wants of others from his own great store of knowledge and shone more by those reflected lights than by direct diffusion of his own rays.[272]

> There is no doubt that Gilbert was an extremely clever man knowing more about politics and science, mechanics and mathematics than he ever cared to admit.[273]

Although Gilbert was to spend much of his time privately with his pupils, it was his public contribution to the world of science that caught the eye of the establishment. The scientific journals happily wrote glowing reports about Gilbert's role in society.

> Gilbert's importance to the development of science in the early nineteenth century lay in his faith that science provided the best means to tackle practical problems and in his facility as a parliamentary promoter of scientific ventures.[274]

> His importance to the development of science lay in his tireless parliamentary promotion of scientific ventures ..… scientific matters and Cornish concerns

However, Todd tells us he found the following, more abrasive newspaper cutting in Gilbert's diary,

> Mr. Gilbert, throughout his parliamentary life, voted, without single exception that I can trace, for every measure now deemed corrupt and infamous, and against every measure now esteemed pure and Patriotic. He opposed the Reform Bill. His 'occupation is gone'.

The file of Gilbert's documents at the Royal Society is composed of some fifty items, mostly letters, not a lot when one considers his many years in office; none is connected with Trevithick. In 1827, the year of Gilbert's election as President, Trevithick eventually returned from Central America. In records held elsewhere, we find him in correspondence with Gilbert who also answered Arthur Woolf's questions on steam engines.

The necessity to write long letters to Gilbert faded when Trevithick broke the link between the two men by going to work at Dartford. Was Gilbert's dismissive attitude to Trevithick after his death a display of his annoyance connected to the loss of his control over their association? It may have been pique because the Halls would have supplied his last remaining pupil with all the attention, facilities and academic advice he required. Trevithick had placed the progress of his high-pressure steam above everything throughout his life; at Dartford he appeared to have eventually found in his old age the friendship, succour and understanding he sought. To this day, the people of that town willingly display the affection they showed the inventor nearly 180 years ago.

Taking the correspondence between Gilbert and Trevithick in isolation one would believe that Gilbert's correspondence with the Cornish engineer occupied a great deal of his time but it is clear from the other associations in his journal that he led a highly complicated life in touch with many people of note both socially and academically. It is noticeable that whenever Gilbert discussed his friends or the importance of the steam engine he barely, if ever, mentioned Trevithick. One could easily believe that Gilbert never mentioned Trevithick to others more than the few instances mentioned in these pages. Trevithick frequently turned to Gilbert as his mentor and confidant but he is addressed and recorded in Gilbert's journal simply as 'Trevithick'. All Gilbert's other correspondents are fully prefixed in the notes and letters with titles such as 'Mr, Mrs, Miss, Sir' and so on.[275]

Educated letter writing in the early nineteenth century followed a prescribed etiquette, much of which appears to have been lost today. It enabled people at different social levels or positions in business to maintain their station when writing to each other. Gilbert would open his letters 'Dear Trevithick' while Trevithick replied, 'Dear Sir' or 'Dear Mr Gilbert'.

Gilbert did serve one important purpose throughout most of Trevithick's life; he was the steadying anchor to whom Trevithick was willing to turn. The governing factor was the difference in social standing between the two, a barrier that was always acknowledged but never apparently mentioned. Gilbert's station in life was achieved by background, education, access to funds and the demonstration of his natural ability. He always maintained the difference in their levels and this was appreciated by Trevithick who was grateful that he was dealing with a gentleman who was prepared to listen to him. Trevithick did not require much of what Gilbert had to say to him, his purposes could have been better served by the good sense of Henry Harvey but Trevithick was reluctant to speak or listen to his brother-in-law.

The Gentleman's Magazine published the following favourable review of Gilbert's re-editing of the Parochial History of Cornwall in 1838,

> This Parochial History of Cornwall must, we predict, make its way into the hands of every intelligent resident in the county, …

But others, who understood Cornwall and what should have been found in such a publication, were not so kind.

Let us sum up Gilbert's enormous activities and responsibilities. In one of his publications, Gilbert described himself as 'One time President of the Royal Society, FAS, FRSE, MRIA &c, &c, and D.C.L. by diploma from the University of Oxford'. He was also High Sheriff of Cornwall for a year, president of the Royal Agricultural Society and the first president of the RGSC. He held a number of posts such as President of the Board of Agriculture. He spent a great deal of time travelling the country on horseback. His claimed interests extended from making recommendations for improvements to the design of the suspension bridge over the Menai Straits to Anglesey[276] and the publication of papers on *Suspension Bridges* and the *Catenary Curve* to the standardisation of weights and measures and the establishment of an observatory at the Cape of Good Hope. Whether he had been invited to contribute from his prodigious understanding of scientific matters to these projects or his connection had been one of well-intentioned interference could be the subject for further investigation. For instance, an examination of the extensive Papers of the Royal Observatory, Cape of Good Hope held in the Janus depository at Cambridge University Library shows that his interest was in the definition of longitude and only three items were recorded in his name.

Gilbert found it possible to influence the outcome of situations, such as the obscurity of Trevithick, and some of his claims must be engaged with uncertainty. There were disputed instances where his influence was reputed to have made a difference. A change in the height of the towers on the Menai Straits Bridge apparently improved the Catenary and as the Chairman of the committee concerned with the building of the 1831 London Bridge, he was reputed to have been responsible for it being constructed ten feet wider than had originally been planned. The bridge was widened by a further eleven and a half feet in the 1900s and sold to the USA in 1968.[277]

There is no doubt that Gilbert would have considered his contributions over a wide range of sciences to have been creditable and very worthy but he tended to spread his intellect very widely and rather thinly; life did not supply him with enough time to accomplish all he and many others thought he had achieved.

John Samuel Enys, 1796-1872
J. S. Enys was a very well educated man of notable lineage who turned his hand to a number of pursuits including farming, road improvements, mineralogy, architecture and being a magistrate. He developed an interest in the pumping of Cornish mines and acquired considerable information from Trevithick and others. He married Gilbert's eldest surviving daughter, Catherine. He wrote a great number of papers for the Institution of Civil Engineers, many of them concerning Cornish steam engines.[278] Gilbert and Enys carried on a prolific correspondence.

The Royal Society, 'The troubled years'
We see many instances in these pages of Trevithick's trusting manner. While it could have been one of his more endearing qualities, it would also stand between him and the success he sought in life. It would never have occurred to him to mistrust Gilbert or Davy, the first he constantly turned to for advice and the second he respected for his ability and the progress he had made. Had he known that the first played with him at his whim and the second dismissed him as being of no consequence he may have chosen different acquaintances.

While the Royal Society may appear to be a long way from the story of Trevithick, its interests were scientific. We find within the Society people who might have paid more attention to the world-changing advances in mechanical engineering that were taking place around them. That is, if they had not wrangling between themselves for more than a decade.

The prominent characters in what Todd and others describe as the 'unhappy years' included Sir Joseph Banks, Sir Humphry Davy, Charles Babbage and Davies Gilbert. The activities of Davy and Gilbert were to have a direct influence on Trevithick's failure to establish his claim as the inventor of the high-pressure steam engine.

As might be expected, proceedings concerning the hierarchy at the Royal Society were complex and subject to considerable debate among its learned members. It did not help that its Fellows were, by the establishment of the Society, divided into two major camps and linked to other vested interests. Again, the full story is well told by A. C. Todd in his biography of Gilbert, and by David Philip Miller in *Between Hostile Camps: Sir Humphry Davy's Presidency of the Royal Society of London, 1820-1827*, in which he describes the career of Davy as 'one of the fairy tales of early nineteenth-century British science'. There are a number of other books and the *Minutes of the Council of the Royal Society*. If anyone thought that the Royal Society of the early nineteenth century was a repository of somnolent geriatric academics, the proceedings of the Society over the course of a certain ten years or so will shatter that illusion. Just off-centre, as self-appointed kingmaker, Gilbert was wheeling and dealing with fractious personalities and desperately trying to save his own skin.

Davy's disputes with other Fellows of the Royal Society allow us to ascertain the nature of the man who chose to denounce the true inventor of the high-pressure steam engine.

In 1819, the President of the society was Sir Joseph Banks, 1743 – 1820, who had held the Presidency for the previous 42 years with an overpowering interest in natural history; he also held the privilege of being permitted to choose his successor.

Banks elected Gilbert as Vice-President although he was not a member of the Society's council. Gilbert reported Banks as saying that he would die in peace if he knew that Gilbert was to be elected as his successor. However, the likelihood of Gilbert being elected was far from everyone's liking and William Whewell spoke of those seeking power in the institution where, 'all sorts of plans, speculations and schemes are afloat and all sorts of people, proper and improper, are penetrated with the design of wielding the sceptre of power.'[279]

Banks' attitude to his opponents inflamed the situation with the Society and as Richard Gregory put it, 'Banks is portrayed as an incompetent natural historian with powerful friends whose fondness for domineering was exceeded only by his distaste for mathematics and mathematicians'.

Contrary to what Banks was reputed by Gilbert to have told him, Sir William Barrow said that Banks thought his successor should be William Wollaston or Davy but Wollaston had refused and he did not think Davy was at all suitable. He thought Davy to be too 'lively' for the post.

Gilbert was said to 'possess all the requisites which science and literature could bestow for filling the prominent station to which he had been called but he had no large and hospitable mansion in the metropolis for the reception of the numerous guests by whom he would have been surrounded and the government or even the management of such a body as the Royal Society required a more rigid and commanding deportment than nature and his limited commerce with the world had bestowed on him.' Gilbert was subsequently elected as Treasurer.[280]

The different factions in the society all had their opinions. There was also the newly formed breakaway Astronomical Society requiring its first president. This post was offered to Gilbert and he accepted but later rejected it because it would be incompatible with his position as Vice-President of the Royal Society.

Gilbert proposed that Wollaston should act as temporary President for a few months in 1820 and he accepted. Wollaston was later to make a number of generous gifts to the Society, demanding that they should not be parsimonious with their distribution of awards for experimentation.

Gilbert appeared by many to be the re-incarnation of the late Banks and so he expected strong opposition if his name was proposed as President. Gilbert's value to the Society was seen as his ability to obtain Parliamentary support for the work of its Fellows. Davy had been given a grant to develop his miners' lamp, after George Stephenson had done all his similar work for nothing, and Babbage received several grants to enable him to proceed with work on his Difference Machine, the forerunner of the computer. These decisions all followed intervention by Gilbert and revealed how he could exercise the considerable influence he held.

Gilbert's demeanour did not shape him to be a leader in what was to become a difficult time for the Society after Banks. Gilbert proposed Sir Humphry Davy as President; he had excellent credentials as an internationally renowned chemist, exemplified by the award of a Knighthood in 1812 and a Baronetcy in 1818. Davy was popular with the public because his lectures in chemistry were well-attended, entertaining, social events. Thomas Rowlandson the satirical cartoonist, well known for his depictions of London life, illustrated a scene where Davy performed some of his tricks with chemistry in a crowded lecture theatre.

Miller holds the view that a group of Fellows who had led opposition to Davy's election now saw promise in his initial attitudes, policies and actions,[281] but that was not to last. His early reformist policies began to lose momentum and he failed to unite, or even placate the many institutions that grouped their interests against the Society.

By the time that Davy came to the Presidency, the Mathematical Practitioners and the other groups had long been joined in opposition to the attitude of Banks and his friends. Similar factions made Davy's path to the Presidency an uneasy one and there were several other contenders. Many considered that Davy, no longer eminent in an avenue of science that he had not pursued for some years, was unqualified for the Presidency.

Davy accepted the presidential nomination and Gilbert was delighted. He believed he had taken a clever young man who was destined to be a provincial doctor from Penzance in Cornwall to the highest, most honoured post among the world's scientists. Under Davy's leadership Gilbert expected the Royal Society to reform

Rowlandson cartoon of a Humphry Davy lecture in London.

following the four decades of conservative rule under Banks. Although he was unaware of it at the time, it would be Gilbert's subsequent downfall that brought about the significant changes required by the Society.

The effect of the Presidency on Davy was immediate and disastrous for him and the Society. He completely changed from being the son of a wood worker and adopted an authoritarian status, treating the Royal Society as his monocracy. The Society was about to go through what some Fellows tactfully described as an 'unhappy period'.

Davy's natural awkwardness, irritability and ill-humour were features of his life that had tactfully been attributed to his inhalation of toxic gases in the cause of science. According to Paris, Davy's authoritarian approach demanded subservience from those about him. Royal recognition and marriage to the wealthy Mrs Apreece changed timidity into arrogance. Paris recorded that Davy showed,

> an inordinate admiration of hereditary rank, was the cardinal deformity of Davy's character ; it was the centre from which all his defects radiated…'.[282] He goes on to say, in equally strong language, that it was sad to see him maligning friend and foe alike, dead or alive. Davy asserted that Banks, his predecessor, was only a tolerable botanist and a lover of gross flattery.[283]

F. F. Cartwright realised that there was a problem and tried to mitigate, saying,

Perhaps it is true that he was suffering from a form of hypertension, which made him intolerable of criticism, deluded him into thinking that he was infallible, and set up within himself a persecution mania.[284]

The crisis is related in much fuller detail by A. C. Todd in his biography of Gilbert and by L. F. Gilbert.[285]

Miller takes a good, hard look at the Royal Society and states that 'the use of Davy's career to illustrate the thesis that 'genius will out' is not without its problems'[286] Davy had come to the Presidency after forty-two years in which Sir Joseph Banks had 'done everything in his power to cultivate and maintain relations between the Royal Society and the antiquarian, natural history, horticultural and agricultural constituencies'[287] that were his particular interests.

Other sections within the Society found this Banksian regime to be irrelevant or, at least, unhelpful to their scientific and social aspirations. The results of these variations in interests were the inevitable formation of other societies. Miller says that Banks and his supporters saw the RGSC as 'a relatively informal venue for polite mineralogical and geological conversation'.[288] He clearly did not appreciate that, when roused, its members were made of stronger stuff.

Davy had been one of the RGSC's founding members in 1808 and had soon been joined by Gilbert. The society was still in its infancy and making progress when Davy returned after four months' illness to find things not as he would have wished. Apparently, he had hoped it would be a social club where the members had the opportunity to enjoy good food and cross-table banter. He said he had no time for the presentation of papers that he described as trivial and boring, making a point of constantly finding fault with everything and interrupting the proceedings. To add to his dislikes, he considered the meals both inferior and expensive at fifteen shillings (nearly £40 today) a head. Mrs James Watt wrote that she and her husband obtained a delightful meal in Cornwall for just twopence (50p); maybe Davy had a point there.

Other members of the RGSC were appalled by this constant bad behaviour and eventually Davy was caused to resign in April 1809. Activities like this could frequently be laid at Davy's door, for instance Paris wrote of Davy's trip to Paris in 1813 when,

> ... his likes and dislikes to particular persons were violent and that they were, apparently, not directed by any principle, but were the effect of a sudden impulse.[289]

In addition to his nature, it was likely that Davy's misbehaviour at the RGSC had a more sinister reason. Thirty-seven of its members were also Fellows of the Royal Society, an organisation that saw itself pre-eminent in the world of all forms of science. There were many who saw the emergence of additional learned societies as threats to the Royal Society and Davy had taken it upon himself to undermine the status of the RGSC, hoping to reduce it to being the harmless dinner and discussion group that Banks perceived. An entertaining account of the early activities of the RGSC can be read in *Whatever is under the earth, the Geological Society of London, 1807-2007* by Gordon L Herries Davies.

Davy turned his attention to the aristocratic patronage that had made his own career possible within the Royal Society. He focussed more of his interests in this direction than he did towards the Society's lack of attention to the sciences; something it had so poorly served over the past half a century. His establishment of the Royal Medals, the foundation of a zoological park and the importation of new breeds of game birds revealed his interests in self-promotion and the shooting season.

Even the award of the Royal Medals, which seemed to be the prerogative of Davy, caused consternation amounting to outrage in the case of Charles Babbage who considered that he was in line for one with his work on the difference machine. There was a widely held belief amongst the reformers that the medal 'affair demonstrated that the patronage of science was more a matter of the *éclat* which accrued to its organisers than a genuine attempt to stimulate ongoing original research.'[290]

Davy further inflamed the situation when he overlooked Babbage's generally recognized wish to become one of the Royal Society's two secretaries in favour of John G. Children, an old friend of Davy's from his chemistry days. Edward Ryan, a member of the reform group, summed up Davy's behaviour in a letter to Babbage,

> The President has behaved infamously, full of his tricks and knavery of every description and treating Herschal with great indignity. The Society, every member almost, as Colly and Herschal inform me, are in the greatest rage at the President's proceedings and nothing is now talked of but removing him.[291]

A more conservative group in the Royal Society that included Davies Gilbert, although he was apparently careful not to say anything, were concerned 'by Davy's ineptitude in managing scientific projects and … the Royal Society had given conflicting advice to the Admiralty on the conduct of the Royal Observatory'.[292]

It is clear from the information acquired by Todd that Davy's reign at the Royal Society could, in the view of many, have been one of terror. On the other hand, Davy was carrying on correspondence with his old friends in the Bristol area on the most amicable of terms. He frequently wrote to Thomas Poole from London or abroad, signing himself variously, 'Your old and affectionate friend' or 'Very affectionately your old friend'. In 1831, Poole wrote to John Davy, Humphry's brother, and remembered Davy in the friendliest of terms, saying, *"... his Heart was as enlarged as his Mind"*.

Davy did not help himself when opportunities arose to reveal any tenderness he may have possessed. On the death of Dr W. Hyde Wollaston in December 1828, not long before his own demise, Davy added a tribute to the memory of the great man who had held the position of President of the Society for an interim period. Sir John Barrow, FRS, records all the tributes in *Sketches of the Royal Society and the Royal Society Club*, and adds that Davy 'has contrived to spoil it, by an ungenerous observation with respect to his application of science for profit – without adverting to the profit that science had so abundantly poured into his own lap'. That Barrow, who started life as a timekeeper in a foundry and progressed to found the Royal Geographical Society, should have chosen to attack Davy in such a delicate situation revealed the views held by some of the Fellows about their President.

Davy would frequently judge that he was deserving of some award to improve his social, financial and academic situations. In a letter to his wife.[293] Davy thought that he should have been made a Privy Councillor or "Lord of Trade". He goes on to assert his fear that, "honours as well as places will go not to those who deserve them; but to those who seek them by all means fair or foul", a line that would have produced a wry smile on many faces.

Davy was also implicated in a scandal that involved a printer and Davy benefiting by £500, mostly from the Society's funds; something described as the 'taste of scandal sauce' by the *Dublin Magazine* of 1840. He also steadfastly resisted Babbage's attempts to oppose him. Babbage found that other members of the council were powerless in the face of their one-eyed President's dictatorship, saying, "there were upright and eminent men on that Council; yet not one of them had the moral courage to oppose the President's dictation or afterwards to set it aside on the grounds of its irregularity".[294]

The Society was in crisis. Miller says 'Davy's basic problem as a leader was that he was unable to reconcile warring interest groups in that community'.[295]

Although Gilbert, as Vice-President, is not mentioned by Miller in his account of Davy's Presidency for having actually done or said anything, Gilbert claims elsewhere that he used all his political ability to uphold the status of the Society, especially in relation to its standing with the government. He was again offered the presidency of the Society of Architects but declined, tactfully hoping that some way could be found to bring the two societies closer together. Meanwhile Davy continued in his usual manner, one that caused great concern to the Council and its Fellows.

While Davy's resignation letter of the 1st July 1827 to Gilbert from Salzburg contained some personal matters and details of his health, his rigid vegetable diet, haemorrhoids and his use of leeches and blisters, it was written in a most formal manner, addressing him as 'My dear Sir' and asks him, under these circumstances to offer his resignation to the Society. This is a distinct change from the letter he wrote to Gilbert on the 22nd February 1799, which began, 'Dear Friend – for I love you too well to call you by a more ceremonious name.' At that time his letters would often end with, 'Yours with sincere affection'. By October the following year, the letters appear to start frequently without a salutation and end, 'With sincere respect and affection, Yours'.[296]

In 1828, Davy suffered a second stroke that left him partly paralysed. However, determination drove him on and he left to seek a cure on the Continent. He arranged with Gilbert that, should anything happen to him, Sir Robert Peel should be invited to be the next President; his credentials and achievements appeared to be ideal for the post. We see here how Davy and Gilbert have changed places; the pupil becoming the teacher. It is Davy who is giving the commands and Gilbert obeying them. In the beginning, Gilbert claimed that it was Davy's acccptancc of his guidance that set him on the path to success.

Davy was in Switzerland in February 1829 where he suffered another stroke and died at Geneva on 29th May of that year. Davy's death is often attributed to his selfless inhalation of dangerous gases in his formative years. Whether those gases can eventually instigate a couple of strokes and a heart attack, the actual causes of his death some thirty years later, we are not qualified to know. His dread of a post mortem examination because of possible residual sensitivity in the body meant that no definitive cause of death was ever recorded.[297]

Davy's wife was charged £142[298] for a memorial window to her husband in Westminster Abbey.

In the absence of Davy the pent-up reformers in the Society, who had been frustrated for the past 49 years, proposed a number of changes. On receipt of Davy's letter of resignation, Gilbert dined with Peel. At the next council meeting, Gilbert was elected as temporary President. Internal politics were still tearing the Society apart and another two Cornishmen entered the scene, Sir Benjamin Hobhouse and his son Cam from Grampound who, in Gilbert's words, "exhaled a scorching air of radicalism". John Ayrton Paris of Penzance added another from Cornwall to those interested in Presidential activities.

In 1822, Gilbert recorded the election of Sir Charles Lemon to Fellowship and, in 1826, Sir Richard Vyvyan joined the fray to make about a dozen Cornishmen as Fellows involved in the dispute. While this says something for their love of a good argument, it also indicates acceptance of the Cornish contribution to culture and the sciences during the nineteenth century. In 1931, J. Hambley Rowe calculated that there had been over fifty Fellows of Cornish extraction in the Royal Society including such characters as Admiral William Bligh of Bounty mutiny fame.

In another of his politically safe, understated but visionary epitaphs following the demise of his failed pupil, Gilbert said of Davy that 'he failed as President of the Royal Society through social confusion'.[299]

Gilbert addressed the Society on the death of Davy and Paris recorded, 'Mr Davies Gilbert, his early friend and patron, has likewise paid to his memory a just and appropriate testimony in respect and admiration from the chair of the Royal Society'. He also mentioned that 'the inhabitants of Penzance, animated by feelings of honourable pride and strong local attachment will shortly raise a pyramid of massive granite to his memory'. In another address to the Society, Gilbert said 'The poetic bent of Davy's mind seems never to have left him …'.[300] On reflection, the inhabitants decided against the pyramid.

The level of argument, and that is a kind word, within the Royal Society would amaze anyone who believed that such learned bodies were the comfortable seat of serene academic contemplation. Davy and Gilbert, who had so ably damned the acknowledgement of Trevithick's attainments, were frequently the butt of the hate.

Looking back at Davy's reign he was, as Miller has said, clearly caught between the traditional Banksians and the reformers. His high-flown actions did little or nothing to appease either side or to merge them. Paris wrote, 'To assert that Davy retained his popularity, or to deny that he retired from the office under the frown of a considerable party, would be dishonest. I would willingly dismiss this part of his life without too nice an examination; but I am writing history, not a eulogy.'[301]

The election of Peel to reconcile matters looked secure and Gilbert was able to write to his wife with some relief, "My heart is lightened by having the burden taken from it which I have cast off this day".

Although Gilbert was doing his best to consolidate the Royal Society, some of the words used by its Fellows and his own biographer to describe him reveal the strength and diversity of feeling at the time. They include vacillating weakness amounting to ineptitude, fear, dishonour, confusion, illogical perversity and hysterical weakness and, there is just one mention of gentleness.

Then Peel wrote to say that it was not his intention to stand for Presidency. Gilbert, the great fixer had become unstuck and wrote to his wife, 'It is very provoking that just as I had got Mr Peel's election sure, he has flown off'.[302]

Gilbert had, at one time intimated that he would consider the Presidency but as he saw Peel leaving the scene, he pleaded with him and stated his own case, 'I feel myself quite unequal to the task. If I were to submit now to be elected I should forfeit all my powers before the end of the year. I entreat you to reconsider the matter'.[303]

It was said of him, "Mr Davies Gilbert is a worthy good man, but a mere child in the affairs of the world and by his own confession he has with the best intentions most certainly misled you."[304]

The Oxford Dictionary of National Biography says of Gilbert, "This echoes the judgements of his contemporaries who found him indecisive and irresolute as president of the Royal Society. Gilbert's repeated refusal of political office and his predilection for behind-the-scenes administrative work were much in character."

Peel left Gilbert to his own devices and the latter prepared the speech of acceptance he knew he would have to give at the next meeting of the council; saying it 'almost made me ill by emotional application and labour'.[305] The labour of writing the speech was indeed painful and the delivery and reception were probably equally so. It is likely that his address was a long affair. Gilbert would put all that he had into his writing and the records of the Royal Society's Library show that on 30th November 1829 his address to the Society consisted of no less than thirty-nine sides of paper; and we know his handwriting was minute.

Davy's Presidency, between 1820 and 1827, was followed by three years in which Gilbert occupied the Presidential chair. For ten years the Royal Society was led by two men in whose judgement Trevithick had implicit faith. He trusted them and never thought for a moment that they would do anything that might adversely affect his engineering career or the rewards it should have provided. Miller concluded the decade of their rule and summed up Gilbert's last days as President by saying, 'The Royal Society 'troubles' reached a climax in 1830'.[306]

Gilbert held the Presidency from 1827 to 1830. By his own admission, he was not up to the job. During this period the Society's politicians and those with particular views tore it apart, a period that its more reasonable Fellows would prefer to forget. Innuendo and downright accusations flew between the factions within the Society and Gilbert was again accused, with some justification of connivance and secrecy. These seemed to be the tools of his trade and his only form of control, being unable to deal with adversaries face to face.

Several entries in *The Literary Gazette* provided damning reports on proceedings at the Society and *The Times* printed a letter, signed F.R.S. that exposed even more. Gilbert's position had long been untenable and, at an unconstitutional extraordinary meeting in November 1830 held prior to the normal council meeting, he was practically put on trial for his deeds. He then announced his intention to resign, got up and left the meeting to return home to his Sussex house where, a broken man, he fired his haystacks.[307]

Gilbert had stepped down without nominating his successor and Warburton was immediately elected to the chair. Power had swung from the philosopher to a timber merchant and, in future, Presidents were to be elected, not as the prerogative of the retiring incumbent, but by a majority of all the Fellows. Gilbert's downfall had brought about the long needed reforms of the Society. He could not see it and spoke miserably of the breakdown in orderly life as he saw it. He wrote, 'Measures were taken which will totally change the character of the Society, reduce it to a level with the minor societies and make me the last real President.'[308]

The election was declared invalid in the days of turmoil that followed. Gilbert found he was unable to walk away but continued his life of patronage, this time with no less a person than HRH the colourful The Duke of Sussex, known as the favourite uncle of Queen Victoria. Sussex was subsequently elected by a narrow margin and held the post for the following eight years. With some relief, Gilbert assumed heroic status and wrote to his wife, 'I have retreated over a Golden Bridge with Purple Banners'.[309]

The reforms of the Royal Society that Gilbert had hoped Davy would fashion had been achieved by himself, at the expense of his personal standing and dignity and in a manner that he probably did not recognise. The eventual election of a nobleman had vindicated his steadfast opinions on the sanctity and sanity of the British class structure and the advancement through the ranks of his fellows solely by academic achievement.

It was about this time that the new general appellation of 'scientist' began to replace 'philosopher' at the Royal Society and elsewhere as the understanding of the sciences tended to move away from dreams and the ethereal. The terms 'physicist' and 'chemist' were being better understood by the public. Many intellectuals still preferred to hide behind the title 'philosopher', as they do to this day.

Gilbert's intended hand in the elevation of Davy to the Presidency may have been understood by the Fellows but it is difficult to find a reference to his work in any report on the discussions. While Davy's name will always be appreciated as a leading chemist and an inventor of the miners' lamp, historians choose to make little or no mention of Gilbert in their writings about Davy. For instance,

> Born in humble circumstances … and by chance brought into

communication with men of wealth who cultivated science'[310] is a typical example of how Davy's career was seen to begin.

Gilbert, Davy and Trevithick

While the story of Trevithick was involved and exciting, Gilbert did not appear to be overly impressed. How many people are there who invent so much that they change the world and yet they fight for their existence in the mountains and jungles of South and Central America? Gilbert did not seem to be too thrilled by anything that Trevithick did. This may have been because he found Trevithick incorrigible.

From his early days, Trevithick saw Gilbert as someone to whom he could turn for answers. When he did not need answers, he did not need Gilbert. Gilbert's early association with Trevithick appeared to be one in which he was fascinated by the inventor's flair and was willing to encourage, support and guide him in his labours. It is clear from the correspondence between the two men that there were two different types of letter from Trevithick. In one he set out his intentions and joyfully explained what he was about to achieve and, in the other, he detailed his queries, provided such information and figures as he could muster and ask for Gilbert's advice. In the latter he would want a simple answer that advised him whether his idea would work, and if so, how well.

Gilbert's answers tended to be similar in both cases. In the first, he would caution Trevithick's aspirations, provide detailed reasoning and sometimes explain why he thought Trevithick should not pursue the course he intended. In the second, he would write at length, detailing the scientific interpretation behind his deliberations. In both cases, Gilbert may have been hoping that Trevithick would see things his way and so improve his mind. While this would have enabled him to work out his own answers to such questions, we must wonder if Gilbert would have wanted that. Gilbert never refused to answer Trevithick's questions and did not stint on the information he gave. As a busy man who had many other things to do, he had good reason to discard Trevithick at any time. Where would Gilbert obtain his pleasure if Trevithick were able to answer his own questions? Gilbert must have enjoyed responding to all those questions over many years, did he never think that the amusement Trevithick brought him with his oddball enquiries deserved some promotion of those ideas in return? Did he only see Trevithick as a member of the lower classes to be employed or used for his amusement? Maybe he thought that his response to Trevithick's questions was sufficient payment, bringing mutual satisfaction and enabling both to benefit from their actions.

We do not know what Trevithick thought of Gilbert's consistent response to his queries, it was useful and he was grateful. He probably ignored most of what Gilbert wrote, all he really wanted was a simple 'yes' or 'no'. It is interesting to note that, during his time in the Americas, Trevithick was without advice from Gilbert. His fortunes there appeared to be no better or worse than those in England.

Trevithick could not think in the same way as Gilbert; he was never destined to become a philosopher. Had he tried to think along similar lines, he would have stymied his mind and interfered with the rare thoughts of a genius. Similarly, Gilbert was unable to innovate; his powers were different. He could exert influence and its use on Hornblower and Thomasin could well have been the cause of their losing their will to continue. Trevithick was made of stouter stuff and impervious to such interference; he probably never noticed it.

Although we know Trevithick struggle throughout his lifetime avoiding food, sleep and responsibilities to his family to achieve greater triumphs with his engine, he failed to live up to Gilbert's expectations. Gilbert credited him with being one of the most ingenious men in the world but, 'he has never done anything himself'.[311] and that he 'failed to reach the rank to which his ability entitled him through his restless and turbulent inner self'.[312]

Gilbert would have been well aware of the social standing of an engineer. The extensive *New General English Dictionary*, originally by the Reverend Thomas Dyche, in its seventeenth edition and published in 1794, explained as follows,

1.   MECHA'NIC (S) a mechanician, one fkilled in mechanics; alfs a manufacturer, a low workman.

2.   MECHA'NIC or MECHA'NICAL (A) fkilled in mechanics, relating to mechanics, regulated by the nature and laws of mechanics; alfo mean, poor, low, or bafe in degree or order, as the fon of a handicraftfman, in opposition to the fon of a nobleman, &c.

3.   Mechanical *Philofophy,* is that which explains the appearance or phenomena of nature, and the principles of mechanics, taking in the confideration of motion, gravity, figure, fize, &c. and is sometimes called the corpufcular philofophy.

4.   ENGINEE'R (S) one who manages engines; in *War,* a perfon whofe bufinefs it is to contrive and infpect attacks, defences, works, &c.

5.   PHILO'SOPHER (S) a wife and judicious man, who applies himfelf to the ftudy of nature, and morality; one who ftudies to know the nature and caufes of all things human and devine, and to attend to ebvery good rule and method of life.

6.   CHY'MIST (S) a perfon fkilful in, or practifing the art of chymifty.

While these definitions were originally published a couple of years prior to the events being recounted here they were still current thinking at the time our characters were in their formative years.

We see from these definitions that anyone holding the position of a mechanic is a 'low fellow' and likely to be poor, low or base, as in the case of the son of a handicraftsman. This explanation of the position of a woodcarver's son in the social order of things must have worried Davy because he was just that. He worked hard to raise his social and financial position from his lowly beginnings. In doing so, he managed to demonstrate Gilbert's theory of attainment by ability.

When one includes the word 'philosophy' with 'mechanical' the situation changes radically and intellectual thought enters the picture. This is where Davy takes the position of the philosopher, and disagrees with the possibility that George Stephenson, a mere North of England brakeman, could have been clever enough to design an effective miners' lamp. There is also a school of thought that suggests that Davy's visit to Sunderland in August 1815 and the contribution by Smithson Tennant, 1761 - 1815, an eminent Cambridge professor of chemistry, were the basis for Davy's lamp; also that both his lamp and that of Stephenson were based on the 1813 work of the Irishman Dr William R. Clanny, 1770 – 1850, who practised as a physician at Sunderland.

Davy referred to Stephenson as an 'engine mechanic' and said that his claims were 'false' and 'absurd',[313] With a stab in the back from his hometown, *Lake's Parochial History of Penzance, 1868,* held that Stephenson's lamp had been in use for some time prior to that of Davy. In a gesture of publicised magnanimity directed at the saving of miners' lives, Davy refused to accept any royalties from those who copied his patented lamp. Davy would receive the Rumford Medal from the Royal Society in 1816 for his 'outstandingly important discovery' and a great deal of prestige to this day for his inventiveness and noble gesture. Stephenson is reputed to have developed a considerable distrust of London academics and then went on to build a number of clever things like his Rocket locomotive. In 1847 Stephenson became the first President of the Institute of Mechanical Engineers, bred cattle, designed light houses and a glass tube in which he grew straight cucumbers, he clearly enjoyed his life and prestige, Davy passed his declining years in disagreement.

This was the age of discovery and it was not limited to new lands across the sea, plants or elements in the ground. The discovery of individuals was of equal importance and Gilbert took the opportunity in his letter to John Wyatt in connection with the Thames tunnel to demonstrate how successful he had been in that respect, dropping in the names

133

of two other people who have no relevance to the content of the letter,

> … I entertained for several years some acquaintance with Mr. Jonathan Hornblower; answering every theoretical question to the best of my power … I had the good fortune to bring forward Mr. Davy earlier than without that assistance he could not have come to notice, and believing Mr. Trevithick to be a sensible, enterprising young man, I ten years ago began to lend him every assistance … and his knowledge in mechanics …'.[314]

Gilbert represented Helston as a Member of Parliament in 1804 until a bill was brought in 'to secure freedom and purity of election' in the borough.[315] He then stood, but never fought for Bodmin from 1806 until 1832. We find that, unknown to Gilbert, his position as High Sheriff was manoeuvred by Sir Francis Basset in revenge for failing to show his political hand in support of Basset's plan for a hospital at Truro.[316] The time consuming position was intended to keep Gilbert away from Oxford. Basset, later known as Lord de Dunstanville of Tehidy, also supported Gilbert's many years as MP for Bodmin.[317] In those days, an election to Parliament was not ordered in the same manner as it is today. Before 1832, when Gilbert ceased to be a MP only men who owned freehold property worth at least forty shillings a year could vote. That meant, at most 435,000 people in England and Wales were entitled to vote, and they were bound to the wealthiest landowners by an intricate web of patronage. In effect the 514 Members of Parliament were elected by no more than 180 land-owning patrons.[318]

It is clear from his biography that many saw Gilbert as an enigma and, although he successfully operated in various authoritative capacities, people queried what he had actually done. While Todd explains a great deal about the meanings of benevolence and patronage as Gilbert saw them, it is difficult to find any trace of annuities or pensions in connection with his pupils. He gave freely, says Todd, of what he prized most, the stocks and shares of his own training, knowledge and experience.[319] We are unable to trace anything of a financial or practical nature that would have aided any of them, especially Trevithick.

Todd says that, 'benevolence always had a prestige rating in the eyes of both the giver and society until it became no more than a fashionable cult; but Gilbert's patronage of Davy, Thomasin Dennis, Trevithick and Hornblower had nothing more to offer [Gilbert] than an inner private satisfaction.'[320] We see that Gilbert's relationship with these four people intended to change their psychological approach to life and, in some cases, even alter their chosen calling. Gilbert's deep rooted contempt for the trader and shopkeeper[321] did not encourage or assist Trevithick to sell his wares, something that Henry Harvey would certainly have done, and several others did.

After the death of Davy in 1829, Trevithick was Gilbert's last remaining pupil. Omitting his eleven years abroad, his exchanges with Gilbert had continued for some twenty-five years. During that time, Gilbert had done his best to deter Trevithick from some of the wildest applications of his steam engines. Towards the end, Gilbert shows signs of losing interest and eventually discards Trevithick, saying he was unaware of the time of his death but thought it was in the autumn of 1833. This is not surprising, Gilbert was a very busy man with many interests and Trevithick had taken up a great deal of his time. If Gilbert had done his best to curb Trevithick's wild eccentricities and raise his social status, it was difficult to identify any instance where he had succeeded.

In 1804 Trevithick was enjoying the success of having built and operated the first self-propelled railway locomotive. It is very unlikely that he ever knew of the following words written by Humphry Davy to Gilbert but they were to influence and control the relationship between Trevithick and Gilbert for the rest of their lives.

In October of 1804, Davy wrote to Gilbert and said,

> Whenever speculation leads to practical discovery, it ought to be well remembered and generally known. One of the most common arguments against the Philosophical exercise of the understanding is 'Cui bono' [who will benefit]. It is an absurd and common place argument: but much used: so that every fact against it ought to be carefully registered. Trevithick's engine will not be forgotten, but it ought to be known and remembered that your reasoning and mathematical enquiries led to the discovery'.[322]

These conspiratorial words were to stick in Gilbert's mind throughout the years as his guidance led Trevithick's inventions to obscurity and unattributed fame. They were to appear at the end of his life in the epitaph that Francis claims was written by his father but now looks increasingly like Gilbert's own work. It is clear from the above passage that Davy was happy to see Trevithick's name and reputation disappear as surely as a wisp of his exhausted steam.

What Almighty power, other than Fellowship of the Royal Society for less than a year, did this twenty-six-year-old son of a carpenter from Penzance have that his treachery could order the destiny and partial obscurity of one of the great inventors of all time?

Contrary to the advice dispensed by Davy and employed by Gilbert, the source of Trevithick's inspiration is available for us all to see. During the years when Trevithick visited the Americas, James M. Gerard, a Scotsman,[323] was his travelling companion on some of his most gruelling journeys. Thomas Edmunds, son of Trevithick's solicitor in Penzance, wrote at length of the two adventurers and recalled that Gerard had said,

The eminence of Captain Trevithick as an engineer is well known. The public are indebted to him for the invention of the high-pressure steam-engine and the first railway steam-carriage. The latter being dependent on the former, Captain Trevithick informed me that the idea of the high-pressure engine occurred to him suddenly one day whilst at breakfast, and that before dinner-time he had the drawing complete, on which the first steam-carriage was constructed.[324]

In his later years[325] Gilbert eventually let his guard down when writing to his son-in-law and explained how, in about 1796, Richard Trevithick had come to him with the idea for a high-pressure steam engine exhausting to air.

We should examine the affect of Davy's words on Gilbert; they had clearly sunk home. The younger Davy had noticed something that even the wily Gilbert had overlooked, something that he could possibly use to his advantage. It would be unwise for Gilbert to disregard the considered advice of another Fellow of the Royal Society. We see a change in Gilbert's attitude to Trevithick. Prior to Davy's letter there were signs of Gilbert working with Trevithick, appearing alongside him and taking a personal interest in his activities. We might put this down to engineering enthusiasm, something he may have been unable to continue as his years and responsibilities mounted.

Gilbert had seen Trevithick as a mechanic and had been advised to claim his genius as his own. Nothing had really come of this and Gilbert's reputation had not been improved by his association with Trevithick or any of his pupils. Apart from recommending Trevithick as a suitable contractor to drive an unsuccessful tunnel under the River Thames, there is no recorded instance of Gilbert taking any opportunity to develop the inventor's career or reputation. Throughout their relationship, Gilberts saw Trevithick as the mechanic from Cornwall, a position he was too busy to rise above although he often considered that he was worthy of greater things.

Gilbert's efforts to introduce Trevithick to notables appeared to be limited to one letter to Davy in January 1802. It was in connection with Trevithick's first application for the patent that Gilbert had prepared on his steam engine. Davy simply passed him onto someone else and on subsequent visits to London Vivian was unable to see Davy.

Trevithick had faith in Gilbert's influence and wrote to him after the patent meetings in London imploring him to be nearby should his influence be required.

> Mr. Davy says that a Mr. Nicholson, he thinks, will be a proper person to assist … We shall not specify without your assistance, and all our friends say that if we meet with any difficulty nothing will be so necessary as your presence.[326]

In the event, the grant of the patent was seriously delayed and Trevithick left the completion of the application to Andrew Vivian.

It did not take long for Gilbert to distance himself from any close connection with Trevithick and to avoid supporting his inventiveness. Within a fortnight of receiving the advice from Davy, Gilbert was responding to a query about Trevithick from a John Trotter and said,

> I am not myself concerned in any Mine or business whatsoever and consequently I have never employed Mr. Trevithick or been connect with him in any undertaking. But having amused myself by investigations on mechanical subjects I cultivated his acquaintance as a sensible enterprising young man.[327]

From the very beginning Gilbert been an advocate of what we would today call 'social mobility through education'. He pursued this ideal in the case of Trevithick and probably missed the personal advantages to be gained from claiming a great share of Trevithick's genius for himself. Remember, Gilbert physically took part in Trevithick's experiments with the Camborne stagecoach to test his theory that smooth wheels could transmit movement. He also travelled from his St Erth home to Tehidy the day prior to Trevithick's intended but ill-fated journey from Camborne to welcome him on his arrival. Samuel Smiles optimistically puts him in the 1803 London Carriage along with Davy in 1803.[328] While at Oxford in 1804 he was host to his father and sister but when the call came from Merthyr Tydfil to witness Trevithick's first railway journey, he left them and rode to Wales.[329]

Things were to change after Davy wrote to Gilbert. Zerah Colburn records[330] that Gilbert wrote to William Nicholson in September 1805 with his observations on the blast effect of steam in the chimney of the Penydarren locomotive. Although Trevithick had explained to Gilbert how he had used that blast to good effect Gilbert did not attribute the invention to Trevithick.[331] While Gilbert probably hoped Nicholson would publish the invention under Gilbert's name, Nicholson was more devious and made the observation that although Trevithick had 'discharged steam into the chimney … he had attached no value to the fact'.[332] Nicholson then undertook some experiments and took out a patent for 'steamblasting' the following year.

The dispute as to who had invented this method of improving the efficiency of the engine continued for a further twenty-odd years with many joining in. Even George Stephenson claimed the invention and installed it on his Killingworth engines.[333]

In the years following the arrival of Davy's letter it is very difficult to place Trevithick and Gilbert together outside of Cornwall; I have found it impossible. Trevithick would still drop in on Gilbert at home in St Erth to discuss his latest wheeze when they were both in Cornwall, otherwise communication was by letter. This suited Gilbert and it has provided us with a considerable amount of revealing correspondence.

While Gilbert had the opportunity to gain from his association with Trevithick, he played his cards poorly. He frequently referred to the development of the steam engine in lectures and letters but he carefully avoided any mention of Trevithick. He refers to Hornblower and Woolf, neither of whom made any of the progress that could have been attributed to Trevithick. Had he allowed Trevithick's inventive genius to shine through he could have benefited from association with him in a similar manner to Boulton's relationship with Watt.

We must put Davy's remarks about the steam engine in context for the period. Today we seldom see steam engines in any number unless we go looking for them at rallies. There they appear as amusing, rather benign, warm, friendly machines that are excellent for animation in children's television programmes: their incredible quiet power is seldom appreciated.

It was not always like this. When Watt's improved atmospheric engine appeared, followed by Trevithick's high-pressure engine, the scientists, engineers and businessmen were very excited. For a thousand years man had sought an alternative, controllable source of power to muscle, wind and water. Just how they should successfully combine water, gravity and fire to produce power had eluded them. Many men knew that, somehow, there was a combination that would solve many problems and bring rich returns. Newcomen had shown the way for those who had the funds to operate his engine and were anxious to achieve the benefits it brought. Other enterprising inventors claimed success but time and again they achieved little but publicity and lost a great deal of their money and that of their backers.

Then, along came Watt with a significant improvement on Newcomen's engine. It was not cheap to acquire and the cost of running it included a share of the savings going to Boulton & Watt as patent holders. Although heavy industry, but not transport, benefited from these inventions, there was still a considerable latent demand for a more convenient power source.

When the high-pressure steam engine arrived, there would be no alternative competition from electricity, petrol, diesel or nuclear energy as there is today. Davy referred to the impact Trevithick's engine would make. Its creator was riding high as the inventor of the age, but clearly did not realise the full implications of the situation, nor how to take advantage of them. Others did, and they could see the importance of his advanced technology. Here, at last, could be the power source that they had all been seeking. Some could see that whoever controlled that engine could have greater power, more influence and considerably more money than Boulton & Watt. We have a similar situation today with the international domination displayed by Microsoft, Google, bankers and the oil barons.

Why Davy should wish to see Trevithick deprived of his well-deserved benefits is not clear, was it just annoyance? Davy did not stand to benefit. What he thought Gilbert could do is also unclear; maybe it was just that he considered Trevithick, a mere mechanic in his eyes, was unworthy of the greatness that was likely to be heaped upon him and unable to handle it. Was he simply pandering to his own vanity by exercising mischievous power? Whatever it was, Gilbert would always be reluctant to credit Trevithick with any of his inventions in the future and, on the occasions when the opportunity arose to do so, he would frequently replace Trevithick's name with that of Hornblower and declare how he had assisted him.

Many historians over the years have examined the copious pages of correspondence between Trevithick and Gilbert concerning steam engines. Their various conclusions have been to describe Gilbert as Trevithick's life-long friend, mentor, patron and guide. None in my research has commented on the fact that, following receipt of Davy's advice, Gilbert never used his unique position as a powerful, confidant in Trevithick's life to promote the inventor's career, other than suggesting him as a suitable engineer to dig that tunnel beneath the River Thames. Gilbert never used his undoubted influence in high places to even mention Trevithick's achievements. He did not suggest in his many reports and lectures that it was Trevithick's ingenuity that produced the high-pressure steam engine, the source of nearly all the power upon which the British Empire's Industrial and Transport Revolutions were based.

References

176. *Beyond the Blaze* A. C. Todd p 13
177. *Huguenot Pedigrees* Chas E. Lart, Volume 2, 1928.
178. *CRO Davies Gilbert DG/37*
179. *CRO Accession no 2622.*
180. Oxford Dictionary of National Biography
181. *CRO DG/117*
182. Review, *Gentleman's Magazine 1838* Volume IX, pp273-8
183. *Memoirs of the Distinguished Men of Science of Great Britain living in the years 1807-8*, Wm Walker.
184. *Sketches of the RS and RS Club,* Sir John Barrow, p103
185. *Beyond the Blaze* A. C. Todd p 15.
186. *Life of Richard Trevithick* Francis Trevithick Volume 2 p93
187. *Beyond the Blaze,* A. C. Todd, p15
188. *Ibid* p16.

189. *Ibid* p285
190. *Ibid* p281
191. Oxford Dictionary of National Biography
192. *Sketches of the Royal Society and Royal Society Club,* Sir John Barrow, p102
193. *Beyond the Blaze* A. C. Todd p25.
194. *Ibid* p24
195. *Ibid* p25
196. *The Engines of Our Ingenuity* 1988-2005 by John H. Lienhard.
197. *John O'London's Weekly.* Issues 704-715, p327
198. *Beyond the Blaze* A. C. Todd pp59 – 60
199. *Science & Technology in the Industrial Revolution,* A. E. Musson & Eric Robinson, pp80-81
200. *John 4:44*
201. RIC 26 June 1813
202. *Beyond the Blaze* A. C. Todd p81
203. Hornblower papers RCM
204. *Richard Trevithick, Giant of Steam,* Anthony Burton p50
205. *Sketches of the RS and RS Club,* Sir John Barrow, p103
206. *Ibid* p104
207. *Royal Inst of GB, Davy papers*
208. *Humphry Davy* Paris p52.
209. *Ibid*
210. Davies Gilbert DG/90, CRO
211. *Beyond the Blaze* A. C. Todd p23
212. National Archives, East Sussex, ref GIL
213. *Parliamentary Representation of Cornwall to 1832* W. P. Courtnay, 1889 p245
214. CRO DG/38/1-2
215. *Beyond the Blaze,* AC Todd p 51.
216. Nat Archives, East Sussex.
217. *CRO DG/139*
218. *An Answer to Poverty in Sussex, 1830-1845.* A. C. Todd
219. Davies Gilbert to John Enys, Courtney Library 29 April 1839
220. Davies Gilbert diary entry 6 March 1839, A. C. Todd
221. Gilbert to Babbage, 8 July 1830, BL, Add. MS 37185, folio 254
222. ODNB
223. *Memoirs of the Distinguished Men of Science of Great Britain living in the years 1807-8,* Wm Walker.
224. Davies Gilbert to Thomasin Dennis 20 February 1799.
225. Ibid 9 July 1807
226. *Beyond the Blaze* A. C. Todd pp188/9
227. *CRO DG Papers* 87/1 & 88
228. *Beyond the Blaze.* Thomasin Dennis to Davies Gilbert 30 May 1800 A. C. Todd
229. *Young Humphry Davy.* June Z. Fullmer, p125.
230. *Beyond the Blaze* A. C. Todd p142.
231. *Ibid* p284.
232. West Penwith Resources website
233. *Beyond the Blaze* A. C. Todd p278
234. *Young Humphry Davy* June Z. Fullmer, p70
235. *Sketches of the RS,* p77.
236. Notable Names Data Base http://www.nndb.com/people/028/000083776
237. Retired Professional Engineers' Club of Bristol www.rpec.co.uk/archive/davy.pdf

238. *Young Humphry Davy*, June Z. Fullmer, p137
239. Ibid, p68.
240. ODNB
241. *Biography of Humphry Davy* T. E. Thorpe, 1896
242. Davies Gilbert to Thomasin Dennis Feb 1799.
243. The New Encyclopaedia Britannica p920.
244. *Medical Discoveries: Medical Breakthroughs and the People who Discovered them.* p158
245. *A Cornish Giant* by Edith K. Harper, 1913, p10.
246. *The Life of Humphry Davy* J. A. Paris, p 34.
247. *The New Encyclopædia Britannica* - p523
248. ODNB
249. *Beyond the Blaze* A. C. Todd p30.
250. *Early recollections: chiefly relating to the late Samuel Taylor Coleridge,* Volume 2 Joseph Cottle, p31
251. ODNB 1888
252. Poole to John Paris, 1 February 1830
253. Oxford Dictionary of National Biography, 1888. Website
254. *Ibid,* 1888
255. *Ibid,* 1888.
256. *Humphry Davy* J. Davy page 160/4
257. http://www.cornwalls.co.uk/history/people/humphry_davy.htm
258. *Davy's Journal* RIC Library
259. BBC Radio 4, 10th March 2009,
260. *Young Humphry Davy,* June Z. Fullmer, p178.
261. *The Life of Sir Humphry Davy*, J. A. Paris p518.
262. http://www.nnbd.com/people.
263. CRO DG/159/1-2.
264. *Penzance* Melissa Hardy p69
265. *Beyond the Blaze* A. C. Todd p280 & ODNB
266. *Ibid* pp278-281
267. *Plato: Misogynist ...* Dorothea Wender. Arethusa 6, 1973: pp75-80
268. *The Town Labourer 1760 - 1832* J L Hammond, p57
269. *Hansard, ix* p798 nn
270. *Beyond the Blaze* A. C. Todd pp116 – 122
271. *Ibid* p281.
272. *The Gentleman's Magazine, 1840* p208
273. *Beyond the Blaze* A. C. Todd, p18
274. Dictionary of National Biography 1888
275. Gilbert Journal CRO
276. Philosophical transactions of the Royal Society, Volume 342, Issue 1302.
277. *Memoirs of the distinguished men of science of Great Britain living in the years 1807-8.* William Walker, Jnr, 1864, p54.
278. *Institution of Civil Engineers,* Volume 36, Issue 1873, January, pp290
279. *I. Todhunter,* Wm Whewell, DD
280. *Sketches of the RS and RS Club,* Sir John Barrow, p104
281. *Between Hostile Camps* p35
282. *The Life of Humphry Davy* J. A. Paris p373
283. *Ibid* pp181-2
284. *The English Pioneers of Anaesthesia, 1952,* F. F. Cartwright p26.
285. *The Election to the Presidency of the Royal Society in 1820 vol 11,* pp256-279

286. *Between Hostile Camps* David Philip Miller p2
287. *Ibid* p4
288. *Ibid* p8
289. *The Life of Sir Humphry Davy* J. A. Paris, Volume 2 p12
290. *Between Hostile Camps* David Philip Miller p38
291. *Ibid* Ryan to Babbage 24 November 1826, p39.
292. *Between Hostile Camps* David Philip Miller p40
293. Humphry Davy to Lady Davy 30.8.1827 National Archives, Royal Institution.
294. *Passages from the Life of a Philosopher, 1864* Charles Babbage, p186
295. *Between Hostile Camps* David Philip Miller p1
296. *Life of Humphry Davy* Paris p300
297. *Memoirs ...* John Davy p368
298. ODNB
299. *Beyond the Blaze* A. C. Todd p284
300. *Life of Humphry Davy* John D Paris p400
301. *Ibid* p373
302. *Beyond the Blaze* A. C. Todd p235
303. *Ibid* p236
304. Barrow to Peel 23 November 1827
305. *Beyond the Blaze* A. C. Todd p238.
306. *Between Hostile Camps* David Philip Miller p46.
307. *Beyond the Blaze* A. C. Todd p258
308. Gilbert diary 11 November 1830. CRO
309. *Beyond the Blaze* Gilbert MSS A. C. Todd, 1 Dec 1830.
310. *The Dublin Magazine*, 1840, p91
311. *Beyond the Blaze* A. C. Todd p111
312. *Ibid* p284
313. *Richard Trevithick, Giant of Steam* Anthony Burton p112
314. Gilbert to Wyatt, January 1808 *Beyond the Blaze* A. C. Todd p90
315. *Parliamentary Representation of Cornwall to 1832* W. P. Courtnay, 1889 p58
316. *Beyond the Blaze* A. C. Todd p35.
317. *Parliamentary Representation of Cornwall to 1832* W. P. Courtnay, 1889 p244
318. *The Ascent of Money* N. Ferguson p235
319. *Beyond the Blaze* p279.
320. *Ibid* p279.
321. *Ibid* p285.
322. Davy to Gilbert, 23 October 1804
323. *Elemental treatise on steam & locomotion, based on the principle of connecting science with practice in a popular form*, John Sewell, 1852 p131
324. *The Best of British Engineering, 1750-1960* Thomas Edmunds
325. *Gilbert to J. .S Enys* 29 April 1839
326. *Richard Trevithick, Giant of Steam,* Anthony Burton p76
327. Gilbert to John Trotter 9 November 1804
328. *Engineer,*1 February 1867
329. Gilbert to Enys 29.4.1839 The Enys Papers
330. *Locomotive Engineering and the Mechanism of Railways*, p82, 1872
331. *The Life of George Stephenson and his son Robert* Samuel Smiles, p171
332. *Ibid*
333. *Ibid*, p170

IV   Richard Trevithick, family and friends

Richard's childhood

Richard's mother and four attentive elder sisters provided him with a comfortable, supportive childhood in his family home. Francis Trevithick, his third son and biographer told us this situation would have been unlikely to change when yet more daughters came along. That arrival could have made the one Trevithick boy even more precious to his doting father. An example of his father's standing and regard for his son is contained in the portrait of young Richard. Such extravagant gestures for young people were usually reserved for the well to do. Francis said:

> He was the first surviving son of five children, and was his mother's pet.[334]

John Wesley, the non-conformist preacher who, with others, developed Methodism, was reputed to be a frequent lodger at the Trevithick household between 1743 and 1787. This is a claim that is made for many Cornish households but it is believed it to be true in this instance.

The first account of Richard junior was in a school report that described him as 'a disobedient, slow, obstinate, spoiled boy, frequently absent, and very inattentive.'[335] These were messages for the guidance of his parents. It was clear that young Richard's schoolmaster had little time for his behaviour and disregard of authority. It is noticeable that, apart from the one word 'slow' that could have referred to anything, the report made no reference to Richard lacking intelligence. In some ways Richard had shown himself to be annoyingly sharp-witted, especially when faced with mathematical problems. He had insisted on using his own mathematics instead of the one he had been taught and arrived at correct answers surprisingly quickly. His schoolmaster once said, "Your sums may be right, but it is not done by the rule", to which Trevithick replied, "I'll do six sums to your one". No one had apparently taught Trevithick this alternative mathematics so we must wonder how he came upon his method and whether he knew how he did it, even if he was actually in charge of the decisions he made.

Throughout his life Trevithick was sufficiently confident to make such challenges. In the case of his schoolmaster, there is no indication that the challenge was ever taken up.

The speed at which Trevithick was able to solve these mathematical problems was reflected in his ability to come quickly to conclusions when faced with similar questions and situations throughout his life. His often offered indifferent responses to problems that did not fit directly into his area of main interest. If he was frustrated by being unable to find a quick answer he tended to either fly into a temporary rage or ignore the problem altogether. His friends and family became very aware of these difficulties and gathered to protect him.

Richard's schoolmaster must have found him to be disruptive and frustrating, even frightening. He was taller and stronger than his fellows and his unruly behaviour and unpredictable antics made him the folk hero of his classmates. His belief in his invulnerability and his feats of strength with leaps over the desks made him less than an ideal pupil. Trevithick's popularity and confidence never left him.

It was not in his nature to sit still during classes that did not interest him. Stories are told of his spending hours by himself, drawing lines and figures on his slate instead of attending lessons. His father wished him to sit at a desk in the mine office but he wandered off. In many ways his slow wits in early life were very similar to those of young Humphry Davy of Penzance.[336]

Penponds, Camborne, Trevithick's home in childhood.

Trevithick's childhood home at Penponds

Thomas Carlyle, 1795 – 1888, told the story of a Scottish youth who was also the despair of his instructors. He said the dunce at the bottom of the class became, 'Sir Walter Scott of Universe'.[337] Along with Davy, Scott will also appear in these pages. Today, we would be likely to classify many of the people in this book as having 'special needs'. It is often recalled that Isaac Newton was described in a school report as being 'idle and inattentive'.[338] Maybe such reports are the mark of future genius and indicate someone who will intensely follow one particular aim or ambition, but that is assumption.

Young Richard was just six years old when James Watt introduced his first atmospheric pumping engines to the Cornish mining scene. Watt was soon to understand that the name Trevithick would always be associated with his adversaries. He wrote that he "could barely keep his temper" after a confrontation with Richard's father and spoke of his 'impudence, ignorance, and overbearing manner'.[339] Nevertheless, the senior

Trevithick was quick to see the advantages of the Watt engines over the existing Newcomen ones and ordered three of the first seven to enter Cornwall.[340]

We see little of Trevithick associating with his children but he did briefly work alongside his son Francis and, in one instance, they calculated the properties of a swallow's wings in order to compute the proportions required to lift a man. Francis, who wrote a biography of his father, refers to him as 'Trevithick' and his mother as, 'the late Mrs Trevithick'. He wrote:

> In these calculations cube roots of quantities were extracted, which did not accurately agree with Trevithick's figures, who, asking for explanations, received a rehearsal, word for word, of the school-book rule for such extractions, which threw no more light on his understanding than did his own self-made rule on the writer's comprehension, though both methods produced nearly the same results.[341]

Trevithick's early adulthood and reputed exploits

Young Trevithick exhibited the character of a man whose unflinching resolve and belief in himself was to overcome tremendous engineering obstacles and criticisms. His will would provide the world with the motive power to drive its industry and transport. Had Trevithick been as other men it is unlikely that he would have achieved what he did. Lesser men, and that includes just about everyone on Earth, would have shied away from the problems he was to face.

The ability in his early life to vanquish all that stood before him must have provided him with the conviction that he was invincible. Being taller and stronger than all those about him reinforced his belief in his insuperable ability to achieve anything he wanted. The stories concerning his displays of strength abound,

> Captain Dick would climb up the great shears, or triangles, fifty or sixty feet high, and, standing on the top of the three poles or shear-legs, would swing around a heavy sledge hammer". He was said to have picked up one of his fellow diners at the Dolcoath count house dinner, turned him upside down and stamped his boot prints on the ceiling, just for fun. Other party-pieces included writing his name on an overhead beam with a hundredweight weight hung off his thumbs and hurling a sledgehammer over an engine house roof.[342]

The stories surrounding heroes and popular figures are often developed in the telling. A despairing Cornish historian spoke of the many unqualified claims that Trevithick had thrown a sledgehammer over most of the engines houses in Cornwall, at least three churches and the drawing office of Harvey & Co. in Hayle. These claims, he said, were even validated by the action of one enterprising museum that had put what it declared to be the actual hammer on display. The story is first told by Francis Trevithick.[343]

Similar anecdotes recounted or invented by Francis[344] about his father's antics with a blacksmith's mandrill, something that could weigh up to half a ton, and a range of other incredible exploits, have to be disposed of as folklore *in extremis*. It was essential in such lawless times that those in charge should be able to control their workforce. Trevithick's proud mine workers held Captain Dick in the highest regard and revelled in such amusing nonsense.

It is very difficult to make footprints on the ceiling when holding a struggling man upside down but numerous pairs of muddy marks were lovingly displayed in mine buildings for many years in a manner similar to the preservation of religious relics. As we will see later, passionately held beliefs often override reason. The *Edinburgh New Philosophical Journal, Vol 41, 1859 p 329* suggested:

> 'His muscular strength was such that he could lift two blocks of tin, placed one on the other, weighing seven cwts.'

While there is no corroborating evidence of these, or any other, of Trevithick's feats of strength, it is very unlikely that tin ingots would be three and a half hundredweight each, something that should have been obvious to the writer. Even the famous tin ingot, now in the Royal Cornwall Museum at Truro and found in St Mawes harbour from the Dark Ages, weighed a mere hundredweight and a half.[345] It is clear that Trevithick's stature and strength were much greater than those of other men but they were outweighed by the folklore he attracted. Francis said that his father had a strong dialect.[346]

The story is told how the shareholders of Wheal Abraham had delayed the payment of some Royalties due to Trevithick but the inventor had his own methods of dealing with such matters. One morning the engine at Wheal Abraham was missing, Trevithick and his men had apparently carried it away in the night!

Davies Gilbert records,

> about the year 1796 I remember hearing from Mr Jonathan Hornblower that a tall and strong man had made his appearance among engineers, and that on more than one occasion he had threatened some people who contradicted him to fling them into the engine-shaft.[347]

Richard Trevithick, Senior 1735 – 1797

Trevithick's father was born into the 18th century Cornish mining scene. It was a prosperous industry but a very difficult environment; it attracted wealthy entrepreneurs, charlatans and labourers from all over the country. Richard, senior, was an outstanding mining engineer when the terms engine and engineer were relatively new words. Francis Trevithick, his grandson, tells us that he was the manager, Captain, at Cook's Kitchen, Stray Park and the mighty Dolcoath mines. This is strongly contested by Charles Thomas who provides evidence from the cost books of those mines that it was John Trevithick, 1730 – 1796, Richard's elder brother and Francis's great uncle who held those positions.[348] Thomas mentions John's son, also called John and the inventor's cousin, joining him to work at the mines. Thomas said we must not judge Francis too harshly for 'he was not accustomed to checking his oral or traditional sources very thoroughly … John Trevithick, who for some inexplicable reason finds no mention in the biography'. Francis described his grandfather as an engineer and assay master. Thomas considered that he contracted himself - as was the custom for several centuries – to a number of mines simultaneously.[349] He was also a roving mineral agent for the Bassets of Tehidy, one of the wealthiest landowning families in the district, and they looked to him to take care of their interests.

While Thomas said that we should be kind to Francis, he continued to find discrepancies in his account of the family and questioned why some of the obvious mistakes occurred. We might conclude that 'the pious grandson'[350] knew exactly what he was doing. From the many mines close to Camborne he chose just those where John Trevithick was manager and assigned their responsibility to his grandfather. By doing so he clearly enhanced his status and Thomas points out that this was 'perforce repeated by most or all subsequent writers'.[351.]

It may not have been necessary for Francis to develop the importance of his grandfather as Richard Trevithick was a much respected man in the Cornish mining community; Davies Gilbert, described him in a letter to John Enys as "the best informed and most skilful Captain in all the Western Mines".[352]

Trevithick married Anne Teague, 1736 – 1810, from a well-respected family of mine managers and Francis tells us they were to have four daughters before their only surviving son, Richard, entered the world in 1771. Charles Thomas again offered evidence that Francis made some errors. After the birth of Richard junior in 1771, the family moved to Penponds where another five children were recorded as being baptised, buried, or both.[353] Thomas suggested that Francis may simply not have known of his father's deceased siblings but his father and his senior aunts must surely have been able to recall Sarah and Prudence who had lived to be five and ten years old respectively. There is also the strange omission of any reference in Francis's work to his successful engineering brothers. While subsequent writers seldom have cause to complain about the detail in Francis's account of engineering history, matters connected to his family come in for frequent criticism.

Working with high pressure steam

Little was generally known of steam for centuries. Many inventors designed engines that required its magical properties. Most of the recorded engines were little more than illustrations of ideas that seldom, if ever, actually performed. Either the inventors had little idea how to create their precious designs or they did not have the money or the materials to do the job satisfactorily.

Each of those who contributed some small but significant feature to the development of any piece of machinery described themselves as an inventor. Over the years, Trevithick's contributions were seen to be much more significant. When he produced a new idea it was complete; a fully operational piece of new technology. While we look upon his work as just one step along the way, the enormity of that step might be similar to Michael Faraday, 1791 - 1867, inventing the electric vacuum cleaner. Whatever Trevithick designed could be put into service immediately and be seen to work efficiently. For instance, he designed a dry dock, manufactured a ship's propeller and used iron as a buoyancy aid. His inventions borrowed little or nothing from preceding technology. If he studied the work of his predecessors at all he only saw the faults he had to correct.

As is often the case with any new technology, those not directly concerned often have little appreciation of what the inventor is trying to explain. The production of an operating model often overcomes this problem. William West built such a model to illustrate Trevithick's concept of a high-pressure self-propelled locomotion and there are mixed reports[354] that it was demonstrated on a variety of kitchen tables. The event was attended by Sir Francis Basset of Tehidy, who had just been created Lord de Dunstanville, his wife, Jane Harvey and Davies Gilbert. Francis was probably right when he said it was in Lady de Dunstanville's kitchen and may also have been right when he identified the model as being made of brass.[355] Her Ladyship turned the cock to start the engine

Believed to be Trevithick's first model high-pressure steam engine credited to William West as builder, c 1797.[398] All the essential features of subsequent locomotives are found in this model.

148

and one can imagine the excitement as the little model trundled along the table top.

The demonstration was twelve years after William Murdoch claims to have built his first model steam carriage. The significant difference of Trevithick's engine was in the cylindrical shape of the boiler that allowed his engine to be scaled up to any size. Francis said that the third model, driven by a spirit stove was taken to London and was the one discovered by Uville.[356]

The little model engines revealed some of Trevithick's early thinking. The design was simple yet comprehensive. It was well known that the steam generated within the boiler would be pressing on the sides of that boiler with tremendous force; a round boiler with reinforced ends was essential to contain what Trevithick called strong steam. It was the shape of this boiler that was the significant step forward into the world of high-pressure steam. His models incorporated a safety valve, something that is attributed to the 'bone digester', or pressure cooker, of Denis Papin but we do not know whether Trevithick had re-invented it.

The experiment was a triumph and Trevithick set about building full-sized high-pressure steam engines to operate in the mines in defiance of Watt's patent. In dealing with high-pressure steam Trevithick would be working with a medium in which he had no previous experience. This was new technology and there were no meaningful reference books. He embarked on the construction of engines so dangerous that Watt had declared Trevithick should be hanged for what he was doing. By introducing the advantages of high-pressure steam, Trevithick led world development of engine power. In this, he quickly did the work of maybe a hundred men. The development of an entirely new, successful engine is usually a process of evolution, this was a revolution.

Trevithick's invention was the result of the profound thought processes of one remarkable man. When the Trevithick Society built a replica of Trevithick's 1801 Camborne road locomotive it copied Trevithick's contemporary designs and the engine worked competently on its first journey. After ten years the engine passed its various examinations with no perceptible sign of wear or deterioration. It was still performing as Trevithick intended without modification and with only one small repair. While the society had the advantages of modern materials and technology, the operation of the engine depended entirely on Trevithick's original designs of two hundred years beforehand. Similar situations occurred with the replicas of other Trevithick locomotives. Their builders never had fears that the engines would not operate satisfactorily. This was because they recognised, in the engines they were building, the features of successful contemporary steam engines. It is possible to trace the major components on all steam traction and railway engines today back to the locomotive that appeared in the little town of Camborne, Cornwall, in 1801.

We may criticise Trevithick for his apparent spontaneity and irrational thought processes but he was acutely aware that the future of his engine relied as much on its safe operation as it did on its performance. Today we would have computer studies, stress analyses and a team of scientists to produce such an item. Trevithick had none of these; he faced fear, ignorance, derision and professional attacks from Watt; he knew he was right and he ignored them all.

Rhys Jenkins, a prolific writer about engineers and locomotion described Trevithick as perhaps the greatest inventive genius that has ever appeared in this country and the man of all others is justly entitled to be styled 'the father of the locomotive'.[357]

Trevithick's boiler

It would be prudent at this stage to investigate that frequently overlooked but essential source of power, the steam boiler. No matter how clever is the design of a steam engine; it is nothing if it does not have a suitable boiler and pipework. Historians research steam engines of all sorts and sizes, built by various inventors in different locations for a multitude of purposes. They examine and compare the performance of the engines and mark their results by the efficiency of the engine to 'do work' for a certain consumption of coal. Boilers are frequently mentioned in these reports but only commented upon if they leak steam or fail to perform in some other way.

What Trevithick achieved cannot be too greatly stressed. We are often misled by the appearance of new technology because we are provided with little idea how it came about. There is the assumption that somehow it just materialised. This is how George Stephenson's Rocket is often seen in accounts of its appearance at the 1829 Rainhill Trials. It appeared on the morning of the trial as though it was made the night before (in some ways it was) with the paint was still wet. In fact the Rocket was only the latest in a long line of engines and locomotives the work of Stephenson and other engine builders.

Trevithick's high-pressure boiler, which subsequently became known as the Cornish boiler, was essential to the future development of the steam engine. We find that several years after Trevithick had demonstrated how a safe, effective boiler could be built there were experienced engineers who had not fully understood what he had done or, driven by their egos, insisted upon something different. Lord Montagu recounts how the lack of suitable boilers hindered otherwise excellent attempts to produce worthy vehicles. He says the steam carriage built by Joseph Bramah in 1821 for Julius Griffiths, which was described as the most perfect example of contemporary engineering, never moved out of the factory yard because the patent boilers did not come up to expectation.[358] Even today, boilers are the essence of a vehicle; the 2009 Steam Land Speed Record Car was fitted with no less than twelve.

While steam engines can be the basis for interesting and, sometimes exciting reports it soon becomes clear that all steam engines work. Some perform their tasks better than others and may use less energy. History provides few reports on the performance of individual steam boilers, their output, efficiency, insulation and so on.

To introduce heat into the cylindrical shape of Trevithick's boiler the furnace had to be built within the boiler. This necessitated the construction of a complicated fire tube with a riveted 180 deg bend that had to be both water and pressure proof. Trevithick said that others had put the boiler in the fire but he put the fire in the boiler. The level of water in the boiler would drop as it was converted into steam and this required a complicated high-pressure pumping system to maintain a safe water level.

The exhausted steam from the cylinder was extremely hot and dangerous; Francis referred to 'waste steam being turned into the chimney' on the 1803 London Carriage.[359] Trevithick employed the pipe used for that purpose to pre-heat water on its way into the boiler.

The location of the cylinder of the engine within the boiler is frequently referred to in these days of fuel conservation as an important contribution towards the efficiency of the engine. While this was undoubtedly the case, the benefits of insulation were not fully appreciated in the early nineteenth century. It would be a few years before we find boilers being insulated to restrict heat loss. There was another engineering issue that was seen to be much more important by the engineers of the day. In virtually all previous engines the boiler and the engine were two separate components; while the boiler was usually static the engine tended to vibrate. They required a connecting length of pipe and at least two joints or unions. These usually functioned satisfactorily when the internal pressure did not exceed three or four pounds per square inch but failed when there was vibration or they were asked to contain high-pressure steam. By inserting the cylinder directly into the steam within the boiler Trevithick avoided the problems associated with troublesome pipework.

Many mine owners upgraded their Watt engines to accept high-pressure steam. Fresh beam engines were designed to use the new propellant and they were to become internationally famous as Cornish mine engines; the Industrial Revolution took a tremendous leap forward.

Trevithick had proved to himself and those about him, that high-pressure steam could be used effectively. The engineering presented many challenges that fascinated him for the rest of his life. The philosophy involved the control of a force that was constantly trying to escape from a strengthened vessel; an action that had already proved fatal for many who stood too close. This unseen malevolent power, in the thinking of the time, was likened to the work of the Devil and it is no small coincidence that a woman who saw fire within the boiler was reported as crying out,

> "Good gracious, Mr Vivian, what will be done next? I can't compare un to anything but a walking puffin devil." when Trevithick introduced his steam locomotive to them on Christmas Day, 1801.[360]

This superstitious attitude was universal. When the American, Robert Fulton demonstrated his steam boat on the Seine in Paris in 1807, Victor Hugo described its as the 'Devil's Boat' and a local preacher questioned, 'Whether man has the right to make fire and water work together when God had divided them (Genesis, Chapter 1, verse 4) … Was it not an attempt to bring chaos again into the universe?'[361]

Trevithick clearly saw himself superior to the evil spirit that existed within strong steam and had no qualms about overcoming him.

Trevithick's work in high-pressure steam attracted the attention of Watt, a level-headed, judicious engineer and inventor who was not above taking control of another's work if he could see a threat or financial advantage in it. Trevithick was so sure of his technology being different to Watt's, which it was; that he would not be infringing the patent that Watt held, which he was.

Watt's patents had been so widely written that he exercised control over the steam engine industry until their expiry at the turn of the century. While Watt had seen the possible advantages of high-pressure steam some years earlier, he had disregarded it because he thought the necessary boiler was likely to explode. His authoritative advocacy of low pressure helped, in the words of the historian T. S. Ashton, '… to clog engineering enterprise for more than a generation.' John Farey, in *A Treatise on the Steam Engine*, said, 'From … 1784, very few improvements were made in the workmanship or execution of steam-engines, until after Mr. Watt's retirement, at the expiration of the patent, in 1800', and also remarked in his Appendix to Dr. Robinson's article on the steam-engine, written in 1814, 'The Act of Parliament extending Mr. Watt's exclusive privilege for the improvements secured to him by his first patent, expired in 1800, at which period he retired from business, having for some years before ceased to take an active part.'[362.]

Watt never changed his opinion of high-pressure steam although he must have conceded that Trevithick had found a way to contain that devil. His hostility to the steam carriage is exemplified in the covenant written into the lease of Heathfield Hall, his retirement home, that, 'No steam carriage shall on any pretext be allowed to approach the house.'[363]

The idea of using high-pressure steam was not Trevithick's; it had been tried before, frequently with disastrous results. It was the challenge to get it right that attracted Trevithick. Trevithick's success with his boiler enabled him to operate his engine safely at the hitherto unbelievable pressure of 50 pounds per square inch. To put this in perspective, few engines had previously worked at more than 3 lbs/sq inch and domestic water systems in the UK can contain water within plastic pipes at 70 lbs/sq inch. The *Flying Scotsman* locomotive pulled an express train using 180 lbs/sq inch. A domestic *espresso* coffee machine operates a safe water tube boiler at over 200 lbs/sq inch.

One person who had come close to achieving an engine working with expansive steam was a contemporary of Trevithick, the Scotsman William Symington, 1763-1831. He had built a model locomotive with a cylindrical boiler in 1786. It had a twin cylinder engine that also had a small condenser and used atmospheric pressure. He had not devised an effective transmission and, had it been built full-sized it would have been incredibly slow. Before dying in London and being buried in an unmarked grave at St Botolphs, Aldgate.[364] Symington also designed and built a twin-hulled steam boat with Patrick Miller in 1788 and the *Charlotte Dunbar* for the Forth & Clyde Canal Co. in 1802.[365]

Trevithick always rose to challenges or, if they were not available, he would issue them himself. Seeking to maintain their sales after their patents expired; Boulton & Watt suggested that a competition between a Trevithick engine and one of their manufacture would show the former to be inferior. Trevithick heard of this and quickly returned to Cornwall to back his engine with a wager of £50. The result was a victory for the little Trevithick engine in spite of alleged cheating by Boulton and Watt. Feeling vindicated Trevithick now believed that his engine could beat all comers and it was only for him to find new applications for its use.

Trevithick continually saw a future in which horses were replaced by his engines. He saw horses as nasty, spiteful things that required to be fed even when they were not at work. While he would ultimately be proved correct, he was many years ahead of his time and there were more urgent demands for his engines.

Trevithick brought the complete engine into existence against the advice of many, including James Watt. Without his vision the engine was likely to have developed slowly, designed a bit at a time by a variety of contributors as was frequently the case with other inventions. Consider how long it has taken for the knife and fork to evolve. Examples of the numerous ways in which an engine develops can be found in an examination of the works of Denys Papin who variously used compressed air, steam and gunpowder to make machines that were intended to pump water out of mines: none of them worked satisfactorily. The slow evolution of the engine would have set

TREVITHICK & VIVIAN'S SPECIFICATION.

(3ᵈ Edition)

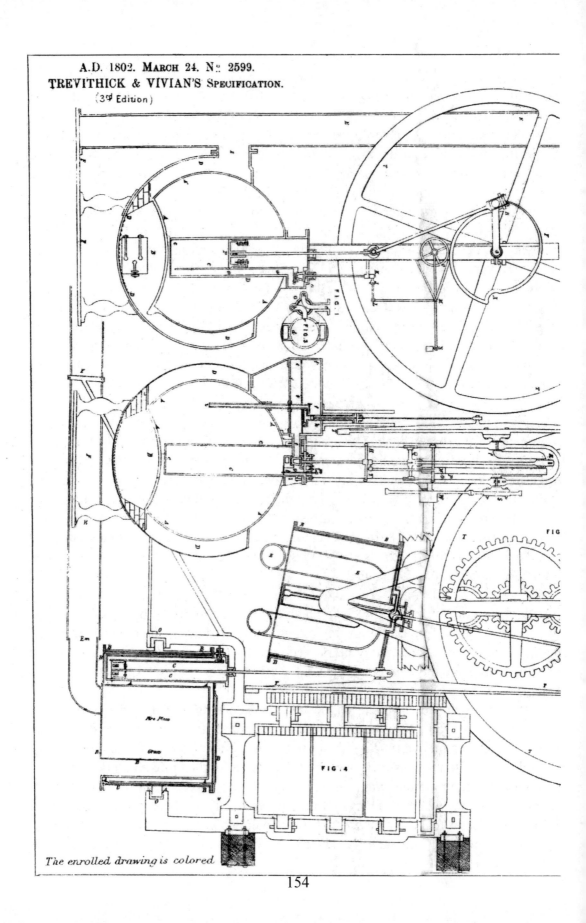

The enrolled drawing is colored.

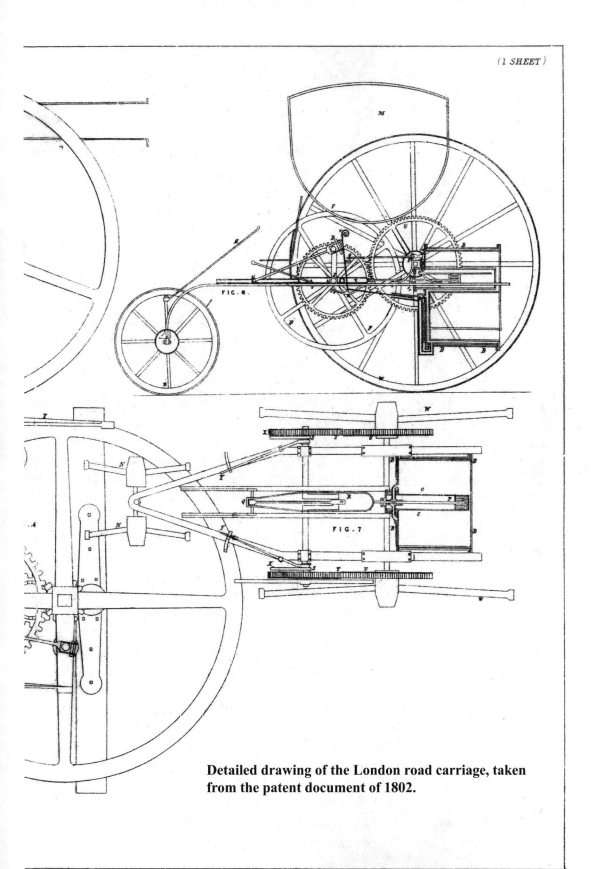

FIG. 6.

FIG. 7

Detailed drawing of the London road carriage, taken from the patent document of 1802.

off many arguments, problems of patent rights, inefficiency and downright danger resulting in death.

It is a tribute to Trevithick's ingenuity and devotion to the cause of his new form of mechanical power that he thought through every aspect of the design before the first 'puffers' were built. By so doing, he produced, at a stroke, a safe, effective working engine complete in every detail. The designs of Savery, Newcomen, Hornblower and Watt were all steps along the way until Trevithick conceived the truly effective steam engine and produced a design that has remained definitive to this day.

In spite of Trevithick's demonstration of many engineering advances, there were frequent examples of inventors taking one step forward and, for no apparent reason, two back. This maybe attributed to a mixture of stupidity, or simply stubbornness and an inability to observe what we see in retrospect, to be the obvious. Take, for instance, the following passage. It is just one of many similar stories of death and destruction in Chapter V of Samuel Smiles' *Life of George Stephenson.*

> Mr Bruton [Brunton] of Butterly Works, Derbyshire, who, in 1813, patented his Mechanical Traveller, to go *upon legs* working alternately like those of a horse. But this engine never got beyond the experimental state, for, at its very first trial, the driver, to make sure of a good start, over-loaded the safety-valve, when the boiler burst and killed a number of bystanders, wounding many more. These, and other contrivances with the same object, projected about the same time, show that invention was busily at work, and that many minds were anxiously labouring to solve the problem of steam locomotion on railways.

In 1813, nine years after Trevithick had proved a couple of times that smooth wheels worked on smooth rails, people were stubborn enough to patent a machine and cause death in an attempt to prove otherwise. This is a typical example of how stubborn inventors frequently take backward steps when they should be moving forward.

Living with Trevithick
Little contemporary material on Trevithick's personal life exists. Such notebooks and letters as there are were almost entirely devoted to his inventions, their operation and the financial and legal problems he encountered. The one person who could have told us so much more was his son Francis but he avoided the great opportunity he had to relate something of Trevithick as a man, a father and, from what he saw of him at home, a husband. We are frequently left wondering whether he thought the story of his father would be better told if he replaced the facts with some of his own imagination. Nevertheless, it is possible to develop some views of Trevithick as a man by sifting his behaviour from his

relationships and the descriptions of his machines. Was he, as many claim, his own worst enemy? Did others combine against him? Could life have been better for Trevithick and should his be a famous household name like Watt and Stephenson?

Young Trevithick grew up a product of the Cornish mining industry like the sacks of copper and tin ore that surrounded him. His abilities entirely suited his environment. Trevithick would have had little outlet for his genius if he had been born in the rural community where power was derived from wind, water and muscle, and machinery would have been almost entirely wooden. Would he have failed to become the man we know and might his frustrations have turned him into a social misfit? We can only speculate and consider ourselves lucky that his birth in industrial Cornwall provided him with the means for expression.

Richard Trevithick's story has been told by many writers. Each has researched a trail of events that led to the high-pressure steam engine becoming the world's prime source of power for well over a century. It is clear from the errors found in books, the media and today on the World Wide Web that some writers have accepted the unproven conclusions of others.

Trevithick has been variously portrayed as being irascible, impatient, single-minded, big, very strong, a good entertainer in some ways but a poor communicator in others who made few, if any, real friends and had little time for his own comforts.

Two hundred years ago, there was not the understanding of the human mind we have today; individuals like Mozart would be described as brilliant by some but mad by others. It was frequently noted that those qualities could be easily confused. Many of those who possessed such virtues fought hard lives and died in poverty, some are mentioned in this book.

Trevithick's mathematical mind could immediately decide upon a course of action. It mattered little to him that he should have no friends to accompany him along the route he had chosen or money to fund his activities. He supported his decisions with challenges to those who opposed him and had a fanatical belief in his ideas for which 'some source would provide' the necessary funds. He was usually right in his assumptions but the sources were often his nearest and dearest, people who would eventually tire of his unappreciative attitude to their generosity.

Had Trevithick not had such a determined, single-minded nature, he would not have achieved all that he did. Businesses respond to people like Trevithick but they do not reward them if they can avoid it. Trevithick was clearly appreciated by the workforces and the mine owners; the latter saw him as a means to reduce their costs.

Trevithick mistakenly considered the government should have granted him the funds to develop his inventions. He also believed that he should have received some recognition. His petitions were poorly supported and he was clearly asking for money to develop a product that was a commercial success, something the government was unlikely to fund. His 'friend' Gilbert at the seat of government was unlikely to have helped him. His engines were readily accepted by industry and their barons offered their assistance but he pursued the development of his projects with unsympathetic government officials. This left industry to develop his engines for their own purposes.

Throughout his life, we find little indication that Trevithick sought the backing of friendship, even the unstinting support of his wife. In the case of Davies Gilbert, it is clear that Gilbert thought of their relationship as one in which Trevithick was an amusing inventor who turned to him for technical advice. Their contact was almost entirely by letter. Gilbert's friends were numerous and lived in other social and academic circles. Trevithick saw his friends as anyone who would share his enthusiasm for high-pressure steam to solve problems.

Those who tried hard to become his friends were cast aside whenever their link to steam was severed for some reason. While he communicated with a variety of people about his engines, there are few or no letters from Trevithick's that might be considered as 'companionable' or 'friendly'. Although he did not seek friends, there is also no sign that he grieved at the loss of one of his acquaintances.

A whole host of people had preceded Trevithick in the world of steam. Some remarkable inventions sought to harness steam and other forms of energy. Most were just flights of fancy because the inventor did not have the money, the materials or the skills he required. We know, having studied their designs in retrospect that few engines would have worked. Like Trevithick, many of these inventors were without a scientific education and so were unable to see the flaws in their work. Trevithick thought it might be possible to build a completely new type of engine using high-pressure steam if that steam were to be allowed to escape after its work had been done. Until that time Hornblower, Watt and others thought it was necessary to condense the steam before it could be of any use. It was Gilbert to whom Trevithick turned and asked 'what would be the loss of power in working an Engine by the force of Steam raised to the Pressure of several Atmospheres*, but instead of condensing to let the steam escape?' Gilbert knew the answer would be the loss of only one atmosphere, regardless of steam pressure. Trevithick's dreams had been vindicated and Gilbert said, 'I never saw a man more delighted'. From that moment, the whole world of steam engineering changed.

*One 'atmosphere' is equal to 14.5lbs/sq" or about one bar at sea level.

John Harvey, 1730-1803

John Harvey was a Cornish blacksmith from Carnhell Green who moved to the Hayle estuary. In the days of Newcomen he saw potential in the new-fangled fire engines and realised the importance of being able to manufacture them and their essential pipework in Cornwall. He needed the necessary iron and coal. He also required to learn more about the manufacturing process. Wales, with its reserves of coal and iron was the obvious place to go and, in a letter to his wife at the outset of his journey he said,

> When I left hayle I was troubled to see you Greaving. I saw you walking up and Down the beach but culd not Speake to me. About ten o'clock I had a little Quame which hould till two, at which time we almost lost Sight of Land with a fresh Gale & a very great Sea. I for amusement imployed my Self in catching of Mackrill. The Next Day we made land, and at Night ankered at Neath.[366]

This letter is interesting; it reveals the educational standard of a Cornish blacksmith at that time. Although there are many spelling errors we find little wrong with the syntax. This shows that, during his minimal schooling, Harvey absorbed the basics of writing but probably had little time or opportunity to learn the accepted spelling of a wide variety of words. It is also, like most letters between close couples, a balance of news and emotions. We will see how Trevithick's letters reveal similar standards of spelling but are devoid of emotion unless it is excitement or exasperation in connection with his engines.

In 1776 Harvey returned from South Wales with a load of iron and set about building the first major foundry in Cornwall. Harvey created an important company that would serve the mining world's demand for pumping engines. His three elder sons helped him in this venture but two died early in life, at 23 and 26 respectively. Then disaster struck again when his third son was killed by a falling section of a mining lift or shear legs at the age of just 22. This left him with only one remaining son, Henry, who was just 15.

During the eighteenth and nineteenth centuries Cornwall produced many men of letters and science; good education was seen as an asset. John Harvey was probably better educated than one would expect of an early Cornish blacksmith. When his circumstances improved, he ensured that his children received the best available schooling. In a similar manner, Trevithick's plans to go abroad involved moving his family to Penzance to ensure that his children received a good education, one for which he unfortunately overlooked to make financial provision. Letters between the characters in this book generally reveal a high standard of education and eloquent letter writing

Edward Bull and Ding Dong

By the age of twenty-one Trevithick was a mining engineer supervising the erection of new engines. This brought him into contact with Edward 'Ned'[367] Bull, who had been an erector of Boulton & Watt's engines for about ten years and a man with his own ideas how to circumvent their patents. He was an accomplished engineer and inventor but without Trevithick's forceful personality.

By the end of the 1700s mining had endured four successive years of losses and the adventurers were willing to support anyone who could rid them of their agreements to pay Watt his premiums. One person who offered hope was Bull. He was determined to solve their problem and reap the rich rewards. Boulton & Watt had not thought of him as a threat until they heard that he had teamed up with Trevithick. Watt became aware of his intentions and wrote to his agent Thomas Wilson saying,

> In respect to Bull the less we have to do with him the better.[368]

This set Trevithick at odds with Boulton & Watt, a challenge he accepted without a moment's thought or hesitation. Bull lost a patent lawsuit brought by Boulton & Watt and was prevented from erecting any more steam engines. This did not intimidate Trevithick and, other than being restricted by Watt's patent he felt free to do as he wished. So he took over the assembly of one of Bull's 'upside down' engines at Ding Dong Mine. This was similar to Watt's earlier design of a Topsy Turvy engine for Wilkinson at Broseley in 1777. Bull was clearly aware that Trevithick would incur the wrath of Watt.

Trevithick was determined to build an engine that would avoid the patents held by Watt. Watt's response was an attempt to serve injunctions on both men. The presence of his bailiffs must have sent them a message but if they troubled Bull they did not deter Trevithick. His miners were reported as having tied a bailiff by a rope over an open shaft. Thomas Wilson cautioned those at Birmingham saying, "This fellow Trevithick in return will certainly raise prejudice so strong against us as may perhaps make it dangerous to go West"

Some years later John Bolitho told Francis,

> Boulton & Watt came down with an injunction printed out, and posted it up on the door of the engine-house, and upon the heaps of mine-stuff, and nobody dared touch them. But Captain Trevithick did not care; he and Bull and William West came and turned the cylinder upside-down, right over the pump rods in the shaft…'.[369]

Trevithick lodged with a Mrs Dennis when working at Ding Dong Mine; her description revealed Trevithick's daily lifestyle.

> Her parents lived at Madron, near these mines and for two or three years Mr Trevithick came frequently to superintend the mine-work, staying at their house a few days or a week at a time. He was a great favourite, full of fun and good-humour, and a good story-teller. She had to be up at four in the morning to get Mr Trevithick's breakfast ready, and he never came to the house again until dark. In the middle of the day a person came from the mines to fetch his dinner; he was never particular what it was. Sometimes, when we were all sitting together talking, he would jump up, and before anyone had time to say a word, he was right away to the mine.[379]

This served to illustrate Trevithick's attitude to anyone who stood in his way.

Visit to Soho

When Bull's engine was complete and working well, something that Watt thought would never happen, he set off with Trevithick early in 1796 to learn the latest engine developments in the Boulton & Watt factory at Soho, Birmingham. While the factory was open to all who wished to examine the ormolu wear and enjoy Boulton's hospitality, the decision for the Cornish engineers to run their heads into such a noose must surely have been Trevithick's. Boulton wrote later to Thomas Wilson,

> I hope this will find you perfectly recov'd from the fateagues of your journey & the better for it. an opportunity offers of sending this Letter to Town but I must be very short. Woodward found Trevethick & his Friends at a publick House faceing my Manufactory & deliverd to him ye Injunction which he rec'iv with much surprise particularly as he thought nobody knew him. He seemed much aggitated & Vexed however he afterwards went w'th Bull & Andrew Vivian to dine with Simon at the Foundry where he found our Men fireing of Canonons & rejoicing at our Victory wch took away his appetite from his dinner. Andrew was admitted to see the Foundry & Manufact'y but not the others. It is rather curious that although ye Injunction could not be served in Cornwall, I should run into the Lyons Mouth & afterwards go to Dine w'th the Man that they had Banished from Cornwall. They afterwards went to Colebrook dale but know not their reception.[370]

This is an outstanding example of Trevithick's unshakable self-assurance and belief in his invulnerability against those who dared to question his decisions. His audacious, foolhardy act attracted the attention of the bailiffs. After all, there were few 6' 2" mine engineers with Cornish accents in Birmingham and the injunctions that he had avoided in Cornwall were duly served. Bull and Trevithick subsequently took dinner in a nearby hostelry in the company of Trevithick's cousin, Andrew Vivian.[371] Vivian was employed at that time as a foreman in the Boulton & Watt factory. John Southern recalled that,

> Bull took his dinner quietly, but Trevithick walked backwards & forwards in the house like a mad man and firmly resisted all temptation to dinner, till the smell of the hot pie overcame his powers, on which he set to, & did pretty handsomely, but in such a manner as shewed him not quiet in mind. The rejoicing that was going forward at the very door, exhibited by fires and gunpowder work, not a little contributed to his *happiness* while he staye'd which was for a very short time indeed. They posted off towards Colebrookdale.[372]

Bull clearly accepted the situation with unanimity and sat down to enjoy a good meal, probably his first after several days of travel. This was not a good time to approach Trevithick who cursed Watt for what any reasonable person could see was a situation he had brought on himself and his friends.

It is interesting to imagine the scene in the hostelry. While fireworks crackled outside, Trevithick, over a foot taller than the average height of men of that time and built in proportion, was stanking* up and down in heavy boots on the wooden or flagstone floor and cursing Watt. Trevithick was in a towering rage and behaving like a caged animal after he and Bull had been successfully served with injunctions.

It had clearly been a good day for Boulton & Watt against the engineers from Cornwall. Their firework celebrations marked the achievement of an injunction in their ongoing battle against Jabez Hornblower and Stephen Maberley although they did not achieve final success until 1799. It was a busy year for litigation and correspondence poured forth from Boulton, Watt and James Watt, Junior at Soho, Smethwick. Early in the New Year, Watt Junior wrote to Wilson and expressed his opinions on the previous concessions made to the mine owners,

> You know perfectly that all the evils in Cornwall have originated solely from the concessions we have made and they more we make, the worse we shall be off, as they will never be regarded as proofs of generosity in us but as tokens of pusillanimity and certain indications that we despair of our cause. This not being the case, but upon the contrary being firmly & fully persuaded that we shall recover all the arrears due to us.[373]

And again,

* Cornish dialect for walking very purposely.

Nothing but perseverance on our side and a determination to make no concessions but what are extorted from us by the law, can ever bring your litigious neighbours to their senses. They have hoped to crush us by the length of their purses and the Audacity of their measures and I have no doubt they are much disappointed & mortified to find that for once, <u>right</u> has prevailed against Violence & against Cunning.[374]

The Hornblowers were clearly the butt of their attention,

> We have obtained an Injunction against Jabez Hornblower and his Employer Maberley which stops the Engines already erected by them and incapacitates them from making any more. But of this you need take no Notice at present as it will be Nine or Ten Days before they can be served with the Writs.[375]

Trevithick frequently appears in the correspondence and, following his application to work for Boulton & Watt we have Watt making his opinions clear twice in the same letter,

> As Trevithick Junr is Dft [defendant] to some of our bills & has never made answer nor suffered the injunction to be served upon him, we should injure ourselves very materialy were we to countenance his being employed in any way unless he first makes his peace by a full & fair confession of the facts in his power to prove. … but as we are situated respecting Trevethick Junr we cannot consent to his being employed, nor do we think it Mr K[evill]s interest to have any thing to do with him.[376]

And yet this cool opinion of Trevithick in May was to change in July when Watt Jnr wrote again to Wilson after a change of mind by his father.

> My father & Mr Weston concurring with us all, in the propriety of disengaging young Trevithick from the confederacy, to which your good character of him has not a little contributed, we have determined to withdraw our suit against him, and if the writs are not already served, desire you will call them in. If they are, they must not be proceeded upon. The inclosed letter to him will sufficiently explain our sentiments upon that head, but with respect to engaging him in our own service, we shall be entirely guided by the inclinations and advice of Mr Murdock, whom we feel ourselves bound to consult and to be governed by in this matter. We inclose a letter to him open for your perusal, but request that both it & the one to Trevithick may be sealed before they are delivered. If William [Murdock] approves of

our employing him, we think it will be best that he should carry the letter himself; if not you will send it to him.[377]

It could have been that young Watt was well aware that Murdoch would veto the appointment so Trevithick would never know of the olive branch being offered by his father. That was the end of the case and the writs were withdrawn.

Leaving home

In 1797, Trevithick's father died leaving him with an enlarged workload and an increased income. It was time for Richard to take a wife. From all the observations Richard was a fine, clever upstanding young man with excellent prospects who had every opportunity to make his way in the world. We hear little or nothing of Trevithick's courting days but know that the building and erecting of engines had brought him into contact with John Harvey's daughter, Jane. She is described as being tall, fair-skinned with brown hair. They must have made a striking couple. Trevithick married her in November 1979 and the match between the two families with substantial interests in Cornish mining looked ideal. We can only speculate what she thought her life would be. Certainly, she was going to have to find reserves of fortitude and patience.

Jane was to find that she was looking at a hard life ahead. Their six surviving children were Richard, 1798 – 1872; Anne, 1800 – 1876; Elizabeth, 1803 – 1870; John Harvey, 1807 – 1877; Francis, 1812 - 1877 and Frederick Henry, 1816 – 1881.

'Hence his [Trevithick's] life was but a series of beginnings.'[378]

We are seeing where Trevithick's determination was taking him. He would get ideas about mechanical things and pursue them to a conclusion without any thought for his own comfort and well-being, or for that of anybody else.

There had been agreement about the terms under which Watt would permit the use of the Ding Dong engine and a similar payment was sought for a Trevithick engine at Seal-hole Mine, St Agnes. This was in excess of Trevithick's estimate and a comparison was arranged.

> … in 1797 Richard Trevithick had worked his first high-pressure steam puffer engine in competition with the Watt low-pressure steam-vacuum engine at the old Wheal Seal-hole Mine, near St Agnes Head. Andrew Vivian was then his companion, and the Cow and Calf, two rocks of unequal size, a mile from the land were, from that time called Capt[n] Dick and Capt[n] Andrew, or the Man and his Man.[380]

164

Jane Trevithick pictured with her children, 1861.
Left-right: Richard, Anne, John, Francis, Elizabeth and Frederick

Trevithick's obsessive devotion to one narrow objective at the expense of all others meant that he disregarded many of the normal qualities of life. This provided his opponents with many ways in which to criticise him. We have no indication that this bothered Trevithick, in fact the contrary seems to be the truth, but it must have hurt his family and friends. His wife was an accomplished but tolerant woman who could probably have found several modern grounds for divorce, including desertion.

Trevithick's fatherly instincts were channelled towards his work. The sacrifices he made of his time, love and attention were bestowed, not on the human offspring of his loins but on the mechanical progeny of his fertile mind. Trevithick clearly considered that nothing was too much trouble for his youngsters. He did everything he thought a good father should do to bring his children into the world, nurture them and create a future where they would prosper and be a credit to their father. Using a strong Cornish vernacular word it would be fair to say he 'cherished' the very ground and tracks upon which his children ran. If he was nothing else, Richard Trevithick was undoubtedly the loving father of all locomotives.

Trevithick was as devoted to developing his inventions as some men were to making money. Although he frequently regretted that life had not afforded him the riches he considered should rightfully be his, he was more concerned with the development of new ideas than the acquisition of a fortune.

Apart from considering he was entitled to receive ample payment for his work and ingenuity, Trevithick's attitude to money was one of indifference. It is clear that, when he required money, he had no compunction about asking for it and when he saw someone in need he would give whatever he had. Francis tells the story of his father being without funds when planning a trip to Holland. He begged two pounds and on the journey came across a man who claimed his pig had died. Trevithick gave him ten shillings of his two pounds. How he got to Holland and back we shall never know, probably by begging.

Jane Trevithick, née Harvey, 1772- 1868

It is often said that behind every great man is a great woman. This was clearly the situation with Trevithick's wife, Jane. Her strong-willed determination kept alive his family and business interests in Hayle. Much like her brother Henry in disposition, her devotion to her husband and family throughout a hard life, during which Trevithick constantly promised riches but never delivered is the substance of novels. Unfortunately, we have not enough material to tell Jane's full story but we know that her commitment ensured Trevithick could travel and develop his inventions without the daily burdens of family life.

At her wedding Jane's husband was described as,

> The bridegroom was 6 feet 2 inches high, broadshouldered, well-shaped massive head, blue eyes, with a winning mouth, somewhat large but having a undefinable expression of kindness and firmness'.[381]

After their marriage the couple lived in the five bedroomed Moreton House, situated in its own extensive grounds on the outskirts of Redruth. Scorning this luxury the couple moved to Fore Street, Camborne after nine months,[382] to a house that was to become their home for the next ten years.[383] Francis suggests that Trevithick left Redruth because of the close proximity of James Watt and his engineer, William Murdoch. Trevithick was unlikely to have been worried by such matters and the possibility that these two adversaries lived 'within a stone's throw'[384] is crediting Trevithick with even greater strength than folklore would have us believe; Murdoch lived about 600 metres away. Francis consistently distanced his father from Murdoch, possibility to avoid the inevitable claims that Murdoch taught him how to build a high-pressure steam engine. Fore Street will feature as the famous 'Camborne Hill' in the song about Trevithick's successful demonstration of his road locomotive. Jane found an indication of what life with Trevithick was likely to be when he left the keys to Moreton House in a coat pocket and had to pay a further year's rent.[385] Trevithick is also recorded as having paid rates on the house for 1798 and 1799 at 2/8d per annum.

Francis offers the following as his mother's description of her life with her husband.

Her husband was good-tempered, and never gave trouble in home affairs, satisfied with the most simple bed and board, and always busy with practical designs and experiments from early morning to bed-time. He sometimes gossiped with his family on the immense advantages to spring from his high-pressure engines, and the riches and honour that would be heaped on him and his children, but thought little of his wife's intimation that she hardly had the means of providing the daily necessaries of life.[386]

Some doubt must be raised here. The passage is attributed to Jane but was written in the third person and published four years after her death. Is it a fair summary of Jane's attitude to her husband? Francis had the opportunity of hearing his mother's views on her husband until four years before the publication of his book. If this was Jane's most reasoned view of her errant husband over a lifetime she must have had patience that exceeded that of the biblical Job, and he had only to deal with the Almighty's treatment of his crops.

Jane appears throughout these pages, patiently contributing to Trevithick's life, looking after his children, being grandmother to twenty-two children, ten of which belonged to Francis, and fending for herself. Her possible influence on her children is revealed in the attitude of Francis, her third son.

Henry Harvey, 1775-1850
Jane's brother, Henry Harvey took practical control of the foundry at the age of twenty-eight on the death of his father in 1803. The deaths of his three elder brothers created his sense of responsibility to the company and family members; he would reveal this in his attitude over the following years. Henry was an educated businessman who operated the largest combined shipping and foundry business in Cornwall, one of the foremost industrial areas of the world. Edmund Vale's description of Harvey in *The Harveys of Hayle* as a young man summarised what a practical, fastidious, hard working employer he was in Hayle.

> … shows him to be meticulous as to detail, checking cargoes by weight to the last pound and never letting any short measure or damaged goods, or such as were inferior in quality pass without an immediate challenge. … We can credit him with industry, acumen, and high principles in business honesty and we know that he shared his father's ideal in the matter of service to his customers …[387]

Henry said of himself,

> I have always made it a rule, whenever I find myself deficient, to endeavour to make it up by industry and perseverance.

It is understandable that with such a view on life he was likely to disagree with Trevithick's wild impulses at every stage of their relationship. Trevithick had been joyfully welcomed into the leading engineering family in Cornwall where he had the opportunity to advance his emerging ideas. What more could any sensible young inventor have desired? At this time he was a mine manager with the ability to supervise the erection of engines. He was also working on his high-pressure steam engines. Trevithick needed someone like Henry Harvey to build his engines and curb his wild excesses. Francis said that Trevithick made his wishes known by a rough hand sketch and a full description.[388] It revealed a great deal of Henry's forbearance and similarity to his sister Jane that he was able to keep many of his feelings to himself and work with Trevithick, producing a number of his engines and permitting him to undertake experiments within the foundry, something for which he was unlikely ever to have been paid.

Trevithick's ability with high-pressure steam clearly left its mark on the foundry. In subsequent years his innovative technology was the foundation for the company's success when put to good use in the hands of other engineers.

In one respect the historians have dealt rather shabbily with Henry. His personal life has either been ignored or dismissed as being of little importance because he never married. His private life was as involved as his business affairs and revealed his patience as a businessman, administrator and father figure.

Henry lived with his spinster sister Elizabeth (Betsey), 1779-1848, at Foundry House. His eldest sister Joanna was married to William West, 1751-1831, the watchmaker and model builder whose skills were an asset to Trevithick and Harvey & Company. The next sister, Anne, 1770-1808, married John Harvey, 1769-1809, in 1794. He was a well-to-do cabinet-maker from Helston but not known to be a relative; they had six children. Disaster struck when both parents died within a year of each other leaving behind their children. Henry and Elizabeth took the orphans into their care at Foundry House, brought them up and educated them. Some, notably Nicholas Oliver and William Harvey, together with John Harvey Trevithick were to take leading parts in the operation of the divided company in future years, creating the line of Harveys that took their surnames from elsewhere but were to head up the later Harvey companies.

Although Edmund Vale produced a very full book on the Harvey company in Hayle he omitted any reference to the Harvey-Tonkings who must have been a significant, well-known part of the community. This is how they came about.

Henry did not marry but kept two houses in Hayle. One was the formal family home, known as Foundry House, where he, his sister Elizabeth, and sometimes their niece, Nanny, 1801-1840, brought up Anne's six children. Henry was a well-known, broadminded pillar of the community and everyone knew that he kept Grace Tonkin, 1793-1865, his lady friend, in another house he owned called Mellanear on Foundry Hill, where, between 1818 and 1837 she bore him no less than ten children, nine of whom survived. Grace was the daughter of Thomas Tonkin, a miner from St Just. A tithe map of the period shows that Henry's Mellanear House was leased to Grace.

At the time their first child was born, Henry was forty-three and Grace eighteen years of age. One can conclude that Grace gave the ever-busy, responsible Henry a new interest in life. The children were all christened at St Erth church with Harvey as their second name and each shown as 'base child of Grace Tonkin'. This may have been at the insistence of the rector as Henry was not shy in claiming them as his. Henry insisted that the name Tonkin should bear an additional 'g' to make it distinctive from the many other Tonkins. It is frequently but erroneously said that Henry's father, John, had forbidden him to marry the housemaid but John had died in 1803 when Grace was just four years of age and about fifteen years before the liaison. Henry was affectionately known locally as 'The little Cap'n', where he was a prominent figure and the major employer in Hayle. In the absence of any evidence to the contrary, we suppose that he was also a model of social responsibility and as such his activities with Grace must have been the subject of much discussion. Although Henry was to live until he was seventy-five and Grace died at the age of sixty-six, the average age at which their children departed was only twenty-five, six of them dying before Henry.

Trevithick's long periods of absence left Henry sharing the responsibility for the upkeep of Jane's children. In all, Henry was father to Grace's nine children and uncle to six of each of his two sisters' children, a total of no less than twenty-one boys and girls who looked to him for financial and fatherly support. He treated his extended family with love and responsibility. Prior to his death in 1850, Henry made a deed of settlement in favour of his many nephews and nieces. In 1838 he made over property he owned in Stithians and St Gluvias and created a trust fund for his illegitimate children and their mother. The children were all suitably educated and many of them set up in business in Hayle where they prospered. To this day their descendents look back in pride on their forebears. Henry would have been proud of his brood and their descendants.[389]

An apprentice at Harvey's Foundry was John Brunton, the son of William Brunton, an engineer, originally based in Birmingham who had a life-long relationship with Harveys including the acceptance of Nicholas Harvey as an apprentice. It is fortunate that John, 1812 - 1899, wrote a biographical book for his grandchildren; it was published in 1939. It recalled many incidents in his life; he seemed to have more than his share of accidents. In one, he was working at Harveys on the mighty Haarlem Lake engines when a 'large and heavy Plummer Block' overbalanced and crushed his foot, breaking a bone. He related how 'the old ladies were kindness itself' and had refused to call the doctor but had insisted upon treating him by the application of leaves. After several days, the painful foot had not improved and his pal in the works, Frank (Francis Trevithick) had called the doctor and had the foot bound up. Although young Brunton had painful memories from this incident, he recalled his good days with Frank and spoke of the way Henry Harvey and one of his sisters (Elizabeth?) had befriended him. Here we have an illustration of the parental kindness and advice meted out by Henry and his sister to the numerous youngsters in their care. Brunton said 'We had to work the same hours as the men from 6 a.m. to 6 p.m. – long hours for a youngster but Miss Harvey used to cut me a large slice of bread overnight and gave me permission to go into her fine dairy every morning and place on my bread a thickness of Cornish cream which was indeed a luxury'. Of Henry he said, 'Mr Harvey not only gave me opportunities of learning matters connected with my profession as an Engineer, but he kept a horse for me and taught me how to ride. He encouraged me to learn boating in the evenings, to practice shooting, and all outdoor manly exercises. While indoors he taught me the art of Carving at table in which he was a great Proficient. I left Hayle and my kind friends there with great regret'.[390]

Henry tried to get on with his brother-in-law; the combination of their two dissimilar personalities would have been essential for a good business relationship. Henry offered advice and gave support on his terms; but Trevithick was having none of it and preferred to walk away. He turned to the foundries at Coalbrookdale and Bridgnorth, Shropshire, to make parts for his engines in Cornwall. Many of his puffer engines were made at Bridgnorth from 1802[391] including the 1808 'Catch-me-who-can' and those destined for Peru. These engines must have been aboard ships that sailed past the mouth of the River Hayle on their voyages to London and other ports. Such niceties were unlikely to have bothered Trevithick. Many years after Henry's death, four 37-inch pumping engines left Hayle in November 1870 aboard the *Bride* for Cerro de Pasco, in Peru. No part was to weigh over 300lbs.[392]

Nevertheless, it would be many years before Henry turned his back on his brother-in-law although, even then, it was probably the other way round. Trevithick's antics must, in many ways, have been a great burden to the Harveys and the Vivians. Family reunions would have been something of a pantomime whenever Trevithick turned up, temporarily eschewing his precious steam engines for the company of his wife and family members. Henry must have been rebuked by the family and his workforce for his continual support of his brother-in-law. In 1810 Henry wrote to his sister,

> My dear Jane
> I am in receipt of your letter of the 22nd inst. I have engaged to Mr. Blewett the £200 he lent Trevithick with the £40 advanced in his illness and also a debt of £60 and costs that Mr. B. has engaged to pay for him … These

sums with the £200 Trevithick had off me in March 1809 amounts to above £500 … I have already given you my opinion & trust you will not ask me anymore about it.[393]

In spite of Henry's settlement of Trevithick's substantial debts we see from the books of Harvey & Co that he was paid a further £50 a few months later.[394]

These were generous gestures by Henry Harvey for the foundry was often short of money. He found it necessary to set up a new company in 1809 called The United Mining Company in which he sold a controlling interest amounting to five-eighths of the stock to Hannibal Curnow Blewett, holding just three eighths himself; small parts of Blewett's share were held by Andrew Vivian, Thomas Ellis and Philip Richards. Henry retained his position as General Manager and, viewed from the outside, the company continued much as before, still generally known as 'Harvey's Foundry'. Blewett had used the company for speculative purposes and the partnership was eventually dissolved in favour of Henry Harvey.[395]

For all of Henry's formality he was receptive to a variety of new ideas. He had regained control of the ideal base for all of Trevithick's exuberance, but Trevithick rejected it, while their interests were similar their personalities were just too far apart.

In the coming years Henry manufactured some of the finest mining machinery in the world and become an accomplished shipwright. From *The 1847 Williams' Commercial Directory*, Harvey & Co. were listed as *Millers, Engineers, Iron founders, Iron and Coal merchants, Ship-builders, Ship-owners, Ironmongers, Wholesale grocers, Tea-dealers, and General merchants and Rope-maker.*[396]

We see that Jane was left out of Henry's will. Was that because he felt she, and her husband, had already had enough of his time and worldly goods? He had certainly been generous to them all his life and had seen their family educated and in good employment. Further than that he probably thought his elder sister was well provided for at the age of seventy-eight. He also failed to mention his partner Grace Tonkin(g) but he had made separate provisions for her and their remaining children.

Henry wisely concentrated on the engines for which there was a ready market. The obvious engine was Trevithick's original small, high-pressure unit that was so versatile it could be used effectively almost anywhere. The mighty single-acting Cornish mine engine, as it became known, was essentially a development of the basic Watt design with the advantages of quality manufacturing and Trevithick's high-pressure Cornish boiler. These remarkably reliable engines were immensely powerful and were used to pump mines and provide domestic water supplies throughout the world. In a way,

171

this use of Trevithick's outstanding design repaid Henry for the considerable time and money that he had invested in his brother-in-law and his family.

William West, 1751-1831

Francis William West of Hayle enters Trevithick's life as a local man married to Jane's elder sister, Johanna Nancy Harvey. He had been in business as a blacksmith and watchmaker at Helston and had been taken into the Harvey family firm on his marriage. An old account book of Trevithick's dated 1800 shows that West received some payment for constructing models. West was also believed to have had a small share with Trevithick and Vivian in their patent of 1802.

In 1803 West was at Felton's in Leather Lane, London, employed for five months helping in the construction of the coachwork for Trevithick's London Carriage. He was just around the corner from the Meux Brewery where Arthur Woolf was employed. Francis described West as the producer of the best time keepers in Cornwall.[397]

Although William was the brother-in-law of Trevithick's wife's the niceties of family ties did not apparently impress Trevithick.

West built many of Trevithick's early model steam locomotives and accompanied him on mine engine erections. Although Francis described the early relationship between his father and his uncle as one of mutual respect and esteem,[399] it was not an easy association. The meticulous, model-making mind of the expert clockmaker did not sit comfortably alongside that of Trevithick's values. West did not make the fortune he had been promised by Trevithick in connection with his share in the steam engine patent and felt he had been very poorly dealt with.

He must have had a forgiving nature as Francis records him working with his father at Dolcoath Mine in about 1811 when Richard Trevithick, Junior, the eldest son, delivered his dinner. This Richard is mentioned only twice again, once when Trevithick used him to test drink cold water from a boiler and again when he is aboard the Falmouth Packet returning to Cornwall with his sick father. Otherwise, Francis makes no other references to his siblings. This is odd for someone who was at the centre of social life when employed by the LNWR Company.

Problems would constantly arise and in September 1815 West wrote to Trevithick in despair.

> Your ill-tempered letter I received, and think you conclude in very threatening terms. Now, sir, in the first instance, what right have you to make me debtor to you for 40£ received of Wood and Murray? …' The

letter goes on for some length, outlining what West sees as discrepancies in Trevithick's accounting and mentions a gift of a pound to Trevithick's children; he concludes. 'Certainly it must distress my mind to think of paying you for your blunders.[400]

In an unusual display of tact and humility Francis says his father elected 'his old friend' William West to superintend the cutting and loading of 300 tons of scantled [measured] Cornish granite fortnightly to London. This request came immediately after the attempt to tunnel under the River Thames and Francis gives no reason for such an order, or any details of it ever being delivered or to whom.

With Trevithick's constant absences from Cornwall, West returned to his craft of clock and watch making and produced some of the finest instruments in Cornwall.[401]

Another William West
While William West made models of Trevithick's intended locomotives and was married to Jane's sister, there was another William West, 1801– 1879, whose work at Dolcoath Mine had attracted the attention of Captain Joseph Vivian. His employment involved him making visits to Harveys at Hayle. He subsequently moved around the mines in the Penzance and Gwithian areas where he introduced insulation to the exposed boiler surfaces with remarkable results. West continued to make improvements to steam engines and was successfully associated with the Fowey Consols. Always one to reminisce, he recalled the days when 'he held the candle to Trevithick while he was engaged in the construction of his locomotives and that he had worked with Vivian and Trevithick when they had been occupied on their road steam carriage'.[402] He later invented the double-beat water valve and patented it in 1839 as an 'Improved Valve for machines for Raising Water or Other liquids' with his business partner Nicholas Harvey, a nephew of Henry Harvey.[403] He must have been very young when he held that candle.

Andrew Vivian, 1759 – 1842
One of the important people in Trevithick's life was his cousin, Andrew Vivian, an accomplished and highly intelligent engineer who had a lathe in his workshop and was willing to form a business partnership with Trevithick. This involved a share in Trevithick's steam engine patent of 1802. Considerably more sensitive to personal relationships than Trevithick, Andrew tried throughout his life to encourage the family interaction that was lacking in Trevithick's correspondence.

After the successful demonstration of steam locomotion during Christmas 1801, Gilbert encouraged Trevithick and Vivian to take out a patent and helped them with its preparation. While Vivian was in London attempting to obtain the patent he wrote cheery letters disguising the frustration and the repeated travels from one office to another to get the paperwork completed.

> I arrived in town yesterday about three o'clock. ... Of course I immediately repaired to Crane Court, where I was informed the patent was to be sealed on Wednesday (tomorrow). ... They recommended me to Mr Davy at the Rolls Chapel Office, for information where I immediately repaired, but could not find the gentleman. From there I shaped my course to Soho Square, and spent two or three hours with Mr Nicholson; had the necessary alterations made in the rough copy of the specification ...

> To-day I have been again at Crane Court, to the Rolls Chapel Office, and to the Patent Office at the Adelphi, and have got the whole business in a proper train.

> Mr Horton promised me to get the specification engrossed immediately. ... To-morrow having no business of the patent until eight in the evening, when I must call at the Patent Office for the great knob of wax.[404]

Having arrived on the Tuesday, Vivian eventually got his 'great knob of wax' on Friday and his is the only signature on the patent. He clearly had to be patient during this process and there is not one word of complaint. He treats Trevithick with kid gloves, does not mention the considerable patent expenses he has had to cover and refers to the necessary seal as a 'knob of wax'. This is likely to have been a reference to Trevithick's opinion of the patent affair as just needing a 'great knob of wax'.

The 1802 patent application included the design of an engine for use in sugar mills, something that was to come quietly to fruition a few years later.[405]

It took Vivian some time to return from London. On arrival he wrote a typically chatty letter to Trevithick that exemplified his attitude,

> I arrived here last evening safe and sound, and missing my wife, was soon informed she was at your house, where I immediately repaired. Your wife and little Nancy are very well, but Richard is not quite well, having had a complaint which many children in the neighbourhood have been afflicted with; they are a little feverish when attacked, but it has soon worn off, as I expect your little son's will also; he is much better this morning and talked to me cheerfully.

> Mrs Trevithick is in pretty good spirits, and requested I would not say a

word to you of Richard's illness, as she expected it would soon be over; but as I know you are not a woman, have given you an exact state of the facts. All my family, thank God, I found in perfect health, and all beg their kind remembrances to you, as does everyone I have met in the village.

"How do you do?" "How is Captain Dick?" with a shake by the hand, have been all this morning employed.[406]

And, as a postscript he added,

Mrs T (your beloved wife) begs her love, and expects to hear from you often.[407]

Anthony Burton rightly observes that 'there is almost as much about Trevithick family life in this one letter of Vivian's as there is in all the surviving correspondence of the man himself'.[408]

Following the approval of the patent, Gilbert wrote to Thomasin,

The patent has very much occupied my attention as … it would give me much pain to reflect that any disappointment … had arisen from my want of care, I shall … put in my claim to a steam carriage gratis as a reward for this labour.[409]

Vivian took an interest in local community matters and in 1805 he was receiving subscriptions in the Camborne area on behalf of the Society for the Suppression of Drunkenness.

According to the *Mechanics' Magazine*, Captain Andrew Vivian sold his part of the 1802 patent right to Boulton and Watt who presented him with a fine piece of [silver] plate.[410.]

In 1845 Captain Henry Vivian wrote of his father, Andrew Vivian, as,

My father was a man of great inventive and arithmetical powers of mind; he has often made up the duty of an engine while we have been walking the road together, multiplying six figures by four figures, and giving the answer without aid of pen or paper, by retaining the figures in memory. Mr Trevithick was a man of still greater powers of mind, but would too often run wild, from want of calculation. They did well together but badly when separated.[411]

Vivian's place might well be seen as a steadying factor in Trevithick's life but he was not always able to supply the sort of stability that Trevithick so sorely needed. He tried various financial ventures without success and one in which he was partnered by Hannibal Blewett involved a considerable amount of money being owed to Henry Harvey. Upon dissolution of Vivian's multiple mining interests, Henry wrote to him strongly,

> Having previously to my Appointment and Manager and Receiver … I have to request you will without delay Settle with me the amount of the debt due from you in your private capacity, and also the several sums due from you as Purser of Binner Downs, Wheal Strawberry, Wheal Trenoweth, and United Hills. I request your immediate answer to this letter.

Harvey saw Blewett as the real villain and was not pleased when he sent a silver tea pot to Henry's sister Elizabeth. Seeing it as a bribe he threw it in the fireplace but Trevithick saw an opportunity, retrieved it, wrapped it up and took it home to Jane.[412]

Andrew Vivian and the first successful road vehicle
Davies Gilbert saw the potential in Trevithick's 1801 locomotive and wisely suggested that it should be patented; it was not.[413] He promptly assisted with drawings for the patent of a subsequent engine[414] and the preliminary application was made in January 1802. He told Thomasin this left him with 'a languor to which I am not very much subject'.[415] This speedy work by Gilbert on behalf of Trevithick indicates his early desire to help him and compares with his obstructive tactics in later years. In the valediction, reputedly written by Trevithick to Gilbert in 1831 there is the reference to the first steam engine being built in 1802. This was incorrect and the error may have been caused by Gilbert having traced his diary entry of the 1802 patent.

Whilst most commentators have referred to Vivian's presence on the 1801 road locomotive, these letters tell us of his closer association with that vehicle. He was involved in the earliest plans to build the engine and contributed significantly to its manufacturing costs, probably those incurred outside the workshop in which it was built. He clearly believed that the high-pressure steam engine had a future and, as a substantial 'cash advance' was still outstanding in his Cash Book, he was anxious to protect his investment by means of a patent.

In March of 1802, Vivian travelled to London to complete the details of the patent application that had been started in January of that year and obtain the necessary seal. He chose to do this himself as he realised it would be a protracted affair and Trevithick was not the best companion on these bureaucratic occasions.

Trevithick, who had other things to do, left the paperwork to Vivian probably saying something about 'waiting for a knob of wax'. Vivian stayed behind and paid the additional costs associated with the patent, something still outstanding in his Cash Book after Trevithick's death.

We do not know the purpose of an enquiry from Richard Tregaskis to Vivian[416] but it elicited a reply from Vivian that quoted the following items from his Cash Book:[417]

> Jan & Feb 1802. Cash advanced to Trevithick procuring patent £100.11.0
>
> 22 Mar 1802. Balance of bill at Patent Office paid by AV. £19.16.6
>
> Other entries for, 'creating a Carriage at Camborne paid wheelwright, smiths & co dated May 22 1801. This carriage runned at Camborne some considerable time before the patent was obtained'.

Vivian's part in the ownership of the 1802 patent now becomes clearer. He had contributed substantially, both financially and with his time to the cost of Trevithick's engines and no repayment was forthcoming. Either Trevithick offered Vivian a half stake in the patent as recompense or Vivian decided to include himself in the patent by way of compensation. We will probably never know the exact details, just as we are left wondering if, because he was unable to pay Vivian, it is very likely that Trevithick never paid his father-in-law for the boilers and engines either.

Trevithick's financial affairs were still being tidied up in 1839. On the 12th August Elizabeth Banfield (Trevithick's married daughter) writes to Henry Harvey referring to him as 'uncle' and acknowledges his payment of £208 6s 8d. '... your very liberal donation for which Banfield and myself return our sincere thanks'.[418]

Francis Trevithick, 1812 -1877

Trevithick's third son was not born until his father was forty-one years of age. It is important to mention something of Francis' personality and his involvement in the story of his father. This is because so much that has been written subsequently about Trevithick first appears in Francis' *'The Life of Richard Trevithick, with an account of his inventions'*, published in 1872. Francis was clearly aware that he had very remarkable parents and felt a duty towards them. His father had been the subject of much criticism during his lifetime and he undertook to protect him from disparaging remarks in the future. He wished to ensure that his father was acknowledged for his inventions. He told us that much of what he wrote was derived from people who outlived his father. He chose many stories that he said were legendary but are difficult to find recorded previously. His mother, Jane, could have been one of his most important sources of information, unfortunately she was hardly mentioned.

Francis' book was the turning point in the history of Trevithick. In the Victorian style of the time, Francis proudly provided the public with a great deal of heroic material about his father's life. Previous accounts had only appeared in learned journals and Francis' story of his father's exciting lifestyle attracted the attention of imaginative authors who filled the many gaps he had left and embellished a life that was already adventurous beyond the dreams of most romantics. Francis was careful to omit family items that must have been known to him but might not have reflected well on his parents. Francis was careful to correct the spelling errors correctly replicated by other writers when quoting from his father's correspondence.

Formal photograph of Francis Trevithick

Richard Trevithick travelled extensively and there is no record that Francis and his brothers accompanied him. Although they were to follow their father's career by becoming skilled engineers, they clearly spent little time with him. It was their mother who looked after the family and established a matriarchal community, signs of which appeared in later generations and their uncle Henry who encouraged their engineering abilities.

Francis saw little or nothing of his father during his formative years. Because of the hardships Jane Trevithick suffered, we draw the conclusion that she was a woman of great resource, patience and forgiveness who provided a stable home for her children. The confidence with which she endowed her children certainly showed up in Francis. He appeared to go through life blissfully happy and unaware of the heavy responsibilities of leadership that fell on his shoulders merely because he was the son of the famous steam engine inventor. At the age of twenty-one, and at the time of his father's death, he was articled to Joseph Locke, the renowned civil engineer. Within seven years, he was Resident Engineer of the Grand Junction Railway (GJR) at Edge Hill and, when it was amalgamated with the London & North Western Railway he created the Crewe Railway Works becoming Locomotive Superintendent there. By this time, his ability and attitude to life were attracting attention and we have a variety of accounts of both. This appeared in the Steam Index:

> Francis grew up very aware of his father but probably of his absence rather than his influence on his education and upbringing. He was a man of friendly, gentle, easy-going temperament, unwilling to hurt anyone or put them in unpleasant situations and he had none of the size and immense

physical strength of his father. At 20 he started his training as a civil engineer and eight years later was appointed as Resident Engineer of the Grand Junction Railway at Birmingham although, having been brought up in Cornwall where there were no railways, he knew little or nothing about locomotives. In 1841 he became Locomotive Superintendent at Edge Hill. The railway system was developing at a tremendous rate and there was a great shortage of any skilled engineers with knowledge of locomotives. One can understand his employers supposing that, being the son of the great inventor, he must have been proficient in the care of engines: he wasn't. He planned the Crewe works and those of the Northern Division of the London & North Western Railway. His civil engineering training was clearly an asset during this period. The locomotive 'Cornwall' was built whilst he was there but, contrary to some reports, he did not design it. He was popular among the Crewe workmen and their families, among whom he was known colloquially as 'Trevvy', and it seems too that his wife was equally gentle and kindly. Trevithick was unwilling and unable to run the works and the whole department on the organised and disciplined base necessary with the growing size of the Northern Division, he also shied away from responsibility. He was diffident even in pressing for a rise in his own salary as his responsibilities grew, but in 1852 his remuneration was increased from £750 to £850 a year. Trevithick's relations with his works chief foreman, Allan, deteriorated as time went on, until after a serious contretemps that came before the Crewe Committee, Allan's resignation was accepted in August 1853; Trevithick was so unhappy at this and the previous atmosphere that he applied for the same job in Scotland that Allan got, and was on the short list with him. Trevithick took a leading part in the establishment of the Crewe Mechanics Institute, and he gave it and other Crewe activities such as the cricket club consistent support. ...[419]

In 1857 Trevithick was forced to resign and was overtaken by Ramsbottom. He was presented with £500 worth of plate by the workmen and Crewe townspeople, and Locke was chairman at the presentation dinner. In the same month Locke rose at the annual meeting of the LNWR and protested against Trevithick's dismissal. Francis is reported to have been given an honorarium of £3,000 'in view of his long service and honourable character.[420]

The report continued and revealed great warmth of feeling for Francis in spite of his shortcomings. In the 1887 Jubilee celebrations at Crewe he was described as 'a man much admired and esteemed at Crewe.' Another article was even more effusive: 'he was a man much admired and esteemed in Crewe, and his memory will always be revered by its inhabitants'.[421]

In his earlier years Francis was fond of outdoor life, and in *The Railway Times* of 25 January 1845 the notorious *Veritas Vincit* warned the GJR directors "to send forth an edict to Mr. Trevithick to put aside his dog and gun and more assiduously apply himself to the interests of the company."

Veritas Vincit had insinuated in an earlier issue that Trevithick really had no ability at all, and that Locke, his former tutor, realised this. Nevertheless, the responsibilities piled on Trevithick grew enormously during 1841 to 1854, the years of outstanding railway development.

Unfortunately, although Francis was clearly a very pleasant, amiable man, opinions are usually written by the more hard-headed amongst his contemporaries and it is difficult to find a complimentary one. In *The Railway Record* we find a long, very critical account written by the editor that begins,

> As for Mr Francis Trevithick, I consider him as nothing better than an expensive supernumerary; nor is this my own opinion merely, but the opinion of everyone connected with this line. He is not possessed of sufficient mechanical judgment for the situation he holds.[422]

It continued with references to the influence his subordinate, Mr. Alexander Allen had over him and that Francis did whatever he suggested without question, no matter how ridiculous it might have been. He gave instances of dangerous practices and accidents that he attributed to Francis' incompetence. A similar account by Brian Reed suggested,

> It is not that Trevithick is not clever and honest but ... we shall never see any vigour or strength in his management.[423]

There are numerous instances where Francis is criticised by subsequent historians for his uneven handling of some events surrounding the story of his father. It is difficult to find that Francis criticised anyone, other than some remarks about Arthur Woolf, no matter how much they may have contributed to his father's problems. We can only suppose that his gentle nature may have been further influenced by his mother's attitude to life. It is clear she would have wholeheartedly agreed with the advice given to her son by Thumper's mother, "If you can't say something nice about someone, don't say nothing at all".

We will never know just how far Francis found he had to go once he had started to enhance his father's image. We know that he adjusted the spelling and syntax of his writings, and he inserted some items into the text that were not from the quoted sources. Just how much he made up of the stories we believe are factual we will never know.

Arthur Woolf, 1766 – 1837

Arthur Woolf was a man associated with Harvey and Trevithick who is frequently credited with a number of inventions. Woolf was an accomplished carpenter and engineer who had an unshakable belief in his own capability and was doggedly determined and intransigent. He was the son of a carpenter who worked at Dolcoath and other mines. He followed his father's craft and, after the completion of his apprenticeship, started his working career in London; it included locks, tools, boilers, insulation and all manner of carpentry. His skill alone enabled him to enter a small, elite circle of carpenters and joiners. He benefited by being employed by Joseph Bramah, 1749—1814, a fine cabinetmaker who turned his hand to quality metalwork. Although Bramah was not the first to think of screw propulsion for a ship he worked at the idea and patented 'a wheel with inclined fans or wings' in 1785.[424]

Some historians credit Woolf with having erected an engine for Boulton & Watt in the North of England but it is more likely that he was working for Hornblower & Maberley and the work was stopped by Boulton & Watt for infringing their patents. Hornblower & Maberley subsequently retained Woolf to erect one of their engines at the Meux Brewery in London where Woolf subsequently became the brewery engineer.[425]

While with Meux he wished to install his design of high-pressure boiler but his employers were concerned by these advances in engineering and called in the second opinion of John Rennie. He condemned both the engine and the boiler. Woolf left Meux shortly afterwards and went into partnership with Humphrey Edwards at Lambeth in October 1808[426] to build his engines and boilers. In 1810 they patented the first compound engine that required steam at a fairly high pressure.[427] They parted company in 1811 and, while there is a report that Woolf left to build steam engines in France with Andrew Vivian[428] and that his 'steam engine was the one most generally adopted in France',[429] John Farey says he returned to Cornwall.[430] The development of steam engines in France is generally attributed to Edwards who obtained a patent (Brevets d'invention et d'importation) for the importation of an improved version of Woolf's engine with a more successful boiler in 1815. After having imported some fifteen engines from England he went on to build 'hundreds' in France where he lived for the rest of his days.[431] Edwards' simplified and improved Woolf boiler was re-introduced to England as the 'French' or elephant boiler. France was at war with England between 1793 and 1815 during which naval blockades must have made the importation of steam engines difficult, but profit-making will always find a way.

T. R. Harris, in his biography of Arthur Woolf,[432.] said that Francis Trevithick created a number of false impressions in the biography of his father, taking every opportunity to belittle the achievements of others. He was, of course, referring to his treatment of Woolf. Harris cast considerable doubt on the claim by Francis that his father employed

Woolf, who was currently being well paid by the brewery at £150 a year, as an engine fireman to deliver or erect his engines at £30 a year.

Woolf received mixed reports from various biographers depending upon their view whether he was remarkably clever but unlucky, or a good craftsman who should never have tried to be clever. He came into the Cornish engineering scene as the opposite of Trevithick. Woolf, five years older and with a very different character must always have seen Trevithick as an unruly upstart. He was recorded as having a nature that provided him with a short temper and a dedication to the decoration and development of others' engines. Vale described him from his researches as 'an irascible and opinionated fellow with a singularly rough tongue' whose boasts were not justified in the long run.[433.]

From about 1820 he was connected to Harvey's Foundry and Rhys Jenkins said that, if Woolf did anything at all towards the steady improvement of Cornish engine building it was 'the art of boiler making, in providing better tools and pressing for more accurate work'.[434] Harris agreed when he said that,

> Although Trevithick may have been the more mercurially brilliant man than Woolf, the former lacked qualities which were necessary to bring the steam engine to that degree of perfection which it attained in the second and third decade of the nineteenth century.[435]

Here we are likely to have the basis for Trevithick's eventual disagreement and departure from Hayle in 1831. It is a story to be related later about the successful installation of three excellent Harvey boilers in HMS *Echo*.

Woolf was described by Matthew Loam as,[436]

> the most pleasant of men when in a good humour, but when vexed, which little would do, he was a Woolf in nature as in name.

Woolf's meticulous attention to detail and quality was quite at odds with the attitude adopted by Trevithick. It was sufficient for Trevithick to prove that his engines could run and do work. It is not surprising that we see little or no sign of these two great engineers co-operating in any way and history records references to their disagreements.

Woolf's personality is seldom, if ever, credited with any redeeming features and it is difficult to discover a record of him ever successfully producing anything that was pure invention. Only once did he ever make anything that had not already been done more simply by someone else. That was his foray into the theory of the elasticity of steam and the patent he obtained in 1804. It was a disaster he spent the rest of his life blaming on boiler inefficiencies but he never renounced his mistaken hypothesis.

John Rastrick, a master engineer whose opinions on engineering matters were similar to Trevithick's, had the following to say after meeting Woolf and being taken to see one of his engines,

> I never had any good Oppinion of Woolfe's Engines, for the Complication was in my mind sufficient to condemn them.[437]

Woolf had a fixation for developing things previously invented by others. They were often referred to as 'Improved Apparatus'. They included a high-pressure boiler that failed to deliver and a substitute for the flywheel which, 'because of its complication it was never used to any extent'.[439] His multi-tubed high-pressure boiler was far more complicated than the boiler we know today.[440] It failed to work satisfactorily.

Woolf developed an ability to append his name to anything he did and to applaud his own work. For this reason a great number of engineered products have been attributed to his invention simply because they are described as such; he even hyphenated his own name to that of the machine. An entry in the *Mining Journal* of 1850 was re-printed in the *Civil Engineer & Architect's Journal* of that year.

> We state these things to show that, although the mining interests in Cornwall gratefully acknowledge themselves indebted to Woolf for first pointing out to the engineers of that important district, the advantages of using high-pressure steam worked very expansively, and led them to adapt their present simple and effectual mode of using and expanding the steam in one cylinder only; ... we cannot perceive what advantage is proposed by the adoption of the *double-cylinder* Woolf-engine. ...
>
> The timidity of James Watt deterred him from employing steam of a very high pressure ... Woolf, having no fears of the kind, had recourse to it. In no other respect was any superiority in the Woolf-engine made manifest. The shrewd, practical, mining engineers of Cornwall soon discovered this; and, in their practice, abandoned the complicated double-cylinder engine of Woolf, for the single cylinder of James Watt. .... Is truly, *and unquestionably*, the simple *single-cylinder steam engine* of the great James Watt.[441.]

While the above denigrated the Woolf engine for its complication, lack of any improvement in performance and likely additional cost it also applauded the common sense and business acumen of the Cornish mine owners and their engineers for looking elsewhere. Surprisingly, it made no mention of Trevithick's high-pressure boiler that made Woolf's venture into advanced engines possible. It made the frequent mistake, from the mid-19th century onwards of crediting Watt with an engine that was a combination of a single cylinder and a cylindrical high-pressure boiler that should have been well known as the Cornish engine, another recorded example of the deficiency in general knowledge between the engines of Watt and those built on the principles of Trevithick's design.

In spite of being advised of his engines' faults, stubbornness was a predominant trait in Woolf's character[442] and he stuck resolutely to his own variations on steam power, patented them and extolled their virtues. In the second appendix of *Arthur Woolf*, T. R. Harris wrote,

> Woolf's patent engine and boiler in Cornwall proved a failure. [William] Pole in 1844, wrote. 'Woolf's ideas respecting the laws of the expansion of high-pressure steam were very crude, and it is difficult to conceive how a man of such excellent practical knowledge could have deluded himself into the belief of principles so palpably absurd as those he had laid down in his specification, and upon which he based his statements as to the proposed advantages to be derived from the use of high pressure steam.

William Pole also said,

> … the credit of having been adventurous enough to break through [Watt's] rule [to avoid high-pressure steam] by introducing high pressure steam into the Cornish engine is generally ascribed to Arthur Woolf but we have undoubted evidence that this first originated with Trevithick, that he proposed this improvement in Cornwall as nearly as possible in the manner it is used at this day and put it into actual practice some time before Woolf took his engine there.[443.]

Although they often worked together, it is easy to see why Trevithick would eventually fall out with him, calling him a 'shabby fellow'[444] and probably being the reason why he left Cornwall for good. While Francis avoids providing the reasons for Trevithick's departure, we know that Woolf was involved and that two inventors with differing obsessions were very unlikely to be friends. Francis, when defending his father, does not hesitate to belittle Woolf at every opportunity. It is clear that Henry Harvey also knew the details of the dispute.

Woolf would not give up and even after he had retired to Guernsey he wrote to Henry Harvey in November 1834 advising him that a Guernsey miller favoured one of his twin cylinder engines, gave the specification and asked for a quotation to include a Cornish boiler. The miller was not convinced by Woolf and eventually purchased an engine from

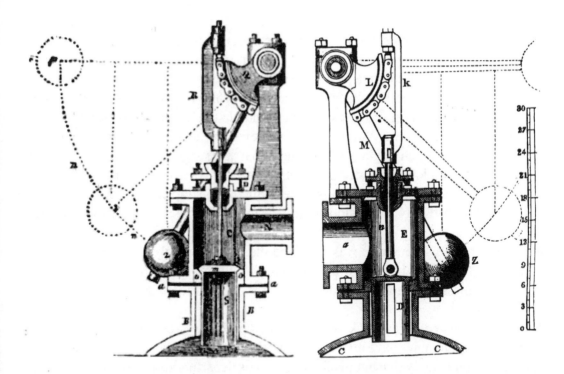

Two variations of the safety valve, both attributed to Woolf in 1803 reveal his propensity for expensively over-designing steam engine components without necessarily adding to their utility or efficiency. If we compare Woolf's 'steam pressure control valves'[438] with Papin's more common steelyard adjustable safety valve it is difficult to find any mechanical improvement. Are they adjustable in the simple manner of the steelyard? However, for 1803 they do appear to include an interesting length of early Simplex link chain to which Hans Renold added roller bushes in 1868.

Neath Abbey, a company that was devoted to the production of Trevithick-type engines and locomotives. Woolf's tenacity was eventually rewarded in 1835 when a Mr Symes ordered and had delivered an engine to his specification from Harvey & Co.[445]
Maybe Francis had a point when he criticised Woolf.

John Farey, in the second volume of his Treatise on the Steam Engine, spoke highly of his friend's work.[446] Those who have seen Woolf's engines remark on their intricate engineering and comely appearance. Woolf's determination to glorify his engines produced an art form in engineering that lifted the steam engine out of the filth and dirt with which it had been so often associated and encouraged engineers to take pride in the cleanliness and appearance of their charges. Woolf would have been overjoyed to have attended the Great Exhibition of 1851 and seen how colour and polished brass had added to the glory of steam power.

From a distance, Woolf's engines and his ability to claim responsibility for their superiority over their rivals set him out as the great developer of the steam engine. In Paris, Sadi Carnot wrote,

... in the years 1814 – 1816 when French interest in British technology was so intense, were the very ones in which the reputation of the Woolf engine suddenly reached a peak in Britain. ... In one important respect the design of the Woolf engine was not revolutionary; for it was essentially an application of the expansive principle that James Watt had patented in 1782. ... It was Woolf's great achievement to show how steam could be used in such engines at pressures that were significantly higher, although they seldom exceeded four atmospheres ... performance not sustained ... Already, British engineers were turning to a simpler form of Woolf engine that had only one cylinder and was more reliable and easier to maintain.[447]

During this period, Trevithick was involved elsewhere, mainly in South America. It was not surprising that he should fall out with Woolf on his return. If ever Trevithick needed a business manager, it was during the period 1804 to 1828.

The problem between Trevithick and Woolf was probably Trevithick's last substantial difference of opinion; we have no records of such problems at Dartford where Trevithick appeared to contentedly live out his final years. His departure from Cornwall after what must have been a small matter of principle between two stubborn men was the saddest of all Trevithick's decisions to leave the scene of a disagreement. Trevithick would never return home to Cornwall. We have no record of any member of his family ever seeing him again. Knowing his thoughtlessness in such matters, it is likely that he left without saying 'Good Bye'; that may have been the final straw for Jane. Henry Harvey was clearly moved by his going but Francis mentions not a word of the feelings within his family.

The rival geniuses of Cornwall are Woolf and Trevithick...[448]

Whatever differences these two remarkably obstinate Cornish engineers might have had in their personalities and their approaches to the evolving technology of high-pressure steam, there is no doubt that the combination of their talents was an asset to the industrial world. Trevithick's basic, effective working steam engine was subject to exploratory development in Woolf's hands. Trevithick did not like what he thought Woolf was doing incorrectly and unnecessarily but Woolf's perseverance[449] developed the engines, not always with mechanical success, but eventually with Henry Harvey's steadying hand, to produce the magnificent, powerful machines that were to grace great pumping halls and factories throughout the world.

John Urpeth Rastrick, 1780 – 1856
John Urpeth Rastrick had the distinction of being named after two small North of England towns; one close to Gateshead and the other near what is now the Beamish

Industrial Museum. He was a master founder at Bridgnorth in Shropshire, a fine engineer who worked extensively in iron for buildings and bridges. Trevithick found in Rastrick someone who understood his approach to invention and engineering. Their relationship was something rare in Trevithick's life and, even over a distance of two hundred years, one can almost feel the dynamic that sometimes exists between people who are attuned to a particular purpose. Rastrick helped Trevithick and undoubtedly benefited from his association with the creative engineer. It is fitting that a memorial erected in Bridgnorth to the two men should link their achievements together.

Rastrick had worked with John Hazeldine at Bridgnorth from about 1807 but is reported to have quarrelled in 1817 and set up his own business. Trevithick diverted his manufacturing from Harvey to Rastrick who built the engines and machinery for South America. The capacity of the Severn Valley to produce quantities of iron foundry work was quite remarkable but partially forgotten today.

Rastrick went on to become one of the three judges at the Rainhill Locomotive Trials in 1829 and his notes, now in the National Railway Museum, give us the best account of the technical qualities of each competitor. He was elected to be a Fellow of the Royal Society in 1837.

John Hazeldine, Bridgnorth
Hazeldine operated the successful Bridgnorth foundry where Trevithick had many of his puffer engines built for sale in this country. One, number 14, is on exhibition at the Science Museum in South Kensington. The 1808 'Catch-me-who-can' locomotive was also built at Bridgnorth. A replica of the latter was built in the workshops of the Severn Valley Railway, Bridgnorth in 2008 to celebrate its bicentenary and

Memorial to Trevithick and Rastrick at Bridgnorth.

IN MEMORY
OF TWO GREAT ENGINEERS
RICHARD TREVITHICK
B. 1771 – D. 1833
INVENTOR OF THE
HIGH PRESSURE STEAM ENGINE
AND
JOHN URPETH RASTRICK
B. 1780 – D. 1856
GREAT RAILWAY ENGINEER
———
NEAR THIS SPOT IN HAZELDINE'S FOUNDRY
RASTRICK BUILT IN 1808
TO TREVITHICK'S DESIGN
THE WORLD'S FIRST
PASSENGER LOCOMOTIVE ENGINE
ERECTED NOV. 1949

The Catch-Me-Who-Can replica displayed at the 2008 bicentenary celebrations at Bridgnorth. Replicas of the Puffing Devil and Pennydaren locomotives also appeared for this event.

took pride of place at a steam weekend organised for the occasion.

Christmas Eve, 1801

Many historians record Trevithick's first road vehicle as running in 1802 because that is the year of his first patent for a locomotive and they look no further. However, his first full-sized road vehicle was one of his industrial puffers with the addition of wheels and it ran late in 1801.

Trevithick's belief was in steam and his determination to build a horseless carriage kept him at work until late one evening. Jane and his young children awaited his homecoming for it was Christmas Eve. Before returning that cold, wet evening Trevithick, his friends and workmen were to take part in the world's first successful self-propelled journey. Trevithick's road carriage pre-dated the first steam railway locomotive, but by only a little over two years, and Trevithick would also build that.

We have a number of reputed accounts but little true evidence of what actually happened. Most of what we believe is based on very doubtful tales collected by Francis several decades later and the legends that have developed over the years. It is clear that Trevithick had a carriage assembled in Tyack's workshop at the Weeth, a part of lower Camborne that stood just opposite the site on which the Gustavus Mission Room was built at the bottom of Fore Street.[450]

At the end of a hard day's work, Trevithick and a number of his workers climbed onto the carriage and set off with their wheels slipping on the wet ground up Fore Street into Camborne. Having got thus far, they managed to turn the vehicle around and returned to the bottom of the hill. The frequent modern references to them having climbed Beacon Hill are preposterous and impossible. The replica would have the greatest difficulty climbing such a hill two hundred years later and the road we see today did not exist at that time. While we summarise their valiant efforts in these few lines we must not forget that this was the world's first significant journey by a self-propelled vehicle that carried passengers. In addition, Trevithick's subsequent journeys on the following days proved this was not an isolated event but the true beginning of self-propelled transport.

These were exciting events for the youngsters who witnessed them and it is clear from an analysis of what they are reputed to have remembered many years later that they confused the events of a few days into one account.

The stories supplied to Francis would be subject to memory loss after fifty-seven years and even the account recorded by the Select Committee on Transport before the House of Commons in 1834 showed signs of confusion between the two events of climbing the hill and the subsequent abortive journey to Tehidy a few days later. We will set out the information we have and leave it to the reader to be amazed at all this 30-year-old man attempted to achieve with his new steam locomotive. Whatever happened during those days of Christmas 1801 it can be fairly said that, from that moment, Camborne was entitled be called the 'Cradle of Locomotion'.

The account allegedly given by a Mr Newton to Francis Trevithick in 1858 described the ascent,

> ... carrying as many passengers as could find standing-room on it – perhaps half a dozen or half a score. A piece of newly-make road with loose stones, just where the incline increased ... heaped an insurmountable barrier against the small wheels of the engine. It was Christmas time: rain drenched the ambitious innovators, and cooled the steam-boiler, and coming darkness added to the gloom. The engine was turned about, and safely conveyed the passengers back again, down this dreadful circuitous hill, to the starting point at Tyack's smith's shop.[451]

And, the *Mining Journal* of October 2nd 1858 printed the following from a Mr. John Petherick.

> I perfectly remember, when I was a boy, about the year 1800, seeing Trevithick's first locomotive engine, worked by himself, come through the principle street of Camborne. [He then describes Trevithick's activities with a steam carriage in London and says it was 'put together in a smith's shop at Wheal Gerry, near Roskear Mine. Wheal Gerry, like Tyack's smith's shop was both later listed as being in the Gustavus district of Camborne.]

Archived by Camborne Old Cornwall Society, Stephen Williams, who co-incidentally, also spoke to Francis in 1858, said

> In the year 1801, upon Christmas-eve coming on evening, Capt. Dick got up steam, out on the highroad, outside the shop at Weith. When we saw that Capt. Dick was again to turn on steam, we jumped up, as many as

189

could may be seven or eight of us. Twas a stiffish hill going from the Weith up to Camborne Beacon, but she went off like a little bird. The second days run it went down to Crane, that Capt. Andrew Vivians family who lived there might see it. An old lady named Paull cried out Good gracious, Mr Vivian, what will be done next. I can't compare un to anything but a walking puffin' devil.

We have no indication that Trevithick had any time for religion, or festive occasions. Certainly, his locomotive was out again on Christmas Day, visiting friends and relatives at Crane, near Camborne. Francis told us that 'The double action bellows … did not answer, … was never used after this first experiment.'[452.]

Christmas 1801 was the best that Trevithick had ever enjoyed. Whether his family got any pleasure from it has never been recorded. A few months later he entered into an agreement to build one of his pumping engines at Shining Sough, the Youlgreave lead mine in the Derbyshire Peak District. Instances like this reveal how commercial interest was quickly generated by an engineer who can offer so much. There is some confusion whether this was a steam or hydraulic engine as the *Sheffield Archives Bag C587/44* has a reference to a Trevithick hydraulic engine being erected at Alport, near Youlgreave, between 1803 and 1805.[453]

Trevithick may have travelled to Derbyshire on this occasion as he was introducing absolutely new technology in an area where nothing like it had been seen before. He must have worked very closely with those involved in the manufacture of the engine's components. This order for an engine revealed Trevithick's establishment in the north of England two years before his railway locomotive ran in South Wales.[454]

Performance of the locomotive, witnesses' evidence
We are fortunate to have a report by an eye-witness who was impressed by what he saw that day and would certainly have recorded anything as exciting as a fire or the locomotive turning over. His testimony is likely to be the most revealing of all and, although clearly confused, probably more accurate than the reports alleged to have been submitted in 1858 by elderly men.

This is an examination of witnesses by a Select Committee of the House of Commons into Steam Carriages, dated 17th July 1834. It was published in the *Mechanics' Magazine* January 31st 1835. It is a compilation of two examinations before the Select Committee on Transport as Trevithick's evidence would have been delivered before his death the previous year. It is one of the very few reports we have of Trevithick's verbatim account of his views.

The main witness was a lad who had been just eight years old in 1801. Although he would be forty-one years of age at the time of the examination he had been an impressionable youngster who was staying in Camborne with a nine-year-old friend called Joseph from their grammar school in Truro over the Christmas period. His friend was the son of Andrew Vivian, Trevithick's cousin, joint patent holder and engineer who had assisted in the building of the locomotive and was reported to be at the tiller that day. Here we will come across what is probably the mention of the modern phenomena of wheel-spin and caterpillar traction; neither was possible until self-propelled locomotion was achieved.

The eight-year-old Goldsworthy Gurney was from near Padstow. The Gurneys were a monied family who could trace their lineage back to their arrival with William the Conqueror. He would be trained as a doctor and later move to London where he took a deep interest in steam and other mechanical matters. He is frequently reported as having built some fifteen steam road carriages but Lord Montagu doubted this and whether his operation of passenger services between Bath and London was as successful as many contend. He developed the Bude Light for lighthouses and other purposes and was charged with heating and lighting the Houses of Parliament. Queen Victoria knighted him for his services in 1863. He was clearly a man with a good memory and an outstanding knowledge of engineering. While Lord

Memorial tablet in Fore Street Camborne, erected in 1919 to commemorate the 1801 run of the Puffing Devil.

Montagu had access to accounts of Gurney's coaching activities and could comment on his financial affairs, he cannot detract from the Select Committee's record that:

> *Mr. Goldsworthy Gurney examined* – From 1824 to 1831, has exclusively devoted himself to locomotion. His attention was first turned to the subject when he was a boy. He was on a visit to Mr. Vivian's, of Camborne, commonly known by the name of Captain Andrew Vivian. He went to school with Mr Vivian's son, and spending his holidays at Camborne, there saw Mr. Trevithick's first experiment with a view to drawing carriages by steam; he (Mr. Trevithick) had an idea that it was practical, and with that view built a carriage for the purpose; he tried it on the common road, but could

not make it start on the level; he then took it to a declivity with a view of getting it to move; the carriage went down by its own gravitation, got into a hollow at the bottom, towards Lord Dunstanville's leading to Camborne. When at the bottom of the hill, he attempted to start the carriage again, the wheels went round upon the ground, but the carriage did not advance.*

This fact made a strong impression on the witness, and he never forgot it in after life. Came to London in 1821, and … found that some of the received notions respecting steam were incorrect. Witness consulted several engineers and eminent men of the day on the subject, who all stated that the insurmountable difficulty propelling carriages on common roads, consisted not in the engine, but in the means of applying it to the road. Being asked to name the engineers he consulted, mentions Sir Humphrey Davy, who, although not an engineer, was supposed to know what had been done on most subjects of mechanical science; and Mr. Moyle, a celebrated engineer in Cornwall. In consequence of the opinion given … he did not feel it worth while to make a single experiment, but took it for granted that it was true.[455]

Gurney's testimony was important for the one major point he made. As a young lad he was so impressed by what he saw that day that, twenty-four years later, he would build his own steam carriages for the common road and still believe that it was essential for his carriages to have a means of propulsion other than the wheels he saw slipping in Camborne during his Christmas holiday in 1801.

Trevithick's experiences of driving on the roads of the day and his mishap when the locomotive was damaged on the way to Tehidy set him thinking that he should find a market and more adequate roads. London was the obvious answer and he built a carriage with wheels eight feet in diameter that would be less affected by pot-holes. The chassis of this locomotive was fitted with an engine similar to that described in the 1802 patent and was destined to have a carriage body built at Felton's Carriage Works in Leather Lane, London.

This is where we come across a frequently overlooked and immaterial part of the Trevithick story, just how did the 1803 London Carriage chassis get from Camborne to London? The stories that it was driven to Plymouth[456] to catch the ferry or that it was driven all the way to London have to be discounted as ridiculous; how thoughtless can writers be?

* In the local folk song attributed to the famous event, there is a line, 'The horses stood still and the wheels went around'. Had the original words of 'Goin' up Camborne Hill' been, 'The carriage stood still and the wheels went around' it would have been more understandable. After all, horses were not involved in that journey and, had any been about they were likely to have left very promptly, having been frightened by the warm, panting machine.

A more frequent and comfortable explanation is that it was driven, or hauled to Falmouth over atrocious tracks and embarked on a Falmouth Packet boat called the *Little Catherine*, under the command of Captain John Vivian, a nephew of Andrew Vivian and so a relative of Trevithick's. This fits well with Captain Vivian being aboard and steering the carriage during one of its journeys through London; but let us look at the facts.

The Vivian Family had a bewildering habit of naming many of their offspring 'John' and not differentiating between seafaring and mining 'Captains': Nicholas was both! There is also the confusing assumption that every ship entering or leaving Falmouth harbour was a Packet ship; they were a famous but small percentage of the busy traffic.

The father of John Vivian, 1784 – 1871, died when he was eleven and he was brought up by an uncle in Camborne who, having sent him to Truro Grammar School and thinking he'd done his duty by the time John was fourteen, packed him off to sea as a cadet from 1798 to 1802 in the charge of another uncle, Captain Nicholas Vivian. There is no evidence that this was in connection with the Packet Service. John became a Post Office Packet Service officer at the age of 21 and, eight years later, in 1813, was given his first command when the H.M. Brig *Little Catherine* was used as a temporary Packet on the run to Corunna in Spain.[457] The chassis was shipped to London by Captain Nicholas Vivian, John's uncle who 'came ashore' soon afterwards, took to mining and by 1809 he was captain at Wheal Abraham where, according to Francis, he purchased a used Trevithick whim engine.

There is sometimes a mention of the *Little Charlotte* but this ship cannot be found and may have been a misprint.

Anthony Burton records Trevithick returning from London in a Falmouth Packet after he had been struck down with illness in 1808. Mail for the Packet ships would normally arrive in Falmouth from London by Mail Coach so avoiding the difficult task of the Packets having to beat westwards in the English Channel.

Andrew Vivian made the following entry in his cash book dated August 1803,

> To paid Messrs. Foxes shippers Falmouth for carriage of the engine to London, £20 14s 11d.

G. C. Fox & Co. was a well-established shipping agent and ship owner in Falmouth. The Foxes were a family of closely-knit Quakers and Trevithick wrote to their London counterparts when he wished to influence the manufacture of his engines at the Foxes'

Perran Foundry. We also find Goldsworthy Gurney's family linked to the Foxes and other Quaker families.

Loughnan St. L. Pendred, founder member and President of the Newcomen Society for seven years, who delivered the eulogy to Trevithick at his Centenary Commemoration in Dartford Parish Church, 23rd April 1933, was editor of *The Engineer* for 40 years and clearly devoted a great deal of time to his research when he declared, in his address to the Newcomen Society in March 1921,[458] that the information supplied by Francis was, 'a great deal that is only guessed'. He went on to state that in his view close examination revealed that not a particle of evidence supported the statement that the cylinder of the engine was horizontal. He brought in the 1802 Tuckingmill locomotive and questioned whether Francis's assumption that it was the same locomotive that was sent to London; much of the mechanical evidence, he said, was against it. He quoted the shipping cost, noted above, and questioned whether it was just the engine that was sent to London. He suggested that a locomotive similar to the 1801 Camborne locomotive ran through London, towing a carriage behind it.

His evidence was based on the writings of Hyde Clarke[459] who was given to making some assumptions[460] although Clark correctly estimated the engine was about the size

Tom Brogden's replica of the London road carriage.

The versatile Trevithick Puffer, used for all manner of applications including operating the dredger on the River Thames. Found at Crewe, this engine was built by Hazeldine and is now at the Science Museum.

of an orchestra drum. Clark assumed that Trevithick had attached a phaeton behind its rear wheels and might have had some grounds for criticising Francis who claiming that Trevithick had exhibited the same engine working machinery at a cutler's shop the following day, something he said would have been difficult had the London Carriage been constructed as Francis suggested from the patent drawing. Here were two correspondents coming to differing conclusions about the carriage but both criticising Francis.

Pendred also raised many doubts about the memories of those who, many years after events offered descriptions of the carriages. He also claimed that the locomotive described by Francis could not have worked. That was a bit bold of him because the splendid replica of the 1803 London Carriage, built by Tom Brogden, does work. Pendred also asserted that Francis was guilty of a 'manifest absurdity' when he said that the engine of the 1808 Catch-me-who-can locomotive was the same size as that used in the 1803 dredger. It is difficult to criticise such a learned and experienced man as Pendred for saying that such a locomotive 'would have been bigger than a mastodon and weighed in the region of 30 tons' but he clearly had found fault in the explanations supplied by Francis and was determined to find fault wherever he could.

Pendred also investigated the life and career of Simon Goodrich, the naval engineer who features throughout Trevithick's life, and the 1808 illustration attributed to Rowlandson. While Pendred criticised Francis he said of his father,

> To Captain Dick, the Cornish giant, the world owes more than to any other single engineer, not excepting Watt himself. To him we are indebted for the double-acting high-pressure engine, and it matters relatively little what else he did or did not do. That fact alone is enough to place him, and to preserve his memory for ever, on the highest pinnacle attainable by engineers.

Simon Goodrich is also reputed, by his wife, to have made drawings of Trevithick's London Carriage in April 1803.[461]

These words by Pendred, who was awarded the C.B.E. in 1934, enable us to compare the views of a critical engineer with those of politicians, writers and others who esteemed Watt. They echo similar words written within a few years of the inventor's death.

> In the establishment of the locomotive in the development of the powers of the Cornish engine and in increasing the capabilities of the marine engine there can be no doubt that Trevithick's exertions have given a far wider range to the dominion of the steam engine than even the great and masterly improvements of James Watt effected in his day. … That Trevithick's application was original there can be no doubt. He had never heard of Leupold nor of Oliver Evans nor was he likely to do so until the close of his life.[462]

The 1802 patent was the first sign many historians found of Trevithick, his life before that time being generally unknown outside his neighbourhood. Although the patent detailed the use of two cylinders and showed a boiler with three tubes, Francis said the vehicle built subsequently was a single cylinder locomotive.[463] The patent also included a simple threshing engine; that will be described later.

Anthony Burton provides a good description of the unsuccessful attempt to introduce the first self-propelled London omnibus.[464]

Going Up Camborne Hill
Gurney was not a stranger to Parliament. At a previous appearance on 12th October 1831 he had informed the Select Committee that 20 – 40 steam carriages were being built in the country.

As the Parliamentary report says, Gurney was not a trained engineer but relied on a mixture of his own ingenuity and the advice of the distinguished. So convinced was Gurney, and many eminent engineers at the time who told him that the situation had been 'settled by actual experiment' and that in spite of Trevithick's work a couple of decades previously, he said, 'it came from such high authority that I looked on it as a settled axiom in mechanics'.[465] Gurney started his steam carriage work in 1824 and took out a patent the following year for propelling carriages by feet! They were a complicated contrivance that operated alternately on the road surface beneath the carriage and were known as propellers. The Select Committee's report continued,

> A trip, between London and Edgware, demonstrated the inefficiency of these propellers, and led to the discovery that there was sufficient friction between wheels and the ground to insure propulsion.

In his *Treatise on Essential Locomotion*, 1834, Alexander Gordon ridiculed the cogitations and subsequent deliberations of close-knit groups of the eminent who forsook the hands-on experimentation of Trevithick in favour of their unfounded theories. Gordon's writing is contemporary with Gurney's unresolved application to Parliament for funding and is recommended for its pertinent information by way of history, theory and perceptive comment on the many varied applications of steam to transport. Gordon's work includes a number of well-drawn plates including one of his father David's patent of August 1821 which depicts a Trevithick-like locomotive inside a large wheel,[466] and Gurney's propellers or feet.[467] Gurney subsequently discarded the propellers in favour of wheels.

We have deviated from what happened on the road to Tehidy to examine the work of other engineers in order to illustrate the fundamental and considerable differences between the thinking and achievements of Trevithick and those who tried to benefit from their developments of his initial concept. It is quite remarkable that, long after Trevithick had demonstrated the essential properties of his engine, there should be people who would depart from his original, proven principles. In 1834 Alexander Gordon said that there were many scatter-brained ideas destined to achieve nothing; was he thinking of his father's 'big wheel'? It is clear that although the fundamental features of Trevithick's high pressure engine were well known and avidly being copied not one of the 'improvements' have come down to us in steam design and we are left with Trevithick's original concept; it just shows how important his thinking and work were.

The account by Gurney continued to explain that he and Mr. Moyle found they were mistaken in their assumptions concerning the reason for the wheel-spin and they

197

Gordon's proposal of 1821 illustrates how subsequent engineers would attempt to enhance a proven invention.[468]

subsequently attributed its cause to the manner in which the steam was applied to the wheels.[469] Lord Montagu said of Gurney's often repeated early exploits with a steam carriage, 'this does not come within shouting distance of the truth,'[470] and, in another instance, commented on the accounts of carriage construction and use, and asked for the 'removal of the ornamental flourishes of mythology from the truth.'[471]

The point Gurney omitted in his evidence[472] was any reference to the locomotive turning over or a fire, surely exceptional incidents that must have been retained in the mind of such a bright young child, had they ever happened.

The Parliamentary cross-examination was reported over seventeen pages and continued in the February 7th 1835 edition of the *Mechanics' Magazine*. The report and Alexander Gordon's *Treatise on Elemental Locomotion, Chapter V, 1838,* contained a great deal of information that would be appreciated by students of early steam on the building and operation of steam carriages, their boilers and the opposition they encountered on turnpikes.

In particular, in the section on the condensation of steam back to water, obviating the need to carry large quantities of water, the report said of Trevithick's evidence.

> As to the originality of the invention, refers again to the evidence of last Committee; when he [Gurney] stated that Mr. Trevithick might fairly and justly be considered to be the originator of locomotion by steam on railways, he would refer to his (Mr. Trevithick's) evidence, to show that he had not been able to move on the common road.

> In one part of his evidence, Mr. Trevithick [who would be sixty-three years of age] says, "Travelling on common turnpike roads would be by far the greatest national advantage, but which, on the present plan, never can be accomplished, because the difficulties of getting a supply of water, and the inequalities of the surface of the roads, will always, under the circumstances, prevent the limited power to ascend the hills; and this objection is irrevocable, because as the power at present increases, the weight increases in nearly the same ratio." Mr. Trevithick further said, - "I

have noticed steam carriages very much; I have been abroad for a good many years, and had nothing to do with them until lately, but I have it in contemplation to do a great deal on the common roads. Railroads are useful for the sake of speed and safety, but not otherwise; every purpose would be answered by steam on common roads." … This is important as far as it goes, because witness [Gurney] believes the only person who can claim originality is Mr. Trevithick; now he himself does not claim it. Mr. Trevithick died since the report of the last Committee. …

Witness considers Mr. Trevithick to be the inventor of locomotion on railways – that to him is due all that has been done on railways; and that the steam engines used at this moment on all railways, are decidedly those invented by Mr. Trevithick, with slight variation. At Manchester and Liverpool there is simply a substitution of a series of flues for the fire flue, the large one which he used. He considers Mr. Trevithick to be entitled to the gratitude of his country for such an invention and has no doubt that his invention will be followed by effects on society scarcely credible at this moment. The high-pressure engine for which Mr. Trevithick has the credit, is the only one (of a sort) capable of effecting locomotion to any advantage on railways or on common roads. Before Mr. Trevithick took up the question, nothing had been done; several reports and statements have been made by the Germans, Americans, Frenchmen, and persons of other countries, all of whom are now anxious to claim the origin of this important subject. In a work lately put into his [Mr Gurney's] hands, a claim was made to the originality forty years ago; but unfortunately for the claimant, the things is said to have been done by a low-pressure engine, which must have weighed a ton at least per horse power, exclusive of the water necessary for condensation; which would have been half a ton more.

In the same *Mechanics' Magazine*, page 304, it says of Goldsworthy Gurney,

At one time he used a revolving chain, which carried the rollers with it; they passed under the carriage to the ground, by which the carriage was propelled. These rollers were armed with projections, so that as they revolved under the carriage, they became stationary upon the ground;

Today we know this feature as track-laying or caterpillar traction.

The journey to Tehidy, Monday 28th December 1801
There is a small point of historical interest that has been exaggerated out of all proportion to the events and it has baffled historians and the people of Camborne for years. When

Trevithick's locomotive went missing for a few hours on the road between Camborne and Tehidy it was variously reported as either having broken down or turned over. Stories have developed to include horses being used to recover the locomotive and it being dragged back to Camborne where it was even reputed to have exploded and demolished a tavern.

The attempt to travel from Camborne to Tehidy on a primitive steam locomotive along roads that could at best be described as tracks and were probably no more than rain soaked lanes of grass and mud was destined for failure. This all smacks of Trevithick's blind enthusiasm for any venture on which he set his mind. Even if they had not had the accident it was highly unlikely the valiant travellers would ever have completed the journey to Tehidy. The route included a substantial hill and a crossing of the Red River in winter; this was probably a ford or, at best, a granite slab bridge, both quite unsuitable for their locomotive.

As there have been two centuries of increasing confusion this might be a good time to look again at the available sources of information. When seeking the facts about an incident in history we should go back to source documents, but what should they be? It is a sad fact that the written word seldom contains the truth or, at least, not all of it. Writings are often abbreviated, misquoted, used as the basis for argument and the creation of myth; then innocent men are hanged on the results. Even letters between the parties associated with an incident should sometimes be viewed with suspicion. This is because writers often seek to portray whatever happened or their personal involvement in a manner that aids them. Letters between loved ones frequently stray from the truth or contain intentional lies. It is only in diaries and journals where the writers believe they are only addressing themselves that one is likely to find the truth.

It is reasonable to believe the naïve writings of Trevithick. They provide the engineering historian with a clear and extensive account of his inventions. For the sake of impartiality and good research, we must examine all the alternative versions of the events concerning the famous but fruitless journey to Tehidy. Francis provides much of the uncorroborated basic information and evidence connected to the event and one wonders if it is not too much. He bases his account on a letter Davies Gilbert wrote to his son-in-law, J. S. Enys thirty-eight years after the event.[473] Gilbert said,

> The travelling Engine took its departure from Camborne Church Town for Tehidy on the 28th of Decr. 1801, where I was waiting to receive [it]. The carriage, however, broke down after travelling very well, and up an ascent, in all about three or four hundred yards. Then, after the overturn, the carriage was forced under some shelter, and the Parties adjourned to the Hotel, & comforted their Hearts with a Roast Goose & proper drinks, when,

forgetful of the Engine, its Water boiled away, the Iron became red hot, and nothing that was combustible remained of the Engine or the House.

Curiously, Burton in *Richard Trevithick, Giant of Steam*, quotes rather differently from what claims to be the same letter written in 1839.

> A very curious sequel followed this disappointment. The Travelling engine was replaced in a building and Trevithick and Vivian and the others determined on supporting their spirits by dining at the inn. They did so and forgot to extinguish the Fire that evaporated the water and then heating the Boiler red hot, communicated fire to the wooden machinery and everything capable of burning was consumed.

While the content is similar the two passages do not match in many instances, uncharacteristically, neither author gives an actual reference and, if there is an original, it is difficult to find. Dickinson quotes Gilbert's account of the incident from Francis' book with the well-known but variously reported lines,

> the party consoled themselves with a roast goose and hot drinks. Forgetful of the engine, its water boiled away, the iron became red hot, and nothing that was combustible remained either of the engine or the house.

Dickinson, who studied all that he could find of Gilbert's papers, does not give a reference and confirms that anyone studying Gilbert's journal and papers cannot find a reference to any mishap, fire or goose dinner. He is left wondering if Gilbert ever made such a report as it is only found in Francis' book. Todd's book about Gilbert contains no references to fires or goose dinners. The whole legend of the exploding locomotive in Camborne, which some people swear is true, has been developed from these few confused words.

As with other questionable instances in the life of Trevithick, the account is first found in the book by Francis as something that Gilbert was reputed to have written. Various versions have appeared frequently since but no one appears to have found the actual source. It may come to light so we should not say that it does not exist.

If one studies the style of Gilbert's letters it appears that he is unlikely to have written the first quoted passage. It seems to be the work of a less educated person. The second passage could be from the hand of someone who wished to tidy the syntax and phraseology of the first account. For instance, 'the Parties adjourned to the Hotel, & comforted their Hearts with a Roast Goose & proper drinks,' becomes, 'and the others determined upon supporting their spirits by dining at the inn.'

It is remarkable that Francis makes no reference to anything other than the burning of the locomotive's wooden parts. Francis would surely have learnt from family conversations and people in the little town where he lived if there had been anything more. It is only in the first passage of all the reports that we have any reference to a fire being related to any form of building and it is just on those three words that the legend has grown. On the other hand, we have to remember that Francis recalls surprisingly little, maybe nothing, from family conversations.

Francis does quote a letter from Henry Vivian, Andrew's nephew, to Henry's father in which he says,

> They started to go to Tehidy House where Lord Dedunstanville lived, about two or three miles off. Captain Dick Trevithick took charge of the engine, and Captain Andrew was steering. They were going very well around the wall of Rosewarne; when they came to the gully (a kind of open watercourse across the road) the steering handle was jerked out of Captain Andrew's hand, and over she turned.[474]

Here we undoubtedly have another example of Francis's interference with the material before him; is it likely that Henry, when writing to his father would have needed to explain what the word 'gully' meant? However, the substance of the letter is enlightening. It refers to the wall around the Rosewarne estate being the limit of the journey. That wall is probably the eight foot high one built of random stone that is still standing today. Rosewarne was an estate on the road between Camborne and Tehidy on the right of the road leaving Camborne. There were few, if any, alternative routes between Church Town and the north as the present Trelawny and Wellington Roads did not exist at that time.

It is likely that there would be gullies across the road formed by rainwater running down the hill and that they would join into a ditch along the foot of the perimeter wall of Rosewarne. We are well aware of the problems faced by the steersman when crossing such obstacles and are not surprised that Captain Vivian had trouble. Looking at the solid stone wall today, two things come to mind. Going down the gentle hill the locomotive, almost certainly without brakes, would have been on the curve of the road and could well have run into a crossing gully and continued until it reached the drainage ditch at the foot of the wall. It would then have partially overturned against the wall, striking in a way that damage was caused and parts of the engine were left in the road to be found later. While these circumstances were quite possible they would not have been sufficient to provide the scene conjured up by subsequent writers of a burning locomotive on its side.

Francis quotes another account of the incident, by 'Old Stephen Williams' in 1858. It could be criticised for suffering from the problem of memory loss over a long period of time but some of it rings true and the first part has a quality not found elsewhere; it is an account of what happened by someone who was there and taking part. Unfortunately, Old Stephen admitted he was not party to the journey to Tehidy. It starts with a possible account of the climb up Camborne Hill.

> … there was a roughish piece of road covered with loose stones; she didn't go quite so fast, and as it was a flood of rain, and we were very squeezed together, I jumped off … Captain Dick tried her again the next day; I was not there but heard say that some of the castings broke. Recollect seeing pieces of the engine in the ditch years afterwards, and suppose she ran against the hedge.

Francis quotes a little more from Stephen's recollections:[475]

> Davies Gilbert waited at Tehidy for the steam-carriage on the 28th December; but it did not reach the end of its intended journey of three miles, because something broke. The gentlemen adjourned to the hotel for dinner and Cornish punch. Meanwhile the engine, being neglected, was burnt.

Here we must question whether Stephen would have known that Davies Gilbert (he would have known him as Davies Giddy) was waiting for Trevithick at Tehidy on the 28th December. The fact was not published but was contained in Gilbert's unsubstantiated letter of April 1839.

We should summarise the evidence and see what conclusions we can draw. We have a number of statements; all made at least thirty years after the event, several are 57 years later, beyond the latest date at which we can expect to obtain reasonable evidence. Although Goldsworthy Gurney's statement to the Parliamentary Select Committee had a ring of authenticity, the events of several days were muddled together. The various accounts are presented with a degree of tangled validity and we are not sure who is supposed to have actually said what. A measure of folklore appears to have crept into all the statements with some of the information so far from the known facts so it can be treated as irrelevant. These included the suggestions that the journey was made from the Vivian's home and that it almost reached Tehidy.

While we have one or two statements by people who witnessed the initial climb up Camborne hill we have no account from anyone who saw the mishap on the way to

Tehidy. All statements in connection with that journey are written in the third person. Therefore all the accounts of the journey to Tehidy were repeats of hearsay as no account appeared in newspapers or other contemporary publications.

The consensus is that the locomotive did not travel very far before it was in trouble. Knowing the handling characteristics of the vehicle and imagining the condition of what passed for a road in those days, it is surprising that it got anywhere at all and the whole foolhardy venture was clearly based entirely on Trevithick's innate enthusiasm for proving he and his engines could do anything.

The factors that arise several times are the condition of the road, its gullies, the wet weather, the down hill slope, the wall of the Rosewarne estate and the ditch alongside it. Fortunately, the wall still stands. 'Overturn' and 'over she turned' appear once each but not in Gurney's account or Gilbert's journal.

We know from Gilbert's meticulous journal that he was at Tehidy that morning anticipating the arrival of the locomotive. After waiting some time, he records that he 'Left Tehidy rode to Camborne Ch T'. While the words 'church town' were used to describe Camborne in 1801, it was little more than a village with a population of just 4,811, a census figure that included the surrounding villages of Tuckingmill, Penponds and Treslothan.[476] Word of a serious mishap with the locomotive and a fire involving Captain Dick is likely to have covered the short distance to the Trevithick household some three hundred yards from where the alleged mishap took place either before or while Gilbert was there. As Gilbert had travelled to Camborne with the sole purpose of witnessing the locomotive, such a disaster would surely have merited an entry in his journal; there was no entry. His notes for the two relevant days are,

> Sunday 27th 1801
> Cousin John Giddy came.
> I rode in the morning to Tehidy for the purpose of meeting Trevithick in the next morn with his Carriage.

> Monday 28th 1801
> After waiting a long time heard that the Carriage had broke down – left Tehidy rode to Camborne Ch. T & returned. Heard of Parson John Vivian's death.[477]

Gilbert's ride to Camborne Church Town was to seek out Trevithick as he and his family lived in Fore Street at the time. Because of Trevithick family relationship with the Vivians it is likely that he would have been told of Parson Vivian's death on that visit. While Gilbert may have left Tehidy Manor by one of three exits, Mount Whistle

House, South or East Lodges, he would have joined the Pool to Gwithian road and it is almost certain that he would have had to cross the Red River at the point where the one road to Camborne crossed it. From there he was on the same road towards Camborne as Trevithick travelling the opposite direction on his journey to Tehidy. There was no note in his journal about their meeting on this narrow track. He clearly reached the Trevithick homestead without having seen Trevithick or the locomotive. Trevithick was not at home. We have a mystery based on folklore; either Trevithick and his companions were enjoying a meal and a few beers in the local public house with the locomotive gathering a crowd of interested spectators nearby or they were putting out a fire caused by their inattention to the engine.

The Richard Trevithick Memorial Committee of 1833 led by HRH The Prince of Wales issued a booklet written by R Trevithick to describe Trevithick's life and achievements; it is another publication that ends with the valediction chosen by Francis. Its account of the journey is brief and to the point.

> On a subsequent trial, a casting broke, and the engine was left by the roadside, caught fire, and was partially burnt.[478]

This account did not stray to include any conjecture or goose dinners. It described a situation that could have occurred; the fire, having been drawn from the furnace, would have lain on the road under the disabled locomotive where it could have set fire to the wooden parts above. That still does not answer the following query.

The entries in Gilbert's journal are the only genuine record we have. In order to reach the Trevithick homestead in Fore Street at the top of Tehidy Road, latterly known as 'Camborne Hill', Gilbert would have had to pass the point where legend has it that the incident is alleged to have happened. He made no mention of it.

Popular belief that the engine might have turned right over on its journey to Tehidy is almost certainly erroneous. Had it done so, its four ton weight would have required the assistance of several stout horses and considerable tackle to right it again. During that time the fire would have gone out, or have been judiciously put out to avoid problems. It would have been unlikely that the fire was relit and steam pressure raised as the total time for all this activity would have meant that Trevithick and his gang would certainly have missed their alleged roast goose dinner. None of the accounts record any such happenings.

Also, the assertion that the engine blew up is incorrect. Steam boiler explosions are as devastating as high-explosive bombs. Had it exploded there would have been fatalities, probably including Trevithick. This rejection of the myth that there was an explosion will come as a great disappointment to the broadcasting media who love the quick exit line and have done so much to propagate this fairy tale.

We can only suppose that whatever mishap occurred, it was a small one and the crew had no difficulty in righting the engine. There certainly was a fire on the locomotive and if it presented a problem, it would have been drawn out of the furnace by the crew as a matter of good practice. The sight of the glowing embers would have impressed, even frightened, the bystanders who were unaccustomed to the operation of locomotives. It is also very likely that the locomotive lost some important parts during its impact with the Rosewarne wall.

Tyack's blacksmith's yard was a very short distance away and the locomotive could have been deposited there while the crew fed themselves, if they ever did. By the time Gilbert came up the road there was nothing to be seen. It's a bit of a disappointment for the imaginative story-teller and a sad end to one of the most famous vehicles that ever travelled on the 'common road', but that is life. Nevertheless, we have not heard the last of an opportunity to enjoy a goose dinner.

An examination of the *Sherborne Mercury,* a local paper at the time, and the *Cornwall Gazette & Falmouth Packet* for the two weeks following the 28th December reveals no report of a mishap to a steam locomotive or a fire in Camborne.

The following line is from a present-day web page. It does not state where the information was obtained but it accords with the above conclusions and makes no reference to a fire. 'On this journey they met with an accident, the engine being overturned in going around a curve; but they got back safely.'[479]

Our information about the mishap on the way to Tehidy is from Francis or from witness statements initially quoted by Francis. Let us examine the various alleged statements by the old men he chose to describe what happened in Camborne that day. There is not a word from his parents and other family members. They must surely have mentioned the incident at some time during his childhood and formative years. Maybe their story did not accord with what Francis wished to tell us.

Elderly readers should try to recall the details of any incidents in their childhood when they were just eight years old. And bear in mind the scientific research that has established, 'By age 60, the rate of memory loss [of British civil servants] had increased to 53 percent, the study found.'[480] Let us look at the timing of these recollections. In 1858 the three witnesses chosen by Francis were fifty-seven years older than they had been at the time of the incident. Had they been ten or fifteen years old at the time, their ages would have been between sixty-seven and seventy-two. It is possible, but the average life expectancy of English adult males at that time was just thirty-eight years.[481] In France the figure was even lower.[482] These often-quoted figures include infant deaths and so are not representative of those who survive their earlier years. With infant deaths running at 20% in 1800,[483] the average English life span would be in the region of 45 years.

The witnesses' accounts of Messrs Williams, Petherick and Newton have the surprising coincidence that they were all obtained in 1858. With John Petherick's account in *The Mining Journal* we have the support of a respected periodical but we do not know who provided the account or if it was checked before publication.

An examination of the Census Records for Camborne District[484] in the years 1841 (by Hundreds), 1851 and 1861 reveal a Stephen Williams, a cooper aged 65 living in Trelowarren Street, Camborne in 1841. He would have been 25 in 1801 and, if he was still alive, 82 when interviewed by Francis.

Another Stephen Williams, 79, from Helstone [sic], who was living in Centenary Place, Camborne in 1851. He would have been 86 at the time of Francis' interview. John Dunstan Newton, a tin miner of Stithians, was 58 in the 1851 Census, making him just eight years old in 1801.

There is only one John Petherick, recorded in the 1861 Census, but he would not have been born in 1801.

We do not have a first name for Mr Newton. The name comes up frequently as an address near Troon but only once as Llewyn Newton, a 55 year old printer of Church Row, Camborne in 1841 and, the same person?, twenty years later as Llewellyn Newton, a 75 year old accountant in Fore Street. If this was the Newton referred to by Francis he would have been 15 years of age in 1801 and 72 when interviewed.

Apart from Mr Newton the characters in the census returns do not appear in earlier or later returns, giving the impression that they were not in Camborne to witness the 1801 event or had died or left the district prior to being available for interview by Francis. There is no real evidence that the three gentlemen with remarkable memories claimed to have been interviewed by Francis or written to the *Mining Journal*, actually existed. May be that evidence will be found one day. There is always the possibility that they all lived elsewhere and happened to be in Camborne on the eventful day. That maybe but we have descriptions of the date, time and weather. It was late on a Christmas Eve, when it would have been dark by four o'clock and it was raining. It was unlikely that Camborne would have had many young visitors at that time, probably not enough survivors to provide Francis with three statements 57 years later. Remember, none were eye witnesses.

We have only one account, of very unconvincing origin, that there was any fire at all beyond that within the furnace of the locomotive. While it is certain that the locomotive did not blow up, it is also very doubtful if the tavern or any other building caught fire. This is an example of an odd word bring taken out of context by an imaginative storyteller, becomes folklore and is eventually argued as fact. We have to be grateful that more people know the name Trevithick than they did a few years ago, but there are few who will recognise it without immediately thinking of a boiler explosion in Camborne followed by the burning of a public house.

So, where can we look for the truth? Gilbert's journal entries provide us with records of the first successful road journey by self-propelled locomotive in 1801. Those entries in his journal for his days at Tehidy and Camborne should counter the mistakes so frequently published elsewhere about the curtailed journey from Camborne to Tehidy.

We have Gurney's testimony that the carriage suffered from the previously unknown phenomenon of wheel-spin. The action of a smooth iron tyred wheel on what passed for roads in those days offered very little adhesion and it is likely that the famous climb in the rain 'Up Camborne Hill' on Christmas Eve was beset with much wheel-spinning.

There is tremendous torque available as the replica of that vehicle starts to move and it requires the most judicious control of the power by the driver to avoid wheel-spin. We do not know how many road wheels were powered in 1801 or if Trevithick had discovered the problem that arose when two wheels are driven at the same time; the vehicle tends to go in a straight line irrespective of where it may be directed.

The new techniques of steering a self-propelled vehicle and managing the supply of steam to make the wheels go round were something quite unknown to the novice crew. The likely explanation is that, after experiencing the problems so well described by Gurney, the crew ran the locomotive into the Rosewarne wall, damaged it and returned it to its workshop, dismissing any further attempt to drive the country tracks to Tehidy. This sad story ends the short life of what Francis realised some seventy years later to be one of the most significant self-propelled vehicles that will ever grace this Earth. As Francis probably had no inkling of what Gilbert had written in his journal at the time, he saw this as too good a story to be left to wither. Let us sum up what happened on that day.

In the year of his death, when he admits to failings of health and memory, Gilbert allegedly wrote a lengthy description of Trevithick's adventures with his steam carriage that included the first references we find of the engine breaking down and turning over. This is at odds with the entries he made in his journal on the day of the event and yet is so detailed as to recall the menu of Trevithick's supposed meal; did Gilbert have a sudden memory recall that superseded the note he made in his journal at the time or was he just enjoying himself by making it up? If this letter exists, and Dickinson has been unable to find it, Francis chooses it as the basis for his story and introduces a number of people to support its content. According to Dickinson, who casts doubt on the whole affair, Francis appears to be the only source of this letter and there is no evidence that the people who so conveniently came forward fifty-seven years later ever existed.

Here we begin to see a similar scenario to that which surrounded the late night story of Murdoch, his model locomotive and the vicar of Redruth. In that case Francis also found an unlikely and uncorroborated witness and got her to substantiate his story. We are again left wondering if Francis took the opportunity to embellish Gilbert's supposed letter or he may well have fabricated the whole story. Whatever the truth, the excellent stories of Murdoch's model locomotive and Trevithick goose dinner are now firmly established in the proud history of two rival towns and they will be joyfully repeated time and time again. Maybe we all have something for which we should thank Francis.

Trevithick and his engine
In many ways Trevithick led a remarkably simple life. For instance, we know that he was happy to indulge in a little social drinking but there are no signs that, unlike many others of the period, Trevithick ever drank to excess. It does not appear that his problems were attributed to alcohol, nor did he apparently resort to snuff for comfort. In spite of what Jane described as malicious rumours whilst he was in South America, there were no suggestions of extra-marital affairs. Nowhere in the various accounts of his life was there the mention of any romance. Although Trevithick was brought up in a strictly non-conformist religious household we find no signs of a zealous evangelical nature. These and the subjects that infatuated other men were clearly not issues that concerned the single-minded Trevithick.

Trevithick brought the complete engine into existence against the advice of many, including James Watt. Without his vision the engine was likely to have developed slowly, designed a little at a time by a variety of contributors as is usually the case with other inventions; think how long it has taken for the knife and fork to evolve. Had Trevithick not existed there would have been the usual drawn-out patent disputes on individual features that are so often an aspect of any development. A great deal of time and money would have been wasted travelling down the blind alleys of exploratory engineering. The slow evolution of the engine would have set off many arguments, problems of patent rights, inefficiency and downright danger resulting in death. The lack of skill shown by designers at the Rainhill Trials twenty-five years after Trevithick's engine had shown how to keep going for nine miles at Penydarren, left only one locomotive performing satisfactorily, Stephenson's Rocket. That locomotive was equipped with Trevithick's steam exhaust blast pipe and a multi-tube boiler, the latter attributed to H. Booth.[485]

At the time Trevithick was promoting his engine there were inventors in other countries, notably France and the United States, who had developed similar technology. This country led the world in steam engine and locomotive development and there were no dramatic alternative engine designs. In the course of the next ten years, the technology based firmly on Trevithick's inventiveness spread like wildfire and high-pressure steam engines proliferated.

The motor car is now safer than it ever has been but people are still killed in their thousands each year. No matter how careful Trevithick was with his designs, there would always be the exception in practice where a steam engine was either poorly made or misused.

Following the financial failure of the London Carriage in 1803, Trevithick faced another disaster later that year when one of his boilers exploded at Greenwich near the site of today's Millennium Dome. Four men died and others were injured. This was due to a combination of misuse and inattention but the implications were predictable. Many boilers had previously blown up but this was a Trevithick boiler and Boulton & Watt seized on the opportunity to draw attention to the dangerous nature of high-pressure steam. They made capital out of it while overlooking their own lethal[486] boiler disasters. During the very cold February of 1784 many men were huddled round a Boulton and Watt brazed copper boiler at the Poldory Mine, St Day near Redruth. It exploded, causing the death of Capt'n Carkeet and several others, many were also scalded. A similar incident at Wheal Chance later the same month revealed that their boilers were incapable of sustaining even the lowest of pressures.[487]

After the explosion Trevithick hurried to Greenwich and fitted subsequent boilers with a fusible plug.[488] Here is an early description of the fusible plug, an essential safety feature on all pressure vessels to this day.

> Fusible metal plugs have been proposed as an additional precaution to the use of safety valves. The suggestion originated with Trevithick, who had holes drilled in the sides of his high-pressure cylindrical boilers, just below the water line, in which the plugs were inserted; so that, should the water, from any accidental circumstance, sink below its proper level, and endanger the explosion of the boiler, by the sides becoming intensely heated, the plugs would melt, and allow the steam and explosive gases to escape. They

have also been recommended to be put into the bottoms of the boilers, in order that, if the boiler should become dry, the plug would fuse, and the fire be put out by the discharge of the steam into the furnace.[489]

Boiler explosions amongst the poorly manufactured engines seriously affected the public's confidence in the steam engine but thick skinned industrialists continued to invest in them while they avoided standing too close.

Trevithick wrote a letter of several pages to Gilbert[490] about the Greenwich tragedy and describes the engine in the fullest detail down to the thickness of the boiler walls, the distance parts were hurled and the size of holes they made in the ground. He asks Gilbert to calculate how much pressure would have been required to burst a cast boiler one inch thick. The letter continues at length with details of the engine, the effect on his sales and the number of Boulton & Watt engines being sold as a result. There are many more technical details and indications how he will avoid such accidents recurring in the future. Although Trevithick was clearly moved by the accusations about his engines and the effect on his sales, he mentions no thought or contrition towards the deceased workmen or their families, the letter finishes,

> I believe that Mr B & Watt is abt to do mee every engury in their power for thcy have done their outemost to report the exploseion both in the newspapers and private letters very different to what it really is.

In spite of the gloom and despondency generated by his competitors, history only records this one Trevithick engine explosion and the deaths were attributed to poor attention by its minder, who had gone fishing. We are fortunate to have a meticulous investigation into the Greenwich explosion by Ms Mary Mills as Appendix II. Trevithick was so thorough and careful in his designs that he was able to work alongside high-pressure boilers all his life without suffering injury.

Penydarren and the exhaust blast.

The following year we find Trevithick building engines in the mighty South Wales ironworks near Merthyr Tydfil. The Iron Capital of the World had been visited by Admiral Lord Horatio Nelson and the Hamiltons in 1802 when he wished to see where many of his cannon balls were manufactured. Samuel Homfray, the iron master, saw Trevithick's ability and employed him from 1802 to build engines for his works.[491] A locomotive was built to take metal from the furnaces to the works forge[492] and it broke many of the tram plates.[493] Always willing to offer a challenge, Trevithick reckoned that his locomotive could move much more iron than horses on the tram road from the Penydarren Ironworks to the Glamorganshire Canal at Abercynon. Homfray bet on his success to the tune of a colossal 500 guineas. An excited Trevithick wrote to Gilbert at Oxford imploring him to be present during the trial.[494] Gilbert had to judge where his interests would be best served and, for a while at least, declined Anna Beddoes' fiery approaches in order to watch the world's first steam train go by.[495] Trevithick had no similar distractions and was also anxious to share his thoughts about diverting the exhausted steam up the chimney.

There is still debate about the first engine to benefit from the use of its exhaust blast to draw the fire in the furnace. While the 1802 patent refers to the dangerous exhaust steam being directed up the chimney it was not until 1804 that Trevithick remarked on the beneficial effect on the fire. There has always been some speculation whether this blast-pipe exhaust effect on the engine's power was carefully thought through and intentional or whether it was entirely fortuitous. Nevertheless, Trevithick was quick to appreciate the improvement to the performance of his engine and said:

> …The steam that is disscharged from the engine is turned up the chimney abt 3 feet above the fire, and when the engine is working 40 St pr mt, 4½ ft Strake, Cylinder 8¼ In Diam, not the smallest particle of steam appears out of the top of the chimny, thro' the Chimny is but 8 feet above where the steam is delivred into it, neither is any steam at a distance nor the smallest particle of water to be found. … The fire burns much better when the steam goes up the Chimny than what it do when the engine is Idle.[496]

There has been so much misinformation concerning the blast pipe that it has tended to deny Trevithick his rightful place in the development of the steam engine. Samuel Smiles, 1812-1904, was a prolific writer who flew to numerous conclusions and enabled his work to be used by those who sought written confirmation of their tales. In the foregoing lines Trevithick clearly explained how he used the blast effect of steam to draw the fire in his Penydarren locomotive. Yet, over sixty years later, Smiles says that 'steam had never been thrown into the chimney for the express purpose of creating a draught until Stephenson so employed it'.[497]

In an article[498] entitled 'The Blast Pipe', R. N. Appleby-Miller, FLA, put the matter firmly to rest when he examined the various claims by Trevithick, Gurney, Hackworth, Hedley and Stephenson to have invented the blast pipe and concluded that Trevithick knew exactly what he was doing in 1804 and illustrated the blast-pipe clearly on the drawing of the 1808 Catch-me-who-can locomotive.

He also countered the misconceived claims that Trevithick fed his waste steam into an expansion chamber to loose its blast effect before channelling it up the chimney. What appeared to some to be an expansion chamber was, in fact, the concentric water jacket employed to pre-heat water before it entered the boiler.

The blast pipe misconception rolls on to the present day with William Rosen, a writer of repute who attributed the blast pipe to Stephenson when writing in 2010.[499]

Trevithick was clearly elated after winning the challenge at Penydarren and was delighted by the effect of his blast pipe. He wrote again to Gilbert,

> The Gentleman that bet five Hundd Guineas against it rid the whole of the journey with us and is satisfyde that he have lost the bet. We shall continue to work on the road, and shall take forty tons the next journey. The publick untill now call'd mee a schemeing fellow but now their tone is much altered.[500]

While the run to Abercynon proved disastrous to the cast-iron tram rails, a subsequent letter to Gilbert confirmed his presence and revealed further journeys by steam propulsion,

> The Tram engine have carryd two Loads of 10 tons of iron to the shipping place since you left this place…[501]

It also indicates that Gilbert managed to extricate himself from the clutches of the amorous Anna Beddoes long enough to attend the trial. In a letter to his son-in-law thirty-five years later, Gilbert preferred to remember that he was at Oxford in the company of his father and sisters during the winter and spring of 1804.[502] Gilbert wrote on an 1808 ticket,[503]

> *1804 I rode in a steam carriage made by Trevithick at Merther Tidville in South Wales. D. Gilbert.*

It must have been many years later that he inscribed the ticket, or Trevithick's business card as some would suggest as it does not bear the cost of the fare, as he would have been D. Giddy at the time and had no knowledge that he would ever change his name.

Little is made of the detail in Trevithick and Vivian's patent application of 1802 that shows a typical puffer locomotive running on both inside and outside flanged iron rails. This reveals that the concept of the 1804 Penydarren locomotive was far from a flash of inspiration brought about by the surroundings in which Trevithick was working in Wales. It also refutes those who claim that George Stephenson was responsible for the first iron edge rails set on square stone sleepers in 1825;[504] they had been in use many years previously in horse drawn days.

According to an account in *The Engineer*, the Penydarren locomotive worked for a period of five months.[505]

These were busy days for Trevithick. Not only did he operate the world's first railway steam locomotive from Penydarren on the 21st February but the *Cambrian* newspaper reported one of his four horse power stationary engines with a horizontal cylinder was set to work at Alexander Raby's colliery in Llanelly on the same day. An elaborate description of this and another eight horse power engine that started operations in London the previous week were reported in the new newspaper on February the 24th. It has to be remembered that no one had ever seen a high-pressure steam engine before and Trevithick must have spent every waking moment travelling and giving instructions how the engines should be built and operated.

Gilbert's signed Pennydaren ticket.

Spurred on by the success at Penydarren locomotive, Trevithick planned an elaborate demonstration of his engines before Samuel Goodrich of the Naval Board. In this the engine would be seen to pump water, work a hammer, lift coal from a mine and then transport that coal on a railway. Everything was set but disaster struck as Homfray was badly hurt when his gig overturned. The display was called off and the locomotive found a new life as a stationary engine in the iron works.

So convinced was Homfray over Trevithick's novel form of power that he entered into an agreement with him to sell the new steam engines. They did not build engines for sale but as joint patentees, they offered to instruct anyone who wished to manufacture them and licensed their construction at the rate of 12 guineas per horse power for smaller engines and at a lower rate for larger ones. With Homfray providing the financial backing, they divided the profits so that Homfray would have three-fifths and Trevithick two-fifths. Trevithick had found a man who could afford to live life in style, who drove about in a coach and four attended by servants in scarlet and buff livery, one who believed in Trevithick and was prepared to invest it in his inventions.[506] This was the encouragement that Trevithick needed. At last, at the height of his genius he could reap the benefits of his inventiveness and endeavours. He could go home to his wife and family and live in luxury for the rest of his life. In addition to encouraging management in South Wales Trevithick had the opportunity of all the foundry, engineering and shipping facilities he required to develop and build a range of his puffer engines.

Following his success with his railway locomotive Trevithick was in demand all over the country and he clearly had a great opportunity to become an engineering industrialist. Just as this wonderful opportunity presented itself, Trevithick's eye was caught by other interests and much of the year was wasted drilling a rocky obstruction on the River Thames. Time and opportunity were slipping by and they would never be so tempting again. He left his Welsh friends wondering where they had gone wrong. James Watt, junior, always one to twist the knife where Trevithick was concerned, wrote to Southern at the Soho Works to the effect that, 'reports that Trevithick and Homfray have quarrelled and that the former has taken himself off in dudgeon. The railway engine is in disgrace and the one sold for winding coals returned upon his hands …'.[507] But there was no evidence of that and the iron founder still encouraged people to buy and use Trevithick's engines. They clearly did not lose touch with one another as in March 1805 they were jointly writing to the Abernant Ironworks at Aberdare, one of their licensees, complaining about the standard of engines they were producing.[508] It is frequently said that Trevithick did not have the Boulton that Watt had; he often had better people but he never recognised them.

This was just another example of Trevithick's consistent and unfailing ability to snatch defeat from the jaws of success.

While in South Wales Trevithick lodged with a Mr Jones at Pontyrhun, Merthyr. 'and was much liked for his amicable character'.[509] There is a confident report that is rather different from the accepted accounts of what happened to the locomotive. It states 'that his engine, after serving for a long time on the tramway, was removed to a pit called Winch Fawr [probably the biggest iron works in the world at the time] and 'in after years' was again moved to the top of the incline owned by the Penydarren Co. and there was restored, patched and repatched, till only the original cylinder remained. Trevithick assisted after this in forming an engine for

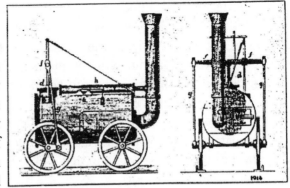

Drawing of the Trevithick-Vivian locomotive from the 1802 patent. Note the alternative flanges on the track.

Tredegar & another for the tramroad between Hirwain & Aberdare & then disappeared from Wales'.[510]

Tales of engines abound and their tellers delight in finding unlikely connections for the characters and the things in their stories. For this reason, it is impossible to confirm whether all the reported subsequent instances of steam engines being used in various locations within the Penydarren works were connected to the famous locomotive. Trevithick made a number of engines whilst working for Homfray and the Penydarren engineers were soon capable of making them for themselves. There is a report that the world's first railway locomotive ended its days causing terrible death and destruction. The *Merthyr Guardian* reported,

Dreadful Accident with Loss of Life at Penydarran Ironworks
On Thursday afternoon, a little after 4 o'clock, the tube [boiler] of the Trevethick steam-engine burst with a loud explosion, threw down in large fragments great part of the cylinders of the engine, scattered in all directions the roofs of several buildings belonging to the works, and shook a considerable number of the houses around. Thomas and William Howel, the sons of old William Howel, well known in the neighbourhood as William of Pencaedrain, were at work in a shed adjacent, the roof of which, made of Iron, fell upon them, and they were taken out dreadfully scalded, and nearly in a state of suffocation.[511.]

We can only suppose that the unfortunate Howel brothers succumbed to their wounds although we will never know how they were 'dreadfully scalded' when an iron roof fell on them in an adjacent building; such was the standard of newspaper reporting in those days.

Some confusion surrounded other locomotives at this time and John Steel, 'a very clever fellow'[512] built a locomotive in Whinfield iron works for Christopher Blackett, a colliery owner at Wylam near Gateshead. It was very similar to the Penydarren locomotive except that the cylinder and beam were located more sensibly at the other end of the boiler away from the furnace door; this would avoid injury to the fireman. There were claims that this was a wholly northern venture but John Steel had been involved with the construction of the Penydarren locomotive with Trevithick and had been despatched from Wales to Gateshead with suitable drawings. The engine suffered a similar fate to its predecessor in that its weight was far too much for the rails and was used very little or not at all.

It was a difficult time for Trevithick, he had always hoped his self-contained steam engine would be the means of mobility, but in his mind he saw that there were possibilities for multiple applications. He recognized it would have no problem proving its worth as a stationary engine hauling, pumping and winding. The lumbering atmospheric engines of Newcomen and Watt had proved the ability of steam to do those simple tasks. Trevithick saw his lightweight, versatile engine as capable of so much more but bumpy road surfaces and fragile iron rails had thwarted him. However, he had ideas of giving steam locomotion just one more chance.

The Penydarren tunnel
While it was intended that the design and detail of Trevithick's engines is really outside the purpose of this book, the aggravating question concerning the locomotive that Trevithick used to haul the first train is frequently raised. The problem appears to be centred on the size of present day replica locomotives and the dimensions of the Plymouth tunnel close to the Penydarren works through which the original locomotive is reputed to have passed; the locomotives of today simply do not fit.

There is also the 1802 Coalbrookdale locomotive about which Trevithick wrote to Gilbert in August 1802 and described it as working between 50 and 145 lbs/sq inch.[513] Although the Dale Company were reported as being satisfied with the locomotive's performance, nothing more was heard of it but today it is confused with the Penydarren and the Gateshead. The model makers of the twenty-first century are mystified.

Trevithick was obviously excited about the possibilities of putting one of his puffer engines onto rails, or tram tracks as they would have been, and worked with William Reynolds, a son of John Reynolds, director of the Coalbrookdale company. The remaining directors were not convinced that this was a good investment and, when

Replica of Trevithick's locomotive based on the Wylam drawings.

217

William died in 1803 there was an opportunity to stop squandering money on this new fangled gadget. Little or nothing more was heard of it.[514]

Conjectural replica of 1802 Coalbrookdale locomotive'

We have ascertained that Homfray invited Trevithick to develop steam power within his foundry. Its prime purpose was the transfer of hot metal from the furnaces. In doing this it would replace the horses previously used. While we do not know the design of the eighteenth century foundry it is reasonable to suppose that the portals through the walls supporting the roofs were adequate for a horse and cart. Trevithick's replacement locomotive would have had to negotiate the same entries. This could explain why the tram tracks in the tunnel, also built to accommodate a horse and cart, would, have been offset to accommodate the drover. While the tunnel would have been large enough for the locomotive designed to operate in the works the rails did not suit the configuration of the locomotive, probably because the chimney, being in the centre of the locomotive but not in the centre of the tunnel, fouled the roof.

Historians are still discussing track widths and tunnel heights with the possibility that what we know as the Penydarren engine with a cylinder projecting horizontally from the boiler at the same end as the furnace door may have been the elusive Coalbrookdale locomotive. The jury is still out deciding whether this means that the Coalbrookdale engine is in fact the Penydarren or whether, having built a suitable locomotive for foundry work at Coalbrookdale, Homfray asked Trevithick to build another for a similar purpose at Penydarren. The better known Gateshead engine has its cylinder placed more sensibly at the opposite end. That leaves us with a Penydarren replica currently at Swansea Maritime Museum that was probably the Gateshead (Wylam) and a smaller locomotive at Coalbrookdale that could have been the Penydarren or another one like it, or even something else. It is not surprising that people are confused and we await agreement from the historians, reputed to be a stubborn group.

Students of accurate history might like to note that the valve gear on the Gateshead/ Penydarren replica was redesigned by the National Coal Board, something that is reputed to have brought about its failure.[515] The front axle of the replica is also subject to failure but it is not clear who is to blame for that.

It is unlikely that there were ever any drawings of the Penydarren locomotive, it probably followed one Trevithick made at Coalbrookdale. This may mean that many of the replicas and models that have copied the Gateshead locomotive drawings and are described as being replicas of the Penydarren are incorrect but we'll let time and further investigation sort that out. It is certain that the Plymouth Foundry tunnel now enhanced and displayed as the one through which Trevithick travelled is man made and did not exist in 1804.

Engine development and sales
In the journal of the *Newcomen Society* for 1970-71, Joan M. Eyles has examined the correspondence between Trevithick, William Smith and Samuel Homfray of South Wales between the years 1804 to 1806.

These years are particularly interesting as they reveal the value of engines driven by high-pressure steam in many industries throughout the country. It is significant that, at a time when communications other than the post were non-existent, news of Trevithick's affordable, compact, portable, safe engine had reached industrialists everywhere. Such was the impact of this news that people who were unlikely to understand the technology but were willing to put their trust in reports that they could save money were placing orders as acts of blind faith. It is likely that they were attracted by the frequent reports of the engine's economy; matters connected to the pockets of industrialists are always important.

William Smith was set upon selling and erecting Trevithick's engines. The eloquent and informative style of his writing revealed him to be educated and thoughtful. Smith wrote to Trevithick.

> Mr Trevithick,
> Inventor of the Improved Steam Engine,
> Pen-y-darren Works near Myrthur
>
> Dear Mr Trevithick …
> I was happy to hear (through the medium of the newspapers) of your great Success in drawing the Trams by means of your Improved Steam Engine … I should therefore be very glad of an outline of your general Charges for Engines of given Powers that I may take every opportunity of displaying the merits of such a superior Invention.

Amongst my numerous acquaintance in different parts of the Kingdom I have had a great many enquiries from Manufacturers Colliers and others respecting the prices of your Engine and the Consumption of Coal therefore your answer directed to the Craven St Coffee House Strand London will very much oblige.'[516]

Smith's enthusiasm for the engine and the opportunities he could see to acquire commission also encouraged him to write to Samuel Homfray:

> I am so much struck with the ingenuity and great utility of the Engine that you shewed me at Pen-y-darran that I have taken every opportunity of recommending it... I have this moment rec[d] directions from the Earl of Sefton to order an Engine for this purpose of sinking to the Coals which I have discovered on his Estate.[517]

The quoted letters and the following excerpts from others in the Newcomen Journal were not chosen for their quantity of engine sales. They reveal that manufacturers of Trevithick's invention were popping up all over the country and a healthy business was developing.

> in a dye-house in Lambeth – the foundry of William Fawcett [Liverpool], where engines according to Trevithick's design were already being made – Earl of Sefton, to the purpose of sinking to the coals, Torbock Colliery – put an engine to work in Worcester – and another in Staffordshire – Liverpool where a founder had made two that worked – one other was finished – three others begun – after having listed the number of engines being made at Manchester, Liverpool, Coalbrookdale and Bridgnorth he went on, at Newcastle I found 4 engines at work and 4 more nearly ready, 6 of these was for winding coals, one for lifting water and grinding Corn – raising water at Longton, Staffs – four engines at work and 4 more nearly ready – one sett to work a month since at one of Lord Dudley's Coal Pitts -- & particularly at Manchester - where they may be sett to work … and can be easily moved – Bath-Easton Coal Company…one of your small engines to sink coal – there is a great numbered ordered since I parted from you – small engine … the Blackwall Rock – Newcastle-under-Lyme…winding coal --- At Manchester I found two engines had been put to work … and three more building --- there are two foundreys at Manchester in full work of them – Walked to see Trevithick engines made by Rowley in Cleveland Row [Fitzroy Square]

The extracts from this correspondence illustrate the impact Trevithick's invention was having on the mining and industrial communities of Britain. Trevithick had frequently told his wife, family and friends how his inventions would one day provide them with riches. Nothing could have more clearly identified the course he should have taken if he really wanted to achieve that ambition. Trevithick had a world monopoly in the supply of efficient high-pressure steam engines. He had the income to patent all the many features he had designed. He was making money from the engines that were being built throughout the country and he could well have afforded to set up a company to exploit his success. Gilbert, Harvey, Vivian, West, Homfray, Smith and Isaac could supply guidance and cash, although such a venture was self-funding and the development costs could be covered by the manufacturers.

Without realising the potential at his fingertips, he summed up the positive sales situation in a letter to Gilbert in which he said,

> ... if I had 50 engines I culd sell them in a Day at any price I wod ask for them.

In this Trevithick referred to his handling of direct sales. Watt had shown him in a most painful manner how to take advantage of patents and Royalties. He had despised Boulton & Watt for the money they had made and yet here was his opportunity to make an even greater fortune. See Appendix III for a list of known Trevithick engine manufacturers at this time.

Following his success at Penydarren, Trevithick was accompanied by W. Smith on his travels around the foundries in the Midlands. It is clear from Smith's correspondence that Trevithick's engines were being made in quantity for a number of end users. Many writers, including Francis, have assumed that Trevithick's visits to Newcastle were to Northumberland but Smith's correspondence clearly indicates that they were in Staffordshire.[518]

Many people could see the benefits of Trevithick's invention and were eyeing the possibilities of accumulating riches by building or employing similar engines themselves. The spread of steam power throughout the country and abroad during the next thirty years was relentless. In addition to applying high-pressure steam to the former Watt engines in Cornwall's mines, Trevithick's new form of power was finding applications in all forms of industry, ocean going ships and the railways that transformed towns, communications and the countryside. It is interesting that all of the engines manufactured during the next twenty years reveal their direct descent from Trevithick's original design. This indicates how important was Trevithick's innovative thinking and how little originality most other people had. It also reveals how Trevithick, or a competent business manager, could have made him one of the richest men in the world. A modern counterpart would be Bill Gates.

In 1809, an iron tramway was laid by the Bassets in Cornwall to connect their mines in the Redruth area to their harbour installations at Portreath on the north coast. While this was the first railway in Cornwall and wagons were winched up an incline by a stationary steam engine, some writers infer it was steam hauled but it was a plateway for horse or mule drawn wagons.

Trevithick would devote more valuable time to a Thames dredger followed by a tunnel under the river planned by the Commercial Archway Company. John Wyatt of Hatton Garden wrote to Gilbert in 1807 asking for his opinion of Trevithick's capabilities and character.[519] This cautious enquiry is not surprising as the Wyatt and Vazie families were prominent shareholders in the company.[520] Robert Vazie was not a Cornish engineer as often reported[521] but had been born and baptized at Hexham, Northumbria in 1758. He had several Cornish contacts and took out patents from a Chacewater address. He had previously attempted to tunnel under the river in 1804 with the assistance of 'Chacewater miners'.[522] Vazie said that he had introduced Trevithick to the Board of the Thames Archway Company and from 1807 they acted as joint engineers.[523]

Trevithick saw it as a mining project with the simple matter of driving an underground level between two shafts. Following a recent succession of failures Trevithick could see

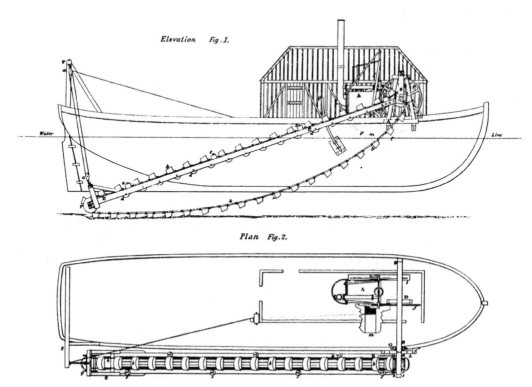

Trevithick's design for the Thames dredger.

222

nothing but profit in a venture where he thought he knew all the answers. Trevithick's mining experience in Cornwall would normally have stood him in good stead for such work but that would have incurred drilling through hard rock; here the ground was mainly mud. Work commenced on the 17th August 1807 intending to construct a pilot tunnel five feet high by three feet wide at the base and two foot six inches wide at the roof level.[524]

One must not forget that Trevithick stood six foot two in height and was broad with it. Undaunted by such trivialities he wrote a couple of optimistic letters to Gilbert in which he said,

> I am very much obliged to you for throwing this job in my way, and shall strickly attend to it, both for our credit as well as for my own profit.[525.]

> I have wrote to Cornwall for more men for them. Its intended to put 3 men in each core six hours' course. I think this will be making a thousand pounds very easey, and without any risque of a loss on my side…

A week or so later his optimism was still high although he admitted to some surprises in the work.

> … the ground is sand and gravel and stands exceeding well, except its when we hole into leareys and holeing to such houses of water makes the sand very quick. We have discovered three of these holes which contain about twenty square yards. … I cannot see any obstickle likely to prevent us from carrying this level across the river in six month …[526]

As with so many of his enterprises, things went from bad to worse and he encountered problems with the ground of the river bed and factions who would have him dismissed for incompetence. Trevithick was seen by Londoners as a strange, almost incomprehensible power in the midst of this project.

Then Trevithick made an unusual decision; he called for his wife and family to join him in London. Jane's sensible brother Henry wrote to Trevithick,

> My sister have commissioned to me her wish of going to London with the Family to live with her Husband but say she cannot think of leaving Camborn unless what you owe there is settled .. If you can give me good security for the Money you owed my Father's time (say about Five Hundred Pounds) I have no objection to let her have what money she want or the £500 given by her will.

This outstanding account is likely to have been connected to Trevithick's earlier boilers; it is doubtful if there was a reply. Henry advised Jane against such a foolhardy mission but it was a mark of her devotion to her husband that she and her four children, all less than ten years of age, made the perilous journey to the squalor and stench of riverside London. Health and sanitary conditions deteriorated during the next fifty years cumulating in the famous Great Stink when it became almost impossible to breath in central London.

Jane's shock at seeing London on her arrival from the fresh, windswept west of Cornwall was compounded when she found the four most recent letters she had written to her husband lying unopened in his coat pocket. Trevithick's excuses are unlikely to have placated his wife and she moved from the miserable lodgings chosen by her husband close to his work at Rotherhithe to more agreeable ones in Limehouse.

There was continual opposition from shareholders to Trevithick's work in the tunnel and Gilbert was called to re-establish his reputation. The directors offered Trevithick a further £1,250 to complete the work;[527] Beamish says it was £1,000.[528]

The pressure was on Trevithick; claims were continually made that he was not the man for the job. He wrote to Gilbert,

> I have no dought of accomplishing my job'[529]

Soon after the arrival of his family there is a report that the roof of the tunnel collapsed. This has been linked to an account from an engineer who claimed Trevithick's tunnel was a foot or so out of line after tunnelling more than a thousand feet.

> Trevithick's tunnel was at Rotherhithe, a short distance from Brunel's [subsequent] tunnel. He committed the usual error of going too near the bottom of the river, the object being a close run, endeavouring to keep the least possible distance from it, and to save labour and expense, as the funds were limited. Had his experiment been carried through, he would also have been able to give a plausible cheap estimate of the intended tunnel, leaving the increased expenses to be met as they could. Trevithick's error was not productive of much inconvenience to him, nor does it seem to have been the immediate cause of the abandonment of the enterprise, for he carried his driftway to a greater extent without impediment that Dodd did before, or Sir Mark Brunel did afterwards. It was not until he had gone 930 feet under the river that he encountered any obstacle, when he got into a hole in the muddy bottom of the river; and at one time a piece of uncooked ship-beef, which had fallen from one of the vessels, drifted into the works.[530]

While reports like this vary a little in content, some suggest that Trevithick was 200 feet from his goal, others 150. Also, that this hole was the end of the project, which it was not. However, the general content is very similar and we can see the usual aspects of Trevithick's character coming through when placed in a challenging situation.

Trevithick found himself in the middle of considerable controversy over the major civil engineering project of sinking a tunnel under the River Thames. There were plenty of armchair critics who had never been down a mine in their lives; they were willing to give advice and warn the company's directors of the dangers they were encountering by employing this impulsive engineer. Trevithick saw all this interference as a challenge to his knowledge and experience as a mining engineer; he immediately rose to it. He was reported as 'displaying the proverbial irritation of Cornish men'.[531]

There is no evidence that he consulted Gilbert on his next move as he would have immediately counselled against it. In fact, in a subsequent letter to Gilbert a contrite Trevithick omits an account of his ill-fated exercise and tells a story how the water broke in. For instance, he overlooks the fact that it was probably he who had made the intentional hole in the tunnel roof. His optimistic letter was full of hope in spite of circumstances that may have incurred multiple tragedies; it was also one of the very few instances where he considered it to be in his interests to be economical with the truth.

> Last week the water broake down on us from the river, through a quick sand, and fill'd the whole of the level and shaft in 10 minutes, but I have stop'd it completely tight and the miners at work again. We are beyond low water Mark on the north side with the drift; and if we have no farther delays we shall hole up to the surface in 10 or 12 days.[532]

> Trevithick had battled against the putrid river mud and the accusations of his critics for more than four months.[533]

The brief account of the incident described in the above letter from Trevithick to Gilbert is at odds with that of a capable third party. This reveals the problem faced by researchers who put their faith, as is generally supposed to be the best way, in the details obtained from a single original document. That method depends on the whole truthful story being contained within the one document.

> He ... soon completed a thousand feet, to the great joy of all parties concerned.

On arriving at this distance, according to a previous arrangement with the committee, Trevithick was to receive a hundred guineas, which, after verification by a surveyor, were paid to him. According to a memoir in the *Civil Engineers' Journal* the surveyor reported to the subscribers confirming the measurement, but asserting that the line had been run a foot or so on one side.[534] This statement, if well founded, was not material. The *Journal* continues,

> Trevithick took exception and chose to consider it as a severe reflection on his engineering skill. His Cornish blood was excited, and with his usual impetuosity he set to work to disprove the assertion, without any regard for his own interests, or those of the subscribers. He is said to have adopted the absurd contrivance of making a hole in the roof of the tunnel at low water, and pushing up a series of joint rods, which were to be received by a party in a boat, and then observed from the shore. ... The work thus ended, having reached 1011 feet, being within 100 feet of its proposed terminus, and it is a melancholy monument at once of his folly and his skill.[535]

One can barely imagine the mayhem in both the tunnel and aboard the boat during this ill-fated escapade on the River Thames. Below ground the men would be working in the narrowest of dark tunnels with their only exit being a fifth of a mile away on the southern bank, a journey that would take Trevithick and the escaping miners to greater depths and through deeper water. The tunnel was low and narrow. The only lighting was by candles attached to the miners' hats and they would frequently be snuffed out on the five foot tunnel roof. The miners were accustomed to working up to their knees in the water of Cornish mines but here it was effluent that flowed in as the River Thames was an open sewer for the increasing number of inhabitants in the capital.

The boat, supposedly moored above them would be swinging about as the tide turned, making the job of feeding in the pipes almost impossible As the water rose and threatened to enter the tunnel there must have been frantic efforts to seal the hole: they failed and the miners had to scramble through the tunnel for their lives.

Trevithick's actions in allowing the miners to escape before him is recorded and appreciated by all the chroniclers. He is reported to have walked home after this incident, streaming wet, without shoes or hat and caked with mud; he almost certainly smelt as well. There is no account of his wife's reaction when he walked in. After tidying himself he returned to the scene to discuss the possibility of a repair. He petitioned the Lord Mayor of London on 7th April 1808 for permission to sink a caisson and was granted permission just a week later for a period of three months.[536]

Local hostility accused Trevithick of incompetence but this was rejected by the directors of the company who called for the opinions of a number of experts. As the tunnel was now flooded it is unlikely that Trevithick received his £100 reward for having achieved the 1,000 ft mark. In true Trevithick manner, his mind had moved on and he now proposed a more complicated method of building a full-sized tunnel from a removable caisson, first with a brick lining and then with the alternative of cast iron.

While Trevithick's mind was seeing workable solutions he was running ahead of his experience and of those who supported his work. With scores of plans on the table from all sorts of people the Archway Company decided it was literally out of its depth and closed. Trevithick, along with his workmen, was out of a job again.

> On a subsequent occasion, being cross-examined as to this occurrence while witness on a trial, he is said to have admitted to fact of ruining the works, and to have asserted his determination, in any circumstances, to defend his own character at whatever sacrifice to other people.

The prodigious author, Richard Beamish, FRS, who had apparently not noticed that Brunel had eventually built a tunnel, said in *The London Quarterly Review* of July 1862 of the problems faced by Trevithick and his men as they approached the end of his tunnel.[537]

> The opinions of scientific men were now sought for; and amongst others Dr. Hutton, the mathematician, and Mr. Jessop, the engineer, were appealed to. The conclusions they came to in the matter is worthy of being quoted, for it has been borne out by the result. 'Though we cannot presume,' they said, 'to set limits to the ingenuity of other men, we must confess that under the circumstances, which have been clearly represented to us, we consider that an underground tunnel, which would be *useful, to the public and beneficial to the adventurers;* is impracticable.'[538]

Here was another example of Trevithick being ahead of his time and not stopping to reason out the whole project before starting. One might have considered that, in 1825, the rather more thoughtful Marc Isambard Brunel would benefit from Trevithick's experience and be able to do the job properly. While Trevithick did not quite complete his tunnel the experiences of Brunel vindicated him when he revealed that there were still many problems to be overcome in tunnelling through a soft river bed. With a brick and steel caisson and a wooden shield, later to be replaced with an iron shield Brunel felt assured of success. However, the river broke in after tunnelling only fourteen feet and the tunnel subsequently flooded five times. Seven men were killed and Isambard barely escaped with his life when his body was broken and he was confined to bed for several months. Brunel's speed of tunnelling, eight feet a week when progress could be made, would have been considered abysmally slow by Trevithick who averaged over seven feet a day including stoppages. Brunel's work was frequently brought to a standstill while the tunnel was pumped dry and eventually the project ran out of money. The government was finally persuaded to loan the company a quarter a million pounds to complete the work. Brunel's useful-sized tunnel ultimately opened after eighteen years in 1843.

Trevithick then sank his savings into a demonstration railway in London. This was a locomotive built at Bridgnorth and set upon a circular track in July 1808. The exact location of the world's first continuous passenger railway is still a matter of discussion.[539] Charles R. King pointed out why the famous drawing of the event, alleged to be by Rowlandson, is a fake and concluded there was the possibility that two different sites appear to have been used, the first in July close to Tottenham Court Road and the second in September at the back of Lower Gower Street over a plot that became Torrington Square. Gilbert wrote to Trevithick and suggested that the locomotive should be called 'Catch-me-who-can', an idea a little out of his character but that of his sister, Mrs Phillipa Guillemard.[540] Trevithick offered rides in an attached carriage for five shillings (£15). It is recorded that it ran for some weeks but failed to attract a buyer or sufficient passengers to pay the expenses in spite of a reduction in the price of the ticket to two shillings and then to just one. Francis recorded that 'the 1808 locomotive engine [ran] on four wheels, two of them being driving wheels made to revolve by crank pins in their spokes.'[541] If, as inferred, both pins were inserted at the same time on a locomotive of 8-10 tons there would have been a tremendous strain on the track that was 'perhaps a hundred feet' in diameter. The effect would have been to cause the locomotive to travel in a straight line and may have contributed to the derailment. It is surprising that Francis, a lifetime railway engineer, was not clearer on this point.

It was noted that, after having employed a horizontal cylinder on his Coalbrookdale and Penydarren locomotives, Trevithick reverted to an earlier design with a vertical cylinder for his Catch-me-who-can demonstration. Without any apparent foundation authors have offered suggestions that Trevithick did this because he experienced faults or wear in the horizontal cylinders. An alternative, commercial decision, might have been considered. The 1808 locomotive was built by the Bridgnorth foundry, builders of a considerable number of 'puffers' and had little or no experience of other Trevithick designs. The puffer engine was very versatile and it was clearly simpler and cheaper for them to attach wheels to a familiar engine than to start new designs for a 'one off' application.

Again, never far from a challenge, Trevithick offered to take the engine to Newmarket where it would compete against any racehorse but there were no takers. The horse was the fastest form of travel in those days. Had Trevithick succeeded in his endeavour, he would have been the fastest man on Earth.

Whilst Trevithick had enthusiasts for his stationary steam engines, self-propelled locomotion had been shown to be no cheaper than horses, susceptible to maintenance costs, likely to break expensive rails and beyond the understanding of anyone but skilful engineers. Trevithick faced his first real setback when his dreams of passenger locomotion came to nothing. In the future it would be simple for others to criticise him for making the rational decision to turn away from locomotion as the day of the passenger railway had not yet dawned. Trevithick was years ahead of the railway companies; when they emerged their object would be to carry freight in the form of coal, iron, stone and wood. They saw no advantage in passenger fares. It was an Act of Parliament in 1844 that made the railway companies convey passengers at no less than 12 miles per hour for a maximum of a penny a mile. In the meantime, Trevithick turned his attention to the growing demand for his stationary engines.

Robert Dickinson
The link with the river and ships opened Trevithick's mind to a whole raft of ideas to

The Catch-me-who-can track, Gower Street, drawn some years after the event.

improve operating practices with his steam engines. Dredging, loading, ballasting, a tug and even the provision of an engine to drive a 100-ton clipper all received his attention but the dreams did not bring in money. This was the time for him to seek a steady, business-like partner but he teamed up with a Robert Dickinson, often described in retrospect as a ne'er-do-well former East India merchant* who shared Trevithick's desire for inventions. One of their joint patents in 1808 was for enclosed paddle wheels.[542] In 1818 the *London Engineer* was the first vessel in England to have this feature with the wheels rotating in a pressurised air-tight casing. The motion of the ship was found to seriously interfere with the water level and the plan to operate the wheels on the London to Margate run was a disappointment. Together they took out another patent on the 'nautical labourer', a complicated, steam driven floating jack-of-all trades. Their enthusiasm was moderated when they encountered a demarcation dispute. The dockers blacked their machine and threatened to drown its inventors.

Trevithick discovered that water did not deteriorate in iron tanks and suggested to the navy that square iron tanks should replace the round barrels in ships that currently occupied more space than the volume of water they contained. When Trevithick and Dickinson issued a pamphlet on the subject the style and spelling suggests that Dickinson wrote it.

> With respect to the Royal Navy, the patentees presume to think that the adoption of iron stowage would be advantageous in a more than common degree. If ships of war were provided with metal tanks for containing their beer, water, provisions, and stores, would not the necessity for ballast be in part done away with?

Dickinson & Titley refer to a letter from Humphry Davy in which he states that water cannot be harmed if it is stored in airtight tanks. They innocently remarked, 'one Cornishman always backs up another'.[543]

Filling iron tanks with water and pumping them out again was suggested by the pair as a simpler way of adjusting a ship's ballast than loading and unloading stone or pig iron bars.

They discovered that iron boxes filled with air would float. Here was an opportunity to build buoys and use buoyancy to lift sunken vessels. Trevithick and Dickinson went into the sea salvage business and lifted a vessel at Margate. A string of demarcation disputes delayed the lifting but it was eventually achieved and the owners then demanded that the vessel should be brought ashore. Trevithick was willing to do this but he would

*The Oxford Dictionary of National Biography says 'West Indies merchant'.

require more money. A refusal to pay the additional charge was more than Trevithick could stand and he had the vessel cut free allowing it to sink to the seabed. Apart from proving that iron could be made to float, nobody won anything out of the exercise and it became another example of Trevithick creating a disaster out of an opportunity.

Sugar plantations and a fire ship

Another patent in 1809 was for a ship in which both the hull and deck would be made of iron. Trevithick was attracted by a number of projects including steam engines for the sugar plantations of the West Indies and he volunteered to sail a fire ship on a suicide mission into the French fleet. He realised this might have been considered foolhardy by those at home and wrote to Gilbert[544] saying, '... be silent abt it home for I shod not like for my family to know I wod engage in such undertaking ...' Fortunately for Trevithick and the French nothing came of the proposal but a simple version of the Trevithick engine was developed for threshing sugar cane.

These engines were as popular as any other of Trevithick's multi-purpose units and he was clearly juggling deliveries in order to keep his customers satisfied. There was a good export market to the sugar plantations in the West Indies and one of the original iron boilers lasted long enough to appear at the World Columbian Exposition in Chicago in 1893. The description mentioned that it was a Trevithick boiler and was one of several that were principally used for threshing. It goes on; 'they were rated at about 4 horse-power, with a moderate steam pressure. They were without safety valves, steam and water gauges, or feed pump, and would run about six hours without requiring a further supply of feed; then the steam was blown off, and the boiler refilled for another run.' It stated that these engines consumed 2½ lbs of coal per horse-power hour and 'the boiler evaporates 9 gallons of water in an hour, and works six hours without being replenished'.[545] It also required very little attention; 'a farm labourer could easily regulate it. The original cost was about £80 ... and some of these engines continued in use for more than fifty years'.

The two illustrations of very similar Trevithick threshing engines probably reveal the differences to be found when an engine is manufactured to the same instructions on two continents.

Just how Trevithick threshing machines appeared in the United States of America is not known but they were clearly manufactured there in numbers, were known as Trevithick engines and enjoyed long lives. We know how the machines were introduced to the sugar plantations of the West Indies and suppose news of them travelled north.

It is impossible to tell if the specification changes that dispensed with such items as safety valves were initiated by Trevithick. Such simplification would have brought

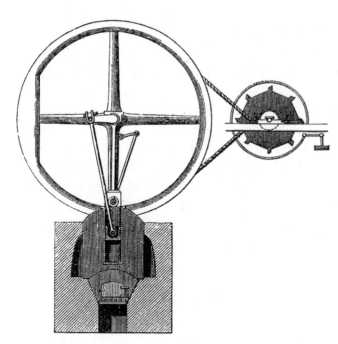

Trevithick's boiler and threshing machine, England 1812.

the price down. Clearly any increase in the comfortable operating speed of the engine, a sign that the pressure was rising, would have indicated to the conscientious operator that he should lower the fire. By careful calculation, the boiler was designed to contain sufficient water to maintain steam during a working shift, frequently quoted as six hours.

In 1812 Trevithick wrote to Sir Christopher Hawkins, Bart. of Trewithen, near Truro describing a very similar four horse power engine that also worked on one filling of water during a shift, 'The steam engine is equal in power to four horses … The boiler … works six hours without being replenished. The engine requires very little attention – a common labouring man easily regulates it'. He wisely avoided mentioning if the engine had also dispensed with the safety valve and other useful features but his description survived in America to be quoted in Chicago nearly a century later. The Americans must have been working from original documents as they repeated the fuel consumption as 2½lbs/h.p./hour. Trevithick quoted the original cost of the engine as £80. As a precaution against damage and loss of profits it was likely that the owner would ration the amount of fuel to be used during a shift.

Sir Christopher was obviously impressed by Trevithick's description of his engine and mentioned it to sugar plantation owners in the West Indies. Trevithick wrote again to Sir Christopher with details for a Mr Pickwood who had enquired about a 10 mule power engine. Trevithick calculated the cost of operating an engine for 24 hours and compared it with the cost of 40 mules as each could only work for six hours but would require sustenance for all twenty-four. He quoted a price of £200 compared with 'a large, heavy, and complicated machine, requiring 2500 gallons of water per hour' at about £2,000.

Mr Pickwood ordered an engine for his mill and, if it proved satisfactory, a further two more, plus several for his friends.[546]

An historian without our knowledge of Trevithick's puffer invention could have considered the simple, single-acting agricultural threshing engine to have been a step towards eventually designing the locomotive; that is the way these things usually develop.

The threshing machine engine made its first appearance in the famous Trevithick and Vivian patent of 24th March 1802 in connection with the locomotive that was to become the 1803 London Carriage. In those early days the threshing engine was a paradigm of minimalism. It revealed Trevithick's ability to dispense with many of the working parts of his engine. In addition to being built with the above parts missing, the patent suggested that the whole vertical engine, boiler and furnace should be built as one and oscillate as it drove the flywheel.[547] William Murdoch invented an oscillating steam engine in 1785 but few people have questioned a possible link to Trevithick's use of the principle. Various versions of the engine were patented by Maudslay, Aaron Manby and others.

The illustration (overleaf) held by the Science Museum clearly shows an 1811 threshing machine with a conventional cylindrical boiler fitted with a safety valve. This was evidently a more expensive model and is similar to the engines designed for shipment to Peru.

Back in London, the partners' business matters in London deteriorated as they developed more ideas. Then Trevithick was incapacitated by illness, variously described as typhoid and gastric fever. Henry Harvey suggested that the family should all return to Cornwall and they did. Even the voyage to Falmouth was not without excitement as the country was at war with France. As Trevithick slowly regained his health in Cornwall his business failed in London and the bailiffs took all his possessions. He managed to settle with his creditors at

Trevithick Columbian boiler and threshing machine as exhibited at the Chicago Exposition of 1893.

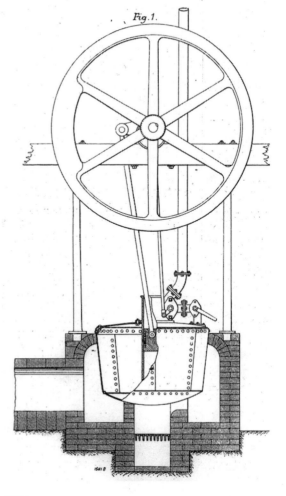

Fig.1.

High-pressure engine built by Richard Trevithick in 1811. This compact engine was built for threshing and chaff cutting duties in agriculture - not all steam engines were destined for heavy industrial and manufacturing use. *Science Museum.*

sixteen shillings (80p) in the pound and was discharged of bankruptcy; something he said was not his fault but Dickinson's. In this, he was probably correct but we cannot overlook his enthusiasm for perusing projects without any hope of remuneration.

Many of Trevithick's ideas with Robert Dickinson were developed and became commonplace in the years to come but with little or no benefit to the pair at the time.

Illness and return to Cornwall

Trevithick's visit to London had provided him with a demonstration railway that attracted little attention, a tunnel to nowhere, a number of maritime ventures with no rewards, an illness that nearly killed him and bankruptcy that ruined him financially. We now find him back in Cornwall within the bosom of his family and in need of work. His usual ebullient, forthright nature would have been calmed as he recovered from his illness. He was not the man he had been and his friends and relatives took advantage of the situation.

In the close-knit Cornish communities of Camborne and Hayle he was, for a while, at the mercy of those who would have supplied a surfeit of advice. Amongst them would have been his supportive wife, now pregnant with Francis, and her sensible brother Henry. Her family, in the form of Harvey's of Hayle and her brother-in-law William West, exerted considerable influence on the weakened giant. In addition, there were his five sisters and cousin Andrew Vivian who had always been at pains to keep the Trevithick family together. It has always been a feature of the Cornish to offer advice, whether sought or not. We can only speculate at the methods used to persuade Trevithick how best to use his talents but we know something was done because the effect was quite remarkable.

As Trevithick's strength and determination returned so ideas poured forth. His illness and subsequent deprivation had taught Trevithick some lessons. He was now reluctant to invest his own money or to do work without reward. He was still disappointed that

234

public funding had continued to evade him.

While his mind still roved over further possible applications for his engines, Trevithick developed the expansive nature of steam, sometimes called 'wire-drawing'[548] and combined it with a degree of condensation. The injection of some Trevithick magic heralded some advances in technology and the design of much more powerful boilers. The success of his work and the manner in which it supplied the means to improve the lives of his family must have been welcomed in the Trevithick household.

This was a time when Trevithick could be seen to be acting judiciously, developing his inventions and selling the products at a profit. New machinery incorporating his high-pressure steam featured in boilers at Dolcoath, a pumping engine at Wheal Prosper, machines for sawing wood and threshing corn. We cannot trace Gilbert having any involvement in these enterprises.[549]

For a while, we see how Trevithick could have lived his life profitably by applying his mind to the improvement of his inventions. This provided him with something of the lifestyle he and his family so desperately craved. However, it was not his way of doing things and, as he regained his strength and lined his pockets, he clearly found life in rural Cornwall was confining.

Rastrick and a change of life?
A change of circumstances at Harvey & Co. found Trevithick developing his association with John Urpeth Rastrick. Rastrick was a partner at the Bridgnorth Foundry and it is likely that Trevithick had met him previously when dealing with Bridgnorth and Coalbrookdale. His arrival in Cornwall and his appreciation of Trevithick's work must have come as a breath of fresh air for the frustrated inventor.

It would be unfair to suggest that Rastrick led Trevithick astray but it is easy to imagine how the two eminent engineers found common ground and enjoyed the banter associated with the development of their technology. They visited the building of the Plymouth Breakwater where Trevithick saw how his versatile engine could cut the mighty granite blocks of which it was being constructed. This was typical of Trevithick's quick appraisal of a situation in which his engine could be put to profitable use. Cornishman John Hosken, father of Lt. James Hosken, captain of Brunel's *Great Western* and *Great Britain* steamships, was in charge of one of the vessels delivering stone to the breakwater and he laid the first inscribed stone.[550]

Trevithick's mind was alive again. His engines were in all advanced transport and technology; in 1813 a 52ft paddle steamer began a regular passenger voyage between Yarmouth and Norwich. In 1815, Trevithick described his plunger pole pump engine in which the pump rod became the steam cylinder. This was Trevithick at his inventive best. The new pumping method required considerable vision and thought but, as happens with the best of inventions, the result was simple and effective.

This change of direction is revealing. Trevithick's ability to see how Mankind could use his engines did not include how they could be manufactured. It would have been to his advantage if he had applied his restless mind to developing the types of engines industrialists had shown they were willing buy in quantity. That would have provided him with the opportunity to pay his debts and put food on his family's table.

Trevithick would usually consult Gilbert for advice on whether to proceed with his ideas. Unfortunately, we do not have all Gilbert's replies so we do not know whether Trevithick took the advice. In the following letter we detect that Gilbert, and maybe others, have got through to Trevithick and told him that many of his ideas were nonsense. It is likely that Trevithick was unable to separate the good ideas from the fancies and this was where Gilbert was useful. In January 1811 he wrote to Gilbert concerning an idea for a blast cylinder to utilise waste heat.

> The saving will be beyond all conception … Perhaps it is like many other wild fancies that fly through the brain, but I do not like to let it go unnoticed without first getting your opinion. I hope you w'll excuse me for so often troubling you.

Later in the same letter his mind wanders when he talks about remuneration.

> I should be content with five per cent on the profits gained by this plan, and would conduct the business for the mines without salary. Should you chance to fall on the subject with his Lordship [de Dunstanville], be pleased to mention something about the mode of payment, as his Lordship is by far the properest person to begin with about my pay, for after his Lordship has agree the sum and Dolcoath Mine is the first to try the experiment, I think all the country will give way to what he might propose. But I wish something to be fixed on before all the agents in the mines know how to be smelters themselves, after which no favour, unless first arranged![551]

Subsequent developments in steam

The development of steam engines by other engineers was permitted following the expiry of the Watt patent in 1800. In 1806 Trevithick discussed the practicalities of using high pressure steam and combining it with a degree of condensation down to less than atmospheric pressure.[552] Of course, this was the basis of the engine designed by Jonathan Hornblower but Trevithick made it work effectively. He suggested converting the mighty Dolcoath engine to high pressure steam from a new boiler of his own construction. However, nothing seems to have come of this, probably because of the reticence of the adventurers and the poor condition of the existing engine.[553] In 1812 Trevithick successfully attached one of his high-pressure boilers to a former Watt 24-inch pumping engine at Wheal Prosper where he was the engineer and drove it on steam at forty pounds per square inch. This was a prototype of the many engines that were to be built for the next hundred years in Cornwall and elsewhere for use throughout the world.[554] They were known by the common name of the Cornish pumping engine and 'between 1820 and 1840, this pumping engine represented the highest engineering achievement in steam power technology'.[555]

It would be wise at some point to clarify the variety of locomotive engines produced by Trevithick. Most inventors produce one or, at the most, two similar versions of their creations in a lifetime. Then they either substantially develop their one invention or proceed to invent other machines. It is unusual for an inventor to produce a number of machines based on the same technical base within just a few years. Also, future historians are likely to be confused if that inventor is dilatory about keeping records or patenting his inventions. This is why the production of half a dozen significant, individual locomotives by one man over the course of a few years was destined to cause confusion.

The several journeys made by Trevithick with his various locomotives on both road and rail should be explained. While there are probably less than a dozen altogether they are all important and have been known to confuse historians who are capable of muddling the early journeys. Their usual mistake concerns the 1803 London Road Carriage that was patented in 1802 but not run in that year. Patenting was not a luxury accorded to the 1801 Camborne road locomotive so it is either ignored or, at best, confused with the London road carriage. The 1803 London Road Carriage has been confused with an 1804 railway journey in Wales and yet another railway journey in London in 1808. There is also the matter of the more understandable confusion by historians and model makers of the designs of the famous 1804 railway engines. A list of Trevithick's locomotives appears in Appendix III.

The man from South America
Before Trevithick had completed development of the plunger pole pump, something happened that would set him alight; a Francisco Uville, described as a Swiss national in *Transactions* by the RGSC and by Gilbert in his diary,[556] arrived at Falmouth from Peru. He was travelling to England to meet the man who had invented the high-pressure steam engine. He had met a passenger on board called Teague who knew Trevithick, the inventor he required, even claimed he was a near relative.[557] Uville was sick from

237

the long trans-oceanic sea voyages that had involved his rounding of Cape Horn four times in his recent life. He had previously visited London and purchased the model of Trevithick's high pressure engine that had been seized by the bailiffs. It had worked satisfactorily at 14,000 feet above sea level and he was seeking its inventor. Such was the greed and hopes of the people with whom Uville worked that they were reputedly willing to pay him $2,000 for the model that had cost £21.

Trevithick's excited imagination added both gold and Mexico to his account of the meeting when he wrote to Rastrick.

> I have been detained in consequence of a Gentleman calling on me who arrived here from Falmouth 11 days since leaving Lima in South America for the sole purpose of taking our steam engine pumps and sundry other mining materials to the Goald and silver mines of Mexico and Peru.

In his excitement, Trevithick made a mistake about the journey time of just eleven days from Peru, around Cape Horn to Falmouth, surely it was eleven weeks. The story of the events that led up to the orders for six engines, boilers and complementary equipment for the silver mines in Cerro de Pasco is well documented by Anthony Burton in his book, *Trevithick, Giant of Steam*.

The pumping engines for Peru were described as specially designed for the mines, a form of enlarged puffer and similar to the threshing engine supplied to Sir Christopher Hawkins of Trewithen. Each was composed of a cylindrical boiler with an integral single-acting 24″ open top cylinder.[558]

At 14,000 feet steam can be generated at 180° F instead of 212° F so making the engine more efficient,[559] but the reduced oxygen at that level called for patience when raising steam.

We have an account of the situation at Bridgnorth from Richard Preen:[560]

> I am now seventy years old, and was working in 1809 in John Hazeldine's engine foundry at Bridgenorth, and have been there most of my time. … The engines Hazeldine was building were called Trevithick engines …Mr. Rastrick was considered the engineer. He quarrelled with Hazeldine and set for himself at West Bromwich, to construct portable engines, the same as they made for Mr. Trevithick … A Spaniard came once or twice with Mr. Trevithick.

The potentially wealthy mines of Peru had, like those in many overseas mining areas, aroused curiosity and rumour in Cornwall. The size of this order caused huge excitement throughout the mining industries. It was far in excess of what Uville had been empowered to spend and would exceed the funds he had to pay for it.

The impact on Trevithick was immediate and significant. Francis reported that his father wrote a flurry of letters between May 1813 and April 1814 urging his contacts at Bridgnorth and Neath Valley in South Wales to make the engines and other components with all due speed. He was also making arrangements for their departure.

> …now I want your immidate answer saying part of these materials you will enter in to an engagement to deliver on Bristol Quay within four months of the time the drawings are sent you, I will lodge in a bank the money to pay for the whole of the matls and it shall be inserted into the same agreement that you shall draw every week for your money as you turn it oute at Bridge North immidly on receipt of yours you will hear from me again.

This was a time for celebration as Trevithick, in his inimitable style could see nothing but good fortune and fine living from this deal. He wrote again to Rastrick,

> I have your favor of the 10 inst containing the invoice of sundrys from Bristol to Cornwall with pipes and Ale all of which being very necessary tools for engineers and miners, the Ale and pipes we are very thankfull for and shall not forget to remember each your health often over a glass of good Shrop Shire ale which will be chearfully joined by my rib as long as we find the can all continue to run.

We see nothing of Henry Harvey building engines for Trevithick at this time.

At a time when no merchantman would sail without an armed escort, Trevithick dismissed a war with France and interference from American pirates as mere irritations. He was much more concerned over the lack of funds with which to pay his sub-contractors. Uville had over extended his credit and Trevithick's display of enthusiasm left him open to the offer of a share in the profits instead of payments in cash. In an agreement dated 8 January 1814 Uville persuaded Trevithick to pay £3,000 for a one-fifth share, a step that greatly improved the finances of the whole deal. It left Trevithick without a salary for his engineering work and at the mercy of the partners in Peru.

It was clear from his absolute devotion to the task of supplying the South American order that Trevithick saw this as the probable climax of his career. All he had worked for, all his inventiveness, hardship and labour was to be fulfilled, not from the government or the many ventures in which he had become involved but by something he had not even considered, rich silver mines on the other side of the world; in his dreams he never enjoyed such delights.

Trevithick was off again, some would say out of control. He had money in his pocket and a demon in his head. He saw before him the solution to all his life's ambitions; surely the riches he so dearly thought he deserved would be his at last.

We see the Trevithick of old; all the careful husbandry of his finances developed when he was under the influence of his family and friends in Cornwall was neglected as he went headlong into an expensive deal that had little hope of being ratified in South America. Everything was to depend upon silver being won from mines about 130 miles north east of Lima and over 14,000 feet (4,338m) up a mountain.

Four pumping engines, four winding engines, two crushing mills and four boilers, together with a ninth engine to roll silver and strike coinage at the Mint in Lima were embarked on the 1st September 1814 aboard the *Wildman*, a South Sea whaler sailing from Portsmouth at a total cost including freight and insurance of £16,152 1s 1d.[561] The machinery, probably the world's first shipment of high pressure steam equipment and certainly the first to South America, was a notable achievement as each item had been specially designed and built in what would be known in the future as 'knocked down' form with a maximum item weight of 70 lbs for transport on mules followed by assembly on site. All had been achieved in just fifteen months without any of the modern forms of communication and digital technology that we take for granted as saving us time.

The climb up the mountains would take weeks, traversing platforms of ice; woollen clothing was essential where the annual mean temperature was 6-8 ° C. Food would have to be carried up the same route and the main fuel for the engines was llama dung although some coal was later found relatively nearby.[562]

Trevithick chose two men to accompany the equipment to Peru and another elected to go. The three Cornishmen that accompanied the shipment were a motley crew but, in accordance with the Cornish attitude and ability, could probably turn their hands to any problem that might arise. They were Thomas Trevarthen, an engineer, and his assistant William Bull from Chacewater.[563] The third was Henry Vivian, a brother to Andrew who had married his cousin, Trevithick's younger sister, Thomasina. Henry was therefore Trevithick's brother-in-law. He was keen to go but Trevithick pointed out that he was reputed to 'make too free with an evening glass'. Trevithick also wanted nothing to do with his employment because, 'should any accident happen to him', his sister might charge him with Vivian's enrolment.[564] Henry had been noted as working Trevithick's first high pressure steam engine at Stray Park Mine and firing a boiler with stone coal (anthracite) at Llanelly [sic], in March 1804 whilst Trevithick was building his locomotive in nearby Penydarren.[565]

It had been an all-consuming time in Trevithick's life and there was little room for attention to problems at home. The health and education of his seldom mentioned eldest son, Richard, caused concern; the symptoms were described as his 'mind and constitution'. Trevithick wrote to the schoolmaster with whom young Richard apparently boarded. The form of this letter is quite unlike Trevithick's usual correspondence and we must wonder whether it had been drafted by Jane, or even by Andrew Vivian.

> At the end of this month I intended to have taken my son under my care to try for a short time what effect a change of education and outdoor exercise would have on his mind and constitution, but I shall be obliged to go to the North and return to London where I expect the Shipping the engines for South America will call my attention two or three months for which reason I should esteem it a favour if you would be so good as to keep him with you one more quarter.

William Williams of Angarrack returned from Cerro de Pasco Mines in March 1872 and stated that he saw two Trevithick 12-inch open top horizontal cylinder pumping engines and one 12 inch winding engine, all with 10 foot flywheels at work. Three 30 foot Cornish boilers were supplying steam at 40 lbs per sq inch.[566] This report suggests that the designs were somewhat different from the threshing machine derived engines thought to have been shipped to Peru, maybe they were the engines in the second consignment.

Who was this Uville who had caused such an upheaval in the lives of Trevithick and his associates?

Francisco Uville, ? - 1818

It is clear from the works of many historians that there is confusion over this gentleman's name and nationality. Don Francisco Uville was born Français Auguste Vuille in Neuchâtel, Switzerland, a member of the famous watch-making family and he trained as a watchmaker. He changed his name on arrival in Peru.[567] Accents on letters in his name do not appear to occur at anytime in his papers. His name is correctly spelt in the Richard Trevithick Memorial Edition of his Life, 1883. He was in partnership with Don Juan Vivez and Arismenda Abradia in the Peruvian Mining Company, a company formed to pump the silver mines at Cerro de Pasco. He visited England, the home of steam technology, seeking suitable engines and pumps. He had been informed that the mighty Boulton & Watt engines would be difficult, if not impossible to transport up the 14,000 feet to the mine and were unlikely to work satisfactorily at such a height where the atmospheric pressure would be reduced to about two thirds that at ground level. He called on Messrs Dupuis & Co, the London bankers, and raised money for the intended purchase of the pumps.[568] While in London he happened upon a small-scale model of Trevithick's high-pressure engine on display and purchased it for twenty guineas. This engine was likely to be one of the possessions of Trevithick seized by the bailiffs when he was declared bankrupt. Upon returning to Peru he found that the engine performed well at altitude and subsequently returned to England, landing at Falmouth, just a few miles from where Trevithick was recovering his health. Trevithick's meeting with Uville was to change his life and provide him with adventures in South and Central America.

The model engine found by Uville may have more significance than has so far been credited to it. The model's performance and Uville's travels have usually been simply dismissed. Uville was a watchmaker, the same as William West the probable maker of the engine, so his attention would have been drawn to what some people might have only considered to be no more than a toy. John Farey[569] mentions that a model of Trevithick's 1804 Penydarren locomotive was offered for sale in the window of Mr Rowley's shop in Cleveland Street, London, in 1806. This was probably the Rowley who was reported as manufacturing Trevithick engines (see page 221) and is the only reference apparently made to the engine being described as a locomotive. It is interesting that Uville would have been able to link the operation of a steam locomotive model to his requirement for a pump; something he hitherto believed looked like a Watt beam engine. Maybe he discussed it with Mr Rowley and so ascertained the purpose of the engine and the name of the inventor.

Uville claimed he had found some of the richest mines in Peru falling into decay.[570] Some years later serious doubts were expressed over the ownership of the Cerro de Pasco mines and the Peruvian Mining Company was forced into liquidation. Abradia's home and property were sold on the spot and he was outlawed. Vivez was banished from South America and his property confiscated. The shares purchased by the clients of Messrs Dubois & Co. were said to be 'not worth a farthing'.[571]

Silver at the great mines of Yaurichoca, more commonly known as the mines of Pasco, was reputably discovered by an Indian in 1630 and were described as producing £400,000 of silver annually.[572] Stories of these rich silver mines abounded and it was reported that during 1819 two steam engines were installed at 13,000 feet by an Englishman who did not find wood for fuel but two seams of coal.[573] Production of silver was reported as 'enormous, and continued so until the occupation of that sierra by the patriot troops, under General Arenales'.[574] A Major Hinde, who served under Arenales, wrote in 1820/1 that he 'actually had under my escort twenty mules, each laden with 250lbs of silver, the produce of the mines, which had been drained by steam engines'.[575] Hindes omitted to say what happened to the silver.

Peruvian silver and gold mines continued to operate and silver became so plentiful that it lost much of its value, being used for knives and other metal implements. The people of the region had little or no idea of money and market forces, their social anthropology was based mainly on reciprocity so the hoarding of silver meant little to them. Europeans had other ideas and, driven by greed 'a party of 40 Welch and Cornish miners and engineers embarked from Falmouth in 1825 aboard the *Ariga* for Valparaiso'.[576]

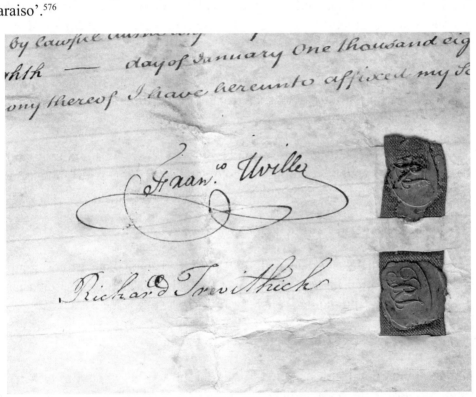

Signatures of Richard Trevithick and Francisco Uville, and seals, on the original agreement for Trevithick's engines to go to Peru. The document is in English and Spanish, on velum. Trevithick Society document, Cornwall Record Office.

There was a great deal of excitement connected to South America's precious metals and many companies were formed with London offices. For instance, the Pasco Peruvian Co. was formed in 1826 with a share capital of £1million with £150,000 paid up in £100 shares. Within three years the company had ceased to exist.

We should not go on without describing something of the voyages experienced by Uville, Trevithick, their engineers and many landlubbers. For this, we turn to Edward John Trelawny of Pelynt, 1792 – 1881, a contemporary Cornishman with a noble background connected to Sir Jonathan Trelawny, Bishop of Bristol, who petitioned against James II's Declaration of Indulgence and was subsequently imprisoned in the Tower of London. John was also a descendant of the God-fearing John Hawkins who was reported as having the doubtful honour of being the first Englishman to engage in the slave trade.[577]

Edward's mother, formerly Maria Hawkins, was sister to Sir Christopher Hawkins of Trewithen, who ordered a steam threshing machine from Trevithick. The progressive Hawkins family brought the first coach to be seen in West Cornwall, "rattling along at a rate of three miles per hour, and riding thus with their cavalcade of belles and beaux, they doubtless thought themselves as grand as Solomon and the Queen of Sheba – till they stuck fast in some hole".[578]

John's father was Charles Bereton Trelawny who packed him off into the navy at an early age thus enabling him to give us an account of his experiences there and later as a privateer. Following Trafalgar he says,

> The food was still vile – biscuits, dusty with weevils and wriggling with maggots; water "revolting in color and swarming with putrescent life", during a long voyage rats became a high prized delicacy.[579]

Later Trelawny describes the Borneo rat as:

> Long-bodied, short-legged, sleek-skinned and fine eared, that when split open, sprinkled with pepper and salt and nicely broiled furnished a salubrious and piquant relish for breakfast.[580]

So much for maritime travel in the early nineteenth century.

With the equipment finally despatched Trevithick turned his attention to his plunger pole engine. During the past eighteen months Trevithick had become thoroughly involved with his new friend Rastrick, with whom he had developed a strong rapport. At the same time he had shown gross insensitivity to the immediate members of his family, his brother-in-law, Henry Harvey and his cousin Andrew Vivian.

Vivian had been with Trevithick from the very beginning, encouraging him in his ideas, helping him with the intricacies of engineering, investing in his inventions and filing their joint patents. He always stood as a strong link between Trevithick and his family at home and, as his cousin, occasionally reaped the riches from his inventions but he received no reward for all his care, support and hard work. It would not be surprising if he were to lose some of the enthusiasm he had developed for his cousin's activities.

Henry Harvey had also supported Trevithick, not only because he was his brother-in-law but because he was the designer of many of the items Henry had manufactured. Henry was a shrewd and accomplished industrialist who had been a pillar of support to the Trevithick family during times of disaster and given him much technical advice. Both he and Vivian must have felt hurt when Trevithick tactlessly ignored them at what he proclaimed was his moment of glory and showered the fortunes of his enterprise on Rastrick and others. Why did Trevithick do this?

Trevithick had found in Rastrick a friend who apparently understood him and saw things his way without argument or a stream of advice that he should change his ways. Trevithick could relax when communicating with Rastrick in a way he found difficult with other people. Let us look at some of his letters to Rastrick. Here he is replying to a number of queries from Rastrick.

> My reason for making the forcing pump with duck-valves is, because they do not bum like the others, and we find them seldom out of repair; but make it whichever way you think best, and work it in any way you like.[581]

And, in answer to query number twelve,

> … I wish you to write a form of an order, in your next, such as you wish, and I will get him to write to you accordingly. Put the engine and drum for Lord de Dunstanville out of hand neat and well, as it will be well paid for; and make the stands, &c., in your own way.

This relaxed attitude to specification is quite remarkable and reveals the absolute faith Trevithick had in Rastrick's ability to interpret his mind and produce a competent engine suitable for its purpose, even for one of Trevithick's wealthiest benefactors. This relationship must have been so different from that Trevithick had with the fastidious Henry Harvey who would have demanded actual dimensions for all the components. It would account for Trevithick turning to Bridgnorth for much of his work. Throughout his life Trevithick had to explain his new technology and to give instructions to people who had never seen a steam engine. It must have been a great relief to him to find someone who fully understood his precious puffer engines, was willing to work with him and sort out his problems. So strong was Trevithick's implicit faith in his friend's ability to read his mind that the tone of his letter would cause a concerned reader today to wonder what medication he was taking.

In another letter to Rastrick, Trevithick explains some changes he has had to make in the allocation of his engines. He does this knowing that he will not be criticised at Bridgnorth as he might have been in Cornwall.

The ploughing engine that I sent you the drawing for, after being used for that purpose, was to have been sent to Exeter for pumping water. I have been obliged to take the small portable engine from Wheal Alfred Mine, and have a new apparatus fitted to it for Plymouth Breakwater. A small engine which I had at work at a mine I have been obliged to send to the farmers for threshing.[582]

While these instructions reveal the versatility of the engine, Rastrick must have been bewildered at times but he was obviously patient and went along with the machinations of his friend; it was good for his business.

Screw propulsion

Trevithick returned to some ideas he had about maritime propulsion and worked on a wheel that was set with a number of steam emitting jets. This 'werling engine' is reputed to have turned at 300 revolutions per minute but nobody showed any interest so he patented it and went off to design the earliest ships' propeller, similar to an Archimedean screw. He sought Gilbert's advice on the matter of screw sizes and received the following intricate reply,

> ...If you are disposed to try various sizes of these screws, moving with different velocities, you must recollect that the propelling zone, with the new screw, increases as the squares of the number of revolutions in a given time; and that supposing velocities of rotation (that is, the number of revolutions in a given time) to be the same in different screws, the propelling zone will vary as the 4th power, or as the square squared, of the diameter; or thus, suppose D = the diameter and N = the number of revolutions in a minute of one of the screws, D = the diameter, and N = the number of revolutions in a minute of the other screws. Then will their propelling power be to each other in the proportion $D^4 \times N^2$ to $d^4 \times n^2$.

> The reason why no limit can theoretically be put to the velocity most advantageous for the propelling screw is this, the faster it goes, the less the loss will be, occasioned by the motion of the vessel through the water.

> The centre of propulsion (as it may be termed) is distant from the centre of the screw (supposing the radius one) $1\sqrt{2}$; that is, if a square piece, equal in size to the triangular vane $\triangle$, were to move with the same inclination and the velocity which the vane has, or $1\sqrt{2}$ (or about c), their effect would be equal. Suppose now, two vessels moving at the same rate through the water, each propelled by screws, one large, and moving so that the centre of propulsion has a velocity double to that of the vessel; the other smaller,

246

but moving with a velocity ten times that of the vessel. In the first one, three parts out of four of the power will be lost; in the second only nineteen out of a hundred. Not one fifth.[583]

This passage is remarkable because it was written at the very beginning of exploration into the modern screw propulsion. It reveals the quality of Gilbert's comprehension of the latest technology, something that he clearly wished Trevithick to appreciate, something he knew he would not entirely understand and so would enable Gilbert to keep them academically apart. It would be another twenty-one years before Sir Francis Petit Smith, 1808 – 1874, in this country and John Ericsson, 1803-1889, in Sweden obtained separate patents for the screw as we know it and their success caused Brunel to adopt the latest technology and change his intended designs for the s.s. *Great Britain* from paddles to a single screw.

News from Peru

All this was going on whilst the *Wildman* was en route to Lima. Trevithick received the news of its arrival and 12,000 dollars with considerable relief.

> Aboute a fortnight since, I recd Letters from Lima, and also letters to the friends of the men who sail'd with the engines. They arrived the 29 Jany after a very good passage and withoute one hour's sick-ness. Both theirs and my agreements was immid'ly ratifyde and they are in big spirits. The ship finish'd dissg the 11 Feby which was the day these letters sail'd from Lima with 12000 Dollars for me which is all arrived save. I shall make another fit oute for them immidly. I expect that all the engines will be at work before the end of October. Half of them must be at work before this time.

We again see the usual Trevithick enthusiasm that was probably not shared by those in Lima. The engineers and their helpers faced a tremendous climb up crude, dangerous mule tracks to the silver mines. So important was the development of these mines to the Peruvian economy that its government ordered all possible funding should be made available together with the services of three thousand mules and four thousand Indians.

The story of the horrendous ascent to Cerro de Pasco at Lauricocha in Tarma province is well documented by Anthony Burton[584] and is recommended reading. It is clear that the outcome of the adventure was satisfactory to the Peruvians and there were reports of torrents of silver and coins being struck in their thousands. All this inspired Trevithick to report that the mines were proving to be richer than had been anticipated and that he looked forward to 'dollars and work plenty'.

However, like all good things, this was not to last and reports came back of problems with the machinery. Trevithick immediately knew what had to be done but the delay incurred when sending messages over such a distance meant months of inactivity at the mine, hungry mouths to be fed, disenchanted mine owners and a lack of financial return for Trevithick. It was clear to him that to maintain the engines in good running order and protect his investment he would have to go to Peru.

Wheal Herland

In the meantime Trevithick had been continuing with his development work on the plunger pole engine for Wheal Herland. He was confident that his new improvement to the steam engine would prove a great success but was bitterly disappointed when the parts from the Bridgnorth foundry did not fit each other. This was due to Rastrick being away constructing the iron bridge across the Wye at Chepstow. Trevithick had highs and lows throughout his life and shared them with everyone.

Trevithick's letters to Rastrick from Penzance were businesslike and to the point. While the originals, before attention from Francis, may have lacked some of their venom because of the manner in which they were written, there is no doubt that Trevithick was well able to express his unhappy feelings. He was well aware that, in Rastrick, he was writing to a friend he did not wish to offend and so addressed the letter generally to the company, Hazeldine, Rastrick & Co, as 'Gentlemen'.

> Gentlemen,
> I have received the Herland castings, and am very seriously sorry to say, after we had fixed together the castings on the mine and made the joints, on attempting to put the plunger- pole into the case it would not go down; neither would either of the rings go to their places into the cylinder and on to the pole; therefore the whole engine must be again taken to pieces and sent to a turning and boring mill to be newly turned and bored. How to get this done I cannot tell, for the founders here will not do it because they had not the casting them. Already great expenses have been incurred by delays, and now to send them back to Bridgenorth at an immense loss of time and money will be a very serious business indeed. I think that either the cylinder is bored crooked or the plunger-pole turned crooked, or both, as it will sink farther down into the cylinder on turning it round on one side than it will on the other. The whole job is most shamefully fitted up, and was never tried together before sent off. Write to me by return of post and say what I am to do in this dilemma.[585]

At Wheal Herland we have an example of Trevithick's relations with his family members when they were also his engineers and suppliers. His original intention had been to erect a plunger pole pumping engine at the mine. In this he may not have had the full agreement of the adventurers to erect the engine but, as many were kin, he reckoned that they should acquiesce to his wishes and what he considered was his better judgement.

Francis said of the situation,

> Scarcely had he smoothed the way with one opponent than another sprung up in an unexpected quarter. His brother-in-law, Harvey, with his once friend, Andrew Vivian, then a partner with Harvey, opposed his plans at the Herland. They were annoyed at Trevithick's sending his orders for castings and machinery to Bridgenorth, and may have had doubts of the success of the new inventions. They had authority in the mine, probably as shareholders, a position generally acquired in Cornwall by those who supply necessary mine material, as well as by the smelters who buy the mineral from the mines. The Williamses and Foxes, controlling the eastern district of mines, were also shareholders and managers, supplying machinery and buying the mine produce.[586]

Here we see Trevithick at his schemy* best. He had a new engine that he fervently wished to see brought to completion but people were trying to thwart him and present him with all manner of problems. He was determined to get his own way by one means or another. He revealed a part of his wily nature by writing to a merchant and printer, James Phillips, 1775 – 1829, at 2 George Yard, Lombard Street to express his concern about matters at the Herland mine and the refusal of Perran Foundry to make parts for him. In doing this he was addressing a well-known and established member of the Society of Friends (Quakers) who was of the same persuasion as the Fox family, part owners of the foundry. We are used to seeing Trevithick going straight to the fountain head when there were matters to be resolved but this revealed his capacity to approach more subtly. On the other hand, Trevithick may have known that Phillips could well have been that fountain head and had a financial interest in the foundry. Francis said that Phillips was the financial manager of the mine.[587] Trevithick knew that a suitable word in his ear about the possibility of placing orders elsewhere may have been more effective than a row with the Foxes. He said,

> Yesterday I was at Herland, where I was informed that Captain Andrew Vivian had been the day before, on his return from Mr. Harvey's, and discharged all the men on the mine, without giving them a moment's notice. Before the arrival of the castings the pitmen, sumpmen, carpenters,

* Cornish dialect word for plotting

and smiths were very busy getting the pit-work ready; at which time H. Harvey and A. Vivian were exulting in reporting that the iron ore was not yet raised that was to make the Herland castings. The day that they heard of their arrival they discharged all the labourers, and ordered the agents not to admit another sixpence-worth of materials on the adventurers' account, or employ any person whatever.

The agents sent a short time since to Perran Foundry for the iron saddles and brasses belonging to the balance-bob, the property of the adventurers; but they refused to make them, with a great deal of ill-natured language about my engine.

I am determined to fulfil my engagement with the adventurers, and yesterday ordered all the smiths, carpenters, pit-men, and sumpmen to prepare the adventurers' pit-work, and ordered the agents to get the balance-bob and every other thing that may be wanted at my expense, so as to fork the first lift, which I hope to have dry by Monday three weeks. The engine will be in the mine this week, and in one fortnight after I hope the engine will be at work, and in less than a week more the first twenty fathoms under the adit will be dry.

In consequence of the Perran people refusing to send the saddles and brasses for the balance-bob, we will make shift in the best way we can without them. The brasses I have ordered on my own account at Mr. Scantlebury's. The coals for the smiths I have also ordered, and the same for the engine to fork the first lift. This is very uncivil treatment in return for inventing and bringing to the public, at my own risk and expense, what I believe the country could not exist without. I am determined to erect the engine at all events and upset this coalition before I leave Europe, if it detains me one year to accomplish it.[588]

While this letter has been tidied by Francis we see Trevithick using all the tactful wile and strategy one would expect in a business letter where the objective is to express one's dissatisfaction of a business acquaintance to someone who was in the right position to influence a favourable outcome. Firstly, Trevithick was using Rastrick and Perran Foundry to make parts for his plunger pole engine just at the time when he is at odds with those at Hayle and is shortly to be leaving for the southern hemisphere. It is a stressful time. We don't know all his problems at Hayle but must expect that, to add to them, Perran Foundry was likely to be wary about Trevithick's credit rating.

By writing to James Phillips in the City of London, Trevithick was involving one of the country's leading Quakers. The Phillips family in George Yard were the current family responsible for the printing and distribution of a great number of Quaker pamphlets. Here is a strong religious connection to Perran Foundry in the country's financial system. The Foxes were a powerful Quaker family in the district and established the foundry in 1791. They had the previously mentioned shipping interests in Falmouth. Clearly, Trevithick knew that James Phillips, to whom he was writing, had Cornish roots, having been born at Trewirgie, Redruth in 1745. James's mother had died whilst giving birth to him and he had been brought up by his stepmother, formerly Catherine Payton, a devoted Quaker.

James had other printing interests and by the end of the American Revolution was conducting both national and international business. He had an elder brother Richard who was engaged in the family's mining business. James was a powerful businessman with a connection to a Quaker called Richard Reynolds who married the daughter of Quaker Abraham Darby III, 1750 – 1791, and later became the manager of Darby's booming iron works at Coalbrookdale. Reynolds was also a secret philanthropist who gave away more than £100,000 through James Phillips, his 'active agent', during his lifetime.

The story becomes even more complicated with the abolition of the slavery and the involvement of the very active Quaker and apothecary William Cookworthy of Devon, 1705 – 1780, who was well-known for having discovered 'China Earth' in Cornwall and developing the manufacture of porcelain. He also had estates in Cornwall and a factory in Plymouth. We can see from all this that Trevithick clearly knew of the personalities with whom he was dealing and was aware that by approaching someone as influential as Phillips, he was tweaking the tiger's tail and likely to get his way at Perran foundry.[589]

Trevithick got his way and the parts he needed. Soon his men were assembling the engine and we are grateful to have an admirable eyewitness account of what happened at Herland.

> I was a boy working in the mine, and several of us peeped in at the door to see what was doing. Captain Dick was in a great way, the engine would not start; after a bit Captain Dick threw himself down upon the floor of the engine-house, and there he lay upon his back; then up he jumped, and snatched a sledge-hammer out of the hands of a man who was driving a wedge, and lashed it home in a minute. There never was a man could use a sledge like Captain Dick; he was as strong as a bull. Then, he picked up a spanner and unscrewed something, and off she went. Captain Vivian was near me, looking in at the doorway; Captain Dick saw him, and shaking

his fist, said; "If you come in here I'll throw you down the shaft". I suppose Captain Vivian had something to do with the boilers, and Captain Dick was angry because they leaked clouds of steam. You could hardly see, or hear anybody speak in the engine-house, it was so full of steam and noise.[590]

It is unlikely that Trevithick realised the heartache he caused his cousin, something that brought about the breakdown in their relations from time to time.

We see this side of Trevithick occasionally and know that he was nobody's fool having the intelligence to negotiate reasonably at a sensible level. However, he seemed to use the skill sparingly and only to procure items for his engines. Furthermore, on these occasions his attention span was limited. Had he been able to sit down more often and discuss company development and financial matters this story might have been much different.

Eventually the engine went well and was proved to be efficient but the mine was disappointing and stories of leaking boilers did not benefit subsequent sales.

Off to Peru
Once he had resolved to make the journey determination set in, no amount of cheerful news would make him change his mind. He made all the arrangements for his departure. We have seen instances in the past where Trevithick had overlooked his and his family's welfare when pursuing a particular project or objective but this was different. This time the project was not the invention or development of a piece of machinery; it was a journey to far-off lands. So we see the departure planned as meticulously as a steam engine; Trevithick starts putting his affairs in order.

His current work on various inventions received particular attention. He adapted the plunger pole and existing Watt engines to work with new high-pressure boilers. Having assured himself that the engine was ready to provide an income for his family he sold half the patent to William Sims, a leading local engineer who was charged with care of the income. To raise cash he sold his interest in Wheal Francis and made the point that anyone seeking an independent report on the mine should not consult Andrew Vivian; their severance appeared complete.

Whilst Trevithick made many thoughtful arrangements for his family's welfare during his absence he was clearly working far outside his sphere and he was to leave many matters unfinished. He arranged for his family to move house to Penzance so that his children could be well educated. However, his assertion that he had paid a year's rent in advance proved incorrect when Jane received a rent demand after six months.

He similarly overlooked the necessity to pay the premiums on the insurances he had arranged for the family.

Journey to London

So intent was Trevithick on going to Peru that he gave the impression to a stranger seven months prior to his departure that he was already on his way. Mr Henry Woollcombe, 1778 – 1847, was a Plymouth solicitor described as the gentleman who founded the Plymouth Institution in 1812 and became mayor of the city the following year.

Woollcombe kept a diary of events in his life and he records that at nine o'clock on the evening of 27th April 1816 he left Plymouth aboard the open Mail coach. His companion on the fine night was silent between Chudleigh and Exeter and the spectacle of the burning hills did not serve to spark a conversation. They stopped for breakfast next morning at Exeter and set off again at five o'clock.

Eventually the stranger talked and Woollcombe discovered he was a Mr Trevithick who was 'about to forward to S. America to introduce into the silver mines there the most improved method used at present in working the mines in Cornwall'. Trevithick clearly impressed Woollcombe and explained how to spell both Trevithick and Uvillé [sic] as he has them carefully recorded in his diary. Trevithick had found a good listener willing to take noticc. The road between Exeter and Andover, where Woollcombe finishes his story, is over a hundred miles long. At a maximum of ten miles per hour Henry Woollcombe spent at least the next ten hours dutifully listening to Trevithick. He relates how he learnt about Mr Uville, whom Trevithick referred to as a Spaniard. Uville is recorded as having lived with Trevithick for some months and travelled with him around the mining districts of Cornwall and elsewhere. Woollcombe was to hear of his dreams and how, 'if the terms which Trevithick has made are duly observed and the produce is anything like what he calculated on; he must make a rapid fortune and … the introduction of machinery will so increase produce that they may well afford to give him a large share.' Woollcombe went on to relate that 'Trevithick apprehends this increase of silver will be chiefly exported in the purchase of British Manufactory'. Woollcombe was so impressed by Trevithick's intention to travel to Peru that he thought he was on the journey. Woollcombe explained that this information occupied the whole conversation to Andover and he ends by saying, 'I was fatigued and soon went to bed.'[591]

It is likely that one of Trevithick's reasons for this journey was to have his portrait painted by John Linnell. The half-length, 20″ x 24″, oil painting of him pointing to distant lands now hangs in the Science Museum and is frequently copied. Was Trevithick sufficiently confident to think something should be left of him for posterity or had he a premonition about his possible demise on the journey to the Americas?

Trevithick, with a small entourage that included Richard Page, the attorney who had drawn up the original agreement between Trevithick and Uville, sailed from Penzance aboard the *Asp,* another South Sea whaler, on the 20th October 1816, some two years after the despatch of the original engines and equipment.

Four months later Trevithick's arrival in Peru was met with considerable excitement and recorded in the *Lima Gazette* of 12th February 1817. The Peruvians saw this giant of a man, now known as Professor Don Ricardo Trevithick, as their salvation. He was not only to be saviour of the silver mines but also for the whole country's economy. Richard Hodge, a mine captain of considerable repute in West Cornwall was captain at Cerro de Pasco from 1819. He helped Trevithick and supplied Jane with news of events in Peru. He eventually returned to St Erth twenty years later.

The political welcome was no less than that of the mining community and the offer to build a commemorative statue in silver to this liberator must have impressed Trevithick. At last he was being acknowledged for his ability and importance, albeit by a race of little people who were quite foreign to him and with whom he could not converse. If, as a latter day Gulliver, he had to travel this far to have his abilities acknowledged, so be it. However, no matter how far Trevithick travelled he would never be far from trouble.

If Trevithick was flattered by this reception the pleasure was not to last as he discovered the state of the machinery and the power struggles where there was money to be made. Henry Vivian had died in May 1815[592] and Trevithick attributed the likely cause to be alcoholic poisoning. Francis does not provide us with any information how Henry's widow, Trevithick's sister Thomasina, was advised of the death or whether Trevithick sent her any letter of condolence. One would also have expected Trevithick to write to his cousin Andrew Vivian, Henry's brother, under the sad circumstances but relationships had broken down so we can only suppose Trevithick ignored the situation. Had he taken the opportunity, it is possible that he could have found appropriate grounds on which to repair their relationship. Would it have occurred to him?

We have a number of predictable letters from Trevithick that deal with technical and financial matters. As usual they are optimistic, such as,

> The Mint is the property of our company, and Government pays us for coining, which gives us an immense income.

There is an unusual letter that includes something by way of an anecdote about life in Peru. That is until one realises the letter would not have been written had it not been in connection with a search for a watercourse to power the Mint. Officials had failed to gain entry to a nunnery but as usual Trevithick saw no problem.

> I walked up and knocked, in my blunt way, at the nunnery court door, *without knowing there were any objections to admit;* it was opened by a female slave, to whom the interpreter told my name and business. … very soon we were ordered to walk in, and all further nunnery nonsense was done away with.[593.]

This letter is probably the only indication we have that Trevithick appreciated he had a blunt nature although he must have been told this frequently by his nearest and dearest. Anthony Burton sums up Trevithick's attitude as follows.

> He was a good deal less well adapted to cope with the convoluted dealings of human affairs. There was a pleasing directness about the man. He said exactly what he thought, and meant what he said. Sadly, such direct honesty too often arrives with a certain naivety, an assumption that others act in the same way.[594]

Trevithick had assumed that his job was to reinstate the machinery to working order and this he did without finding problems he could not overcome. He showed his remarkable ability to run the mine but this was not to the liking of Page or Uville. The latter now saw himself as the mine operator and opposed Trevithick's interference. In spite of his achievements Trevithick found himself blamed for gross mismanagement. His reaction was predictable; he lost his temper and walked off the site to seek employment elsewhere in the Andes. One Peruvian director called Abadia, who was prepared to stand by Trevithick, offered him $8,000 a year to stay but reported his reply as,

> On no conditions would he consent to contend with the jealousies and ill-treatment of the persons with whom he had to deal.

Trevithick travelled through many mining districts and saw several areas that would have provided a good return on mining ventures had there been capital to exploit them. News reached him that both Uville and Bull had died. With Uville out of the way Abadia was able to reinstate Trevithick in full control but he still had to contend with Page who attempted to stir up trouble with the shareholders in London.

Trevithick found he had strong support from a source he had probably not considered. His wife, Jane, came to his defence as she wrote to the shareholders and set right the malicious rumours being put about by Page. Her letter reveals Jane as a determined lady who was quite capable of running both a family and a business, often under the greatest stress. Jane's supportive part in the development of early powered engineering has never been told but it was clearly substantial.

Page had been shamed and Trevithick, with Abadia's blessing, was in charge of the flourishing silver mines at Cerro de Pasco. He was also receiving a share of the profits from the Mint and all was well.

As so often happened to Trevithick, his moments of good fortune were few and short-lived; this was to be no different. The Spanish, who controlled Peru at the time had tended to take their responsibilities apathetically and were prey to Bolivar's men. They ransacked the wealthy mines of Cerro de Pasco and were followed by the Spanish who did the same thing. [595] Trevithick found himself in the midst of a very confusing situation and lost a fortune in silver. He subsequently lost 300 tons of ore destined for England. Burton mentions a Cornish miner who returned home in about 1830 claiming back pay for guarding Trevithick's ore. No one had turned up to claim it so he came home and left it.[596] Remember Major Hinde, who had twenty mules, each laden with 250lbs of silver.[597]

The story of the silver that attracted Trevithick to Peru is one of greed. While Trevithick inevitably saw the rich pickings he knew he rightly deserved, he was also driven by the vision of Peruvian money being spent in the purchase of more mining and other machinery in England.

With no work and his fortune stolen, he travelled 'south into the wild regions of Chile to mine copper and then, after six years of rough and dangerous living, he wandered north along the western coast of South America'.[598] We turn to Burton again for an explanation of Trevithick's various exploits in the countries along the Pacific coast, his adventures with Bolivar and his wasted days of pearl fishing. He had made a great deal of money by salvaging the frigate *San Martin* but instead of sending a much needed £1,000 home to his wife, he invested it all, and lost it.[599] Burton suggests that Richard Hodge told him to send £2,000 back to Jane[600] but as he later explained to his wife, 'You see my dear, I thought of you. I wanted you to be the richest woman in Cornwall, and so I bought an interest in a pearl fishery. I thought it was certain to double the money. It didn't work. That ended the fortune'.[601]

The possession of silver and gold was seen by the Europeans as a path to wealth and access to all it would bring. Little thought was given to how a great deal of money in a poor country could provide the pleasures it would have done elsewhere. Once a mine owner had spent a lot of money on the construction of his lavish home there was little on which to spend it. Too much money chasing too few goods generates inflation. Without going into the details of the financial debt crises that all too frequently hits the apparently rich nations it is interesting to note that by 1826 Peru was one of six Latin and South American nations to default on major loans issued in London just a few years earlier.[602]

256

We now know enough about Trevithick's attitude when faced by certain situations to realise that he would rise to any occasion and the links between his various adventures were influenced by his instant decisions. There is well-known advice to stop digging when at the bottom of a pit. Burton explains that this was seldom Trevithick's approach and he would accept another challenge to make a fortune in preference to a journey home followed by a comfortable lifestyle.

Trevithick planned a public steam railway in Peru from Lima to Callao in 1817. Had he raised the capital the world's first passenger railway would have run in Peru instead of England.[603]

Whilst Trevithick busied himself with his projects it is unlikely that he gave much thought to his family and friends in Cornwall. He frequently sent letters to England and news of his exploits filtered home to Jane. But it is very difficult to find Trevithick showing any concern for his wife or growing family. Rumours about his activities in South America and especially one that he had another family there, lost him a few of his remaining friends but Davies Gilbert remained steadfast, although he sent him a stern letter about the way in which he had apparently deserted his faithful wife and family.

Jane again came to his aid at this crucial time, writing to the shareholders of the company formed in London to fund the developments in Peru and assuring them of his steadfast devotion to her and his family. Jane would have known more about her husband's proclivities in that direction than anyone. Had Trevithick been inclined to wander from his marriage it is likely that he would have done so with such enthusiasm and openness that, like Mozart, it would have become a feature of his life that even Francis could not have concealed.

Trevithick teamed up with a Scotsman called James Gerard at Guayaquil in Ecuador.[604] Gerard had been trading along the Pacific coast but his boat had been wrecked and he told Trevithick in 1822 of rich gold deposits in Costa Rica[605] so they headed north. Burton tells us that Trevithick's subsequent association with the Montelegres in Costa Rica may have sparked the rumours about his personal life. They were the parents of two young lads, José Mariá and Mariano. The trusting Montelegres were wealthy coffee plantation owners[606] and descendants from the Conquistadors[607] who allowed their boys to travel from Costa Rica in the company of two hitherto unknown English engineers in order to receive an education in England. The youngsters would spend weeks trekking through jungles and over mountains, white water rafting, taking their chances with bandits and wild animals. Francis tells us that they also contacted measles on the journey to add to their woes; life with Trevithick was seldom dull.

The lads survived, José Mariá, 1815 – 1887, studied in Scotland to become a doctor and returned to serve Costa Rica as its President, 1859 – 1863, while his brother studied engineering in England and a descendant, Felicia Montelegre married Leonard Bernstein of West Side Story fame. Before his return to Costa Rica, Mrs Robert Stephenson, George's daughter-in-law, presented José Mariá in November 1839, with a copy of *Drawings of the London & Birmingham Railway* by J. C. Bourne, 'as a memento of esteem and regards from a sincere friend'.[608] José Mariá had clearly infiltrated Stephenson family life more deeply than Trevithick ever did. Was this episode with the Montelegres a typical example of Trevithick's many contributions to the life and well being of others without gaining any benefit or acknowledgement for himself?

Jane wrote to Davies Gilbert from Penzance on 4th May 1819. We have little of Jane's handwriting but this was immaculate, spelling and grammar excellent and her style was sophisticated and erudite. It reveals her respect for Gilbert, the level of her education and it can be compared with that of her father, page 159. She said:

> I feel the greatest anxiety respecting my husband and trust you will excuse the liberty I take in inclosing the letter for Mr. Abadia to you to ask your advice whether my addressing him as I have done is improper – Should you approve of it and would do me the great kindnefs to add a few lines to that Gent[n] in my behalf to give it the greater weight I should feel the greatest obligation. The South Whaler will shortly sail and you would further oblige me by …[609]

It is not known whether the letter to Mr Abadia ever reached him or if it arrived in time to influence his relationship with Trevithick. Whatever happened, Trevithick was off on his adventures in South America. Jane's plight caused Davies Gilbert to write a lengthy letter to Trevithick in the strongest terms; it reveals something of his opinion of Trevithick's personality,

> Although many years have now elapsed since any direct communications have reached me from you, or since those who had much stronger reasons for hoping that you would not neglect to inform them at least of your proceedings, have known anything about them: yet I entertain a firm opinion of your still continuing the same honest, thoughtless, careless man that I ever knew you …

Gilbert also wrote to a Mr Mal MacGregor, the British Consul at Panama who replied to say that he had not met Mr Trevithick but had forwarded the letter to the coast of Guatemala 'where Mr Trevithick has his establishment'. He states,

> From the present disorganised state of Guatemala, I fear, Mr T's Mining

Aspirations will be much impeded – I think until Order & Regularity are established under Governments <u>capable</u> of affording the protection of Laws; it will be in vain for any Individual, or Body, however enterprising he, or they, maybe, I hope for succefs in any Undertaking in these New States ...[610]

There are several Guatemalas. We understand Trevithick was in Costa Rica for four years.[611] If MacGregor was referring to the Guatemala on the Pacific coast of Costa Rica it was some 450 miles from Panama. But, if it was a country as described by

Letter from Jane to Gilbert, dated May 4th 1819, referring to Abadia.
Courtney Library, Royal Institution of Cornwall, Truro

Map of Central America showing the countries and distances involved in Trevithick's untold travels.

MacGregor, it bordered Mexico, 800 miles away. Wherever it was, Trevithick was clearly on the move. Eventually circumstances prevailed and he set out for home. Again, we refer to Burton's account of the adventures that brought our party to Cartagena de Indias on the coast of Columbia. This is one of those instances where Francis's account of what happened or his geography seems woefully amiss. He said that Trevithick's party arrived at San Juan de Nicaragua (Greytown) and that they took a small boat to one of the West Indian islands.[612] San Juan is on the Pacific side of Nicaragua. In addition to their exploits in the jungles and mountains of Central America, they probably sailed across the Caribbean Sea to Cartagena, the alternative would have been a very long walk around. Further east they came across the River Magdalena and one of Francis exciting reports about his father's adventures.

Trevithick and the alligator
While we should not hesitate to castigate Smiles and subsequent imaginative writers for their corruption of the truth, few conquer the dizzy heights of embellishment attained by Francis when writing adventure stories connected to his father.

There was undoubtedly an incident with a boat on a South American river; Francis has succeeded in turning it into an adventure that will be quoted for years to come.

Not being one to omit a story that will make a book popular, the trusting Gavin Weightman has, in the manner of a true historian, returned to the original source for a quotation in connection with Trevithick's well known adventure with an alligator. He has not adorned the story in any way; it is more than sufficient as it is. He may have been concerned that Francis produced the only account of the incident in history, but it was too good a story to dismiss.

> Mr Trevithick had been upset at the mouth of the River Magdalena by a black man he had in some way offended, and who capsized the boat in revenge. An officer of the Venezuelan and Peruvian services was fortunately nigh the banks of the river, shooting wild pigs. He heard Mr Trevithick's cries for help, and seeing a large alligator approaching him, shot him in the eye, and then, as he had no boat, lassoed Mr Trevithick, and by his lasso drew him ashore and much exhausted and all but dead.

> It turned out that the Venezuelan officer was in fact British. He got Trevithick back to Cartagena where they found a fellow engineer whom Trevithick, as if in a dream, addressed cordially as 'Bobby'.[613]

Maybe Francis was led astray in his description of his father's adventure because the letter he may have read is apparently in the Enys Papers. Firstly, the officer with the gun was identified by James Fairbairn as a Mr Bruce Napier Hall of Carlisle[614] and Hall identified the River Magdalena in a letter[615] to Edward Watkin of December 1864. This mighty river is nearly a thousand miles long and is several miles wide at its mouth. Trevithick, accompanied by his three companions was close enough to one shore for the offended black man to overturn his boat. Had the officer with the gun been on the same side of the river he would not have required a boat to go to his aid so we are left with the impression that he was on the other side of the river, a formidable distance to shoot an alligator in the eye or throw a lasso. The armed officer of the Venezuelan and Peruvian army was a little off track in Columbia. Venezuela is a very long way from Peru, there are two large countries, Columbia and, to some extent, Ecuador, in between. These South American countries have a history of notorious border clashes; it is very unlikely that an officer would officially serve more than one country unless he was a mercenary. Vale said he was serving in Bolivar's army.[616] The Magdalena River is tidal for many miles; American alligators usually live in freshwater swamps. Unfortunately, Francis and the subsequent story tellers all omit to tell us how Trevithick's three companions survived the allegedly alligator infested waters but we know they eventually arrived at Cartagena. As the River Magdalena is some 60 miles, Vale said 100, east of their destination of Cartagena, one has to wonder why they were trying to cross it; but that mystery is not for these pages.

The unpleasant peccary or skunk pig was indigenous in the region at the time but we should remember that Francis spent a lot of his life as a sportsman with a gun and wonder if that part of the story is based more on his reflections than the fauna of South America.

In a story full of improbabilities we now have a coincidence that the writer of any soap opera would reject. As third parties are involved we have no reason to question what appears to be a most unlikely twist of fate. On their arrival at the Gulf of Darién by the southern Caribbean Sea, Trevithick's bedraggled group met Robert Stephenson, son of George, who had just completed his contract with the Columbian Mining Company. It was not reported to be a cordial meeting but the young Stephenson contributed £50 towards Trevithick's return home. It is very unlikely that they all embarked for England via New York as Samuel Smiles records.[617] Gilbert recounted the homecoming of the prodigal in a letter to his daughter Kitty, 'I must add that last Tuesday [*i.e.*, October 9th] Captn Richard Trevithick … during the whole of which he has not held any communication whatever with his family, arrived suddenly at Hayle'.[618]

James Gerard set off with Stephenson and the two Montelegre lads for New York aboard the brig the *Bunker Hill*. The ship was wrecked soon after departure but they survived and, after reaching New York, made for Canada as Stephenson wished to see the Niagara Falls. Gerard reached Liverpool with the two lads in November 1827[619] but was 'short of the needful' as he tells Trevithick.

Trevithick had landed in October 1827 after an uneventful passage of just forty days travel during which he transferred to the regular Falmouth Packet from Jamaica. His arrival was a mere month earlier than Gerard. Just what happened to the money from Stephenson is not recorded; neither will we know just how long he had dallied before leaving Cartagena. It is thought that either someone else paid for his passage.[620] or, more likely as Francis tells us, having discussed the matter with his father on his return, that the fare was never paid and he was assisted to jump ship on arrival at Falmouth by a friend on board.

We can guess that the ship owner was chasing his errant passenger for his fare and that Trevithick apparently intended to pay. In January 1828, Trevithick wrote to Gerard to say that he wanted to draw £100 from the company to pay the £70 passage and have £30 left over for his expenses in London. He was clearly unable to understand why the bankers would not honour the cheque, probably because there was no money in the account. The Ships List gives the cost of a fare with provisions from the West Indies to London at between £10 and £30.[621]

Elsewhere in the same letter to Gerard, Trevithick says,

Yesterday I saw Mr. M. Williams, who informed me that he should leave Cornwall for London on next Thursday week, and requested that I would accompany him. If you think it absolutely necessary that I should be in town at the same time, I would attend to everything that would promote the mining interest. When I met the Messrs. Williams on the mining concerns some time since, they mentioned the same as you now mention of sending some one out with me to inspect the mines, and that they would pay me my expenses and also satisfy me for my trouble with any sum that I would mention, because such proceedings would be satisfactory to all who might be connected in this concern. I objected to this proposal on the ground that a great deal of time would be lost and that the circumstances of your contracts in San Jose would not admit of such a detention; for that reason alone was my objection grounded, and if that objection could have been removed I should have been very glad to have the mines inspected by any able person chosen for that purpose, because it would not only take off the responsibility from us, but also strengthen our reports, as the mining prospects there will bear it out, and that far beyond our report.[622]

Greed clearly replaces good sense when listening to Trevithick's convincing tales of South American fortune. This letter suggests that Michael Williams had offered to pay Trevithick's expenses and fees on a voyage to South America to develop the mines. Trevithick had turned down the offer on the grounds that it would waste time and be contrary to arrangements that Gerard had made in San Jose; so another opportunity was ground into the dust. Later, Williams told one of Francis' brothers of an offer of £8,000 from some of his friends for Trevithick's interest in the copper mines in South America. Trevithick had refused. When asked by Williams why he did not pocket the £8,000 before refusing he replied that he would rather have kicked those concerned down the stairs. Another opportunity was gone; a pity that Jane was not present during this exchange, the prospect of £8,000 after her privations during the previous eleven years would have been very attractive. At today's Retail Price Index values that £8,000 would have been about £600,000.[623]

During those eleven years of absence, Jane had been steadfast in her devotion to her family and tried to obtain the dues owed to her from the contracts on the plunger pole engine. Few mine owners paid and it was for her brother, Henry, to come to the aid of his in-laws again when, in 1824, he built the White Hart Hotel in Hayle and set her up as its keeper. She stayed at the hotel until she retired in 1837 and it was taken over by William Crotch. This suited both Henry and his sister well as it provided her with an income and his company and Hayle with accommodation for business visitors.

263

Homecoming

There was no sign that his adventures in South America had changed Trevithick's attitude to those about him. Francis says he returned after eleven years' absence without a word as though it had been but a week. He expected to be able to sell mine shares and collect his dues on the £500,000 he estimated the Cornish mine owners had saved by virtue of using his plunger pole engine. Little came of these hopes but Trevithick was far from disappointed. He continued to invent things that nobody seemed to want. His gunnery and maritime experiences came together to design a remarkably easy-to-load gun for the Royal Navy but the Admiralty rejected it. Simply, the recoil action drove the gun up a ramp where the rear wheels remained until barred forward after the gun had been reloaded. This meant that a gun crew could be reduced from nine to two. A wrought iron ship driven by steam, as later built by Brunel, also received the same short treatment from the conservative Admiralty. Trevithick's mind was still on the reserves of silver he had left behind in South America. His way of life had provided him with knowledge and experience. These enabled his ideas and inventions to flow faster than ever. He was also sure that he was the only man capable of unleashing the wealth awaiting him in the South American silver mines.

One has to compare Trevithick's refusal of £8,000 for something on which he was unlikely to capitalise with just £200 he received from William Sims in 1815 for a half share of his patent on the plunger pole engine.

Needing money, Trevithick visited John Williams at Scorrier House on 31st October 1827 and was told that his patent had expired. Trevithick then did something wise and out of character by asking Richard Edmunds, his solicitor to write to John Williams in November pointing out that the patent would not expire for a further two and a half years. Trevithick called again at Scorrier to seek his dues on the plunger pole engine. Next day he wrote to Edmunds,

> Yesterday I called on Mr [John] Williams, and after a long dispute brought the old man to agree to pay me 150*l.* on giving him an indemnification in full from all demands on Treskerby and Wheal Chance Mines in future. He requested that you should make out this indemnification. I could not possibly get them to pay more, thought it most prudent to accept their offer rather than risk a law suit with them.[624]

There is a discrepancy here and whether the problem lies with Richard Edmunds or the Williams is not clear. Michael Williams of Scorrier recalls a rather different meeting when writing a couple of years later,

> I remember our house at Scorrier paying Mr Trevithick £300 as an

acknowledgement of the benefits received by us in our mines from this source alone.[625]

Whatever the truth, Trevithick is unlikely to have received more than £150, less Edmunds' fees for correspondence and preparation of the indemnification.

It was soon after Trevithick's return that his fifteen-year-old son Francis remembered him arriving during October 1827 at his school in Bodmin; his sun bronzed father walked into the room wearing a broad-brimmed Leghorn* hat looking for him. This was a reunion that Francis would always remember but he does not tell us why he was at school at the age of 15 in far-away Bodmin, supposedly as a boarder; who was paying the fees and where were his siblings? Francis also suggested that, at the age of ten, he was going to find his father in South America.[626]

Trevithick was now back with his family, telling stories of his adventures and spending some time with Francis who, forty-five years later was to tell us very little about this father. Maybe, like a lot of people, he simply forgot the stories and was left embroidering the snippets he could remember. In a letter to Gerard Trevithick said,

> We had a very good passage home, six days from Cartagena to Jamaica, and thirty-four days from thence to England; and on my return was so fortunate as to join all my family in good health, and also welcomed home by all the neighbourhood by ringing of bells, and entertained at the tables of the county and borough members, … which will give you new ideas and enable you to make out a prospectus that will show the great advantages in Costa Rica mines over every other in South America.[627]

Later, having seen the proposals for a system of pneumatic engines to be employed at St Katharine's Dock, he wrote to Gilbert, told him of his encounter and explained his sensible thinking on a series of hydraulic engines,

> …by having one powerfull steam-engine to force water in pipes round the dock, say 30 or 40 pounds to the inch, more or less, and to have a worm shaft, working in to a worm wheel, exactley the same as a common roasting jack, and apply to the worm shaft a sprouting arm like a barker's mill horizontally, and the worm shaft standing perpenduclear would work the worm wheel thats on the chain barrell shaft of the crane, which would make the machine very simple and cheap, and accomplish a circulear motain at once, instead of a piston alternitive motain to drive rotarey motain. This report of mine had som weight with them; and an arrangement is on foot

* Archaic English for Livorno, Italy

to make inquirey in to the plan propos'd by me, so as to remunerate me provided my plan is good.[628]

This letter to Gilbert is a typical Trevithick communication and must have made Gilbert smile. Trevithick's suggestion is to use the power of his steam engine to pump and pressurise water in a pipe. This was probably new thinking as previous hydraulic engines appear to rely on a natural head of water.

Chance remarks set Trevithick's mind racing and one concerned the cost of bringing ice to England from Iceland. In a letter to Gilbert he described what we would call refrigeration.

> A thought struck me at the moment that artificial cold might be made very cheap by the power of steam-engines, by compressing air in to a condencer surrounded by water, and also an injection in to the same, so as to instantly could down the verry high compress air to the tempture of the surrounding air, and then admitting it to escape into liquid. This would reduce the tempture to any state of cold required.[629]

A trip the Netherlands in July 1828 presented Trevithick with an opportunity that could have given anyone else the prospect of living in luxury for the rest of their lives. He could see the potential and wrote to Gilbert on 31st July 1828 to explain the situation. Nicholas Harvey, son of John and Nancy Harvey was engineer of the Steam Navigation Company at

The house for the mighty 144-inch annular compound pumping engine at Cruuqhuis, the survivor of three engines sent to the Netherlands. This is the largest steam pumping engine in the world.

Rotterdam. Trevithick introduced the Dutch to high-pressure steam power and designed engines to pump their low-lying lands. Then he threw it all away as a difference of opinion resulted in the engines going for scrap. As in so many of his failed enterprises, others would benefit and in this case Harvey's of Hayle and the Cornish Copper Company built the largest steam engines in the world to pump the polders at Haarlemmermeer. Part of the land they exposed is now the site of Amsterdam's airport at Schiphol.

Closed cycle steam engine
In later life Trevithick was still inventing and the salt in the sea water used by ship borne engines was clearly a problem that stood between him and the universal acceptance of his engines at sea. His answer was to use the longstanding method of condensing the expelled exhaust steam and pumping the condensate back into the boiler as feed water. We find Trevithick writing the following letter, probably aimed at exciting an investment, to a W. H. Wyatt in London in 1829. Remember a John Wyatt of a well-established family of jewellers in Hatton Gardens who asked Gilbert about Trevithick twenty-two years earlier.

> Since I returned to this place I have made an engine and set it at work on board a vessel which answers every expectation and will be employed on almost every ship. It will drive the ship, discharge & pump it, cook their meat, lift the anchor and all heavy work on board and is light, simple, stands in a little room and cheap both in erection & coals, and requires no fixtures.[630]

Trevithick had designed and built a closed cycle steam engine that continued to use the same fresh water. This clearly had prospects in maritime use but this was one of the few Trevithick inventions that did not work perfectly from the drawing board. Some problems arose during the development stages in Harvey's foundry and an apprentice called John Brunton, whom we have met previously, wrote of what he saw:

> I saw a good deal of him for he had persuaded Mr Harvey, his Brother-in-law, that he had invented a great improvement in Steam Engines – by which the Steam having passed through the cylinders was to be pumped back into the Boiler before it condensed. … I soon saw that it was a mistake – but dare not tell Mr R. Trevithick so – for he was a very violent and passionate man. However the Boiler and Engine were completed and tested and then it was shown to be a failure on wrong principles. Old Richard Trevithick was very angry about this and it weighed heavily on his mind so as to derange his judgement.[631]

Here we have a description of Trevithick's rigid personality. It was all getting too much for him and in February 1830 he fell out with those at Harvey's Foundry again,[632] turned his back on his family and left for London. Next we find him at Lauderdale House, Highgate, the home of William Gittings, a boarding house where the Montelegre boys from Costa Rica had been accommodated.[633]

All the domestic and industrial coal fires in London were producing its first smog haze. In March 1830 Trevithick wrote to Gilbert, apologising for not having been in touch and complaining about his health. He records how he can hardly breathe whilst in the city and was probably suffering from some form of asthma or bronchitis. He would die from this complaint three years later and his letter reveals how unpleasant his health was during those years.

Henry Harvey, always keeping a watchful eye on Trevithick, wrote to Gilbert,

> … As you summarise Trevithick did not leave here in a very satisfactory manner. When I have the pleasure to see you I will explain, however he assures, his own temper, always ungovernable, led to this last.[634]

This is another example of Henry being composed at times of stress. Because he annoyingly refuses to give an explanation for Trevithick's departure, historians have been left without a reason why he left home for the last time. Within a few weeks something happened at Hayle that would have delighted Trevithick had he been there. Harveys were awarded an Admiralty contract to remove the three Boulton & Watt boilers from HMS *Echo* and replace them with Trevithick return flue Cornish boilers of 24 feet in length, 'to exert a pressure of twenty pounds, or more, to the square inch'. The valve gear and engines were also to be modified to enable them to work expansively.[635]

HMS *Echo* was a wooden paddle vessel launched with Boulton & Watt engines only three years previously and this approach by the Sea Lords revealed, for the first time, a willingness to conduct a test with high-pressure steam. Naval officers and crew were a superstitious lot and most had no time for this dangerous contrivance. When Francis went to Falmouth to discuss details with Captain King he was plainly told, 'Mind, young man, what you are about, for if there is a blow up, by God you'll swing at the yard-arm'.[636]
The award of this contract to Harveys illustrates the standing of the Cornish foundry in the eyes of the authorities and it caused a great deal of excitement in Hayle. It is easy to see who were involved at the foundry. In addition to Henry there was Woolf, holding some sort of design engineer position and William Burell, the foreman of the boiler-makers' shop. Had Trevithick known he would almost certainly considered this contract to be the justification for all his years of knocking on the Admiralty door. To add to the tension William Brunton, John's father, to whom Nicholas Oliver Harvey had been apprenticed and who was now an engineering consultant in London, had been drawn in with Samuel Goodrich, the leading expert on the Naval Board. Trevithick had first encountered him in 1804 when attempting to demonstrate at Penydarren how

useful a steam engine could be to the navy.

> The three boilers were ready to be installed in the *Echo* at Devonport by April 1831 but poor weather delayed their arrival from Hayle. However, they were eventually installed satisfactorily with Burell's advice and the ship completed its sea trials. The story does not end there and the activities of Goodrich and the Maudslays to sabotage the boilers is best read in *The Harveys of Hayle*. The Cornish boilers and the engines modified by Harveys were fully vindicated as HMS *Echo* sailed away to the Mediterranean with the mail. She continued life in the navy as a tug boat for another fifty-four years and was then sold while still on active service.[637]

Henry Maudslay had worked for Joseph Bramah as a shop superintendent in 1798 at 30/- (£1.50) a week. He sought an increase but Bramah refused so he set himself up in Oxford Street, London where he employed 80 men by 1800 and nearly 200 by 1810. He followed the idiom that progress follows profit and vice versa, a fact of life sadly unobserved by Trevithick.[638] Trevithick sold his patent for the iron tank to Maudslay in 1814.[639]

Sadly, the success of this conversion to high-pressure steam was not reflected in further orders for the Hayle foundry; they probably went to Maudslays. In spite of many ships subsequently being fitted with steam engines the Admiralty was unwilling to encourage use of the engines because of the cost of coal. The Admiralty List of December 1860 stated,

> "...steam power shall not be resorted to when the service on which the vessel is employed can satisfactorily be performed without it." and, "… all Commanding Officers are whenever steam is raised, to cause the same to be noted in the Log Book, together with their reason for so doing, stating whether it be the emergency of the occasion, the necessity of performing the service with the utmost dispatch, or other cause which, in their opinion, may justify them having recourse to steam power".

The conversion of HMS *Echo's* boilers did reveal the quality of workmanship emanating from Woolf's painstaking design and Burell's craftsmanship. These were heady days and it is not difficult to see many instances where Trevithick might have been at odds with his workmates. What eventually caused his departure we may never know but it is clear that the egotistical Woolf, now well established as an engine designer and never one to hide the pleasure he found in his achievements, undoubtedly claimed the design and manufacture of the successful Harvey built boilers for himself. He had reluctantly embraced the Trevithick boiler, attached his name to a slightly modified form and was benefiting from its technology. Henry, who throughout the year had the job of keeping all the people involved to remain focused on their tasks and not squabbling, must have felt a mixture of elation and sadness.

At Lauderdale House Trevithick shared his idea of the closed-circuit engine with Gilbert who saw its advantages. He worked out the duty of the engine, suggested an improvement and did not let the opportunity pass without offering sound advice.

> I earnestly recommend you to complete your experiment at the higher Pressure with all speed, to secure a Patent and beware of associating yourself with Strangers: and to apply yourself to Steam Navigation.[640]

Trevithick subsequently wrote to the Admiralty, asking Gilbert to forward the sealed envelope on his behalf. In a covering letter Gilbert supports Trevithick's application but makes his own rather barbed personal points, 'My extraordinary countryman Trevithick has sent me the enclosed letter … I presume it relates to steam and knowing Trevithick to be one of the most ingenious men in the world, although he has never done anything himself, I have complied with his rather singular request.'[641]

Gilbert joined Trevithick and Simon Goodrich of the Admiralty to inspect the plans at Lauderdale House and recommendations were made.[642] By this time, Trevithick's mind was wandering and little was done about developing what would be the very significant closed-circuit steam engine. However, Gilbert did persuade Trevithick to take out a patent, dated 21st February 1831, for what Trevithick called the 'differential engine'.[643]

Trevithick spent Christmas 1831 at Lauderdale House at Highgate with James Gerard. Whilst still at Lauderdale House Trevithick was engaged upon the design of boilers

LAUDERDALE HOUSE, HIGHGATE, THE NEW CONVALESCENT HOME FOR ST. BARTHOLOMEW'S HOSPITAL

Lauderdale House, built in 1582, and at various times home to Trevithick and the Montelegre brothers.

The blue plaque at the Victoria & Bull, Dartford.

with steam pressures up to 150 lbs per square inch and what he variously describes as his werling or wirling engine. He wrote to Gilbert and enquired about the use of steam pressure.

> I have sent for your consideration three different sketches, the one a boiler the other, a propeller, and the third a plan for a parshall back for the steam in a wirling machine. I first wish to know what the difference on the pressure or strain on the sides of the boiler, suppose a … [he then typically goes into elaborate details of the proposed engine] … be so good as to bring me a coppy of the data that you made for the wirling engine.[644]

Although it was a long letter full of technical detail there was no enquiry about the welfare of his family or any of his friends that he had left in Cornwall and Gilbert would have known.

Dartford

In August 1832 John Hall, Senior, of Dartford wrote to Trevithick[645] saying, "We are proceeding as fast as we can with the work for you" and asking him to come and inspect it. Trevithick did, moving from Highgate to settle at The Bull in Dartford, although the plaque on what is now the Victoria & Bull Hotel at Dartford says he lodged there from 1831 to 1833; maybe he had also been an occasional resident. Vale describes Hall as 'young' in 1832 whilst Burton gives his birth year as 1764, seven years before that of Trevithick; this is where confusion arises again because there were two John Halls. John Hall, Senior (1764-1836) had six sons and four daughters. The best known of the sons are John Hall, Junior (1792-1850) and Edward Hall (1799-1875). They were both apprenticed to the business and later taken into partnership.[646]

It was time for Trevithick to respond to his former acquaintance, John Hall, Senior, a distinguished Methodist preacher, engineer and businessman who warmed to Trevithick's ideas and encouraged some hitherto unknown developments in steam propulsion. Outstanding among these was Trevithick's turbine or werling engine. His previous failure to make this engine work properly is explained further in his letter of January 1832.

> When I made the wirling engine several years ago, I found that the great loss of power was ocasioned by not being able to drive the sprouting arm at the

**The author unveils the blue plaque to Trevithick outside the Victoria &
Bull Hotel, 2007**

> extream end, not above 200 feet per second, which bore a small propotain
> to the volosity of the sprouting steam …

This engine was a development of the Hero Aeolipile from ancient Greece. But Trevithick
found a way of making it work and the company sold several of the engines.[647]

The last letter I have found from Trevithick to Gilbert was dated 14th May 1832
and concerned his idea for propelling a boat by means of a water jet.[648] The patent
specification for this engine involved a remarkable vertical water tube boiler to drive a
steam piston in a cylinder, jacketed by hot waste exhaust gases, that was directly coupled
to a water pump on its connecting shaft. This was an example how Trevithick was still,
in his latter years, developing engines that were at the very edge of contemporary
technology with features that would not find their way into engineering practice for
many years to come.

There is no trace of any further communication with Gilbert about Trevithick's patent of
1832, nor the famous proposal to build a 1,000-foot tower in London to commemorate
the passing of the Reform Act. While historians imply that Trevithick's proposal to the
King was ill advised as the Monarch was unlikely to favour the Reform Act, we know
enough about Gilbert's opposition to Poor Laws and the Act to suggest that he was
at the seat of power and likely to have had some involvement in the collapse of the
proposal.

At Dartford, John Hall and his sons made a significant contribution to ease Trevithick's demise. Although they clearly developed a rapport with the mellowing inventor, their sensitive intervention came too late to provide Trevithick with the recompense he always thought was his due. It is frequently said that Trevithick lacked the assistance of a partner like Matthew Boulton; that is not altogether true.

In his earlier days there was John Blenkinsop who could see the future of steam locomotives and induced Matthew Murray of Leeds, 'one of the most inventive mechanics of his day'[649] to construct a number of locomotives for Middleton Colliery, the first appearing in 1812 with two vertical cylinders. Blenkinsop offered to help Trevithick and Murray was one of the few manufacturers who paid Trevithick a thirty pound royalty for each of the engines he built, many of which were exported.

Christopher Blackett of the well-establish family of colliery owners at Wylam Colliery near Newcastle was very interested in the development of steam as locomotive power and Trevithick supplied him with drawings dated 17th September 1804. The engine was constructed by Mr John Winfield who

Trevithick's proposed 1,000-foot tower to commemorate the passing of the Reform Act.

had a foundry at Pipewellgate and was running in May 1805, just seven months later.[650] It was subsequently known as the Gateshead or Wylam locomotive. Again, its weight was too great for the rails and it did not see the service that its owner had intended. When, in 1808 Blackett came back to Trevithick with the news that he had built a new iron tramway and asked him to build a suitable locomotive Trevithick shunned him, saying that he 'was engaged in other pursuits ... and could render no assistance'.[651]

Winfield became an agent for Trevithick. Later Thomas Waters of Gateshead acquired the agency and built further locomotives to a similar design.[652]

While all these men would have benefited financially from a relationship with Trevithick, they were also prepared, as Boulton did with Watt, to accept the failings and foibles of a partner on whom they depended for design and inspiration. It was Trevithick who did not see the advantages of these associations and preferred to follow his dreams.

Unusually for Trevithick, he kept in touch with James Gerard, his companion from the journey through Central America and they devised several abortive schemes together. They had survived all the terrors of the jungle and now Trevithick was unwell. This is one of the few letters in which Trevithick ever wrote concerning his health or personal feelings, rather poignantly he said,

> Yesterday I took the coach to Highgate, by way of Camden Town and of course had to walk up Highgate Hill. I found I was able to walk up that hill with as much ease and speed as any of my coach companions. However strange this maggot may appear in my chest and brain it is no more than true. I wish among all you long-life-preserving doctors you could find out the cause of this defect, so as to remedy this troublesome companion of mine.

Gerard died shortly afterwards in France.

The 'maggot' in his chest eventually got him and Trevithick died in the Bull Hotel on the 22nd April 1833. His funeral took place four days later conducted by the Vicar of Dartford, the Reverend Francis Bazett Grant. No one from Hayle attended, it would have been difficult although Vale says it would not have been impossible to get there in time. Francis does not provide a date of his visit to Hall & Co. in Dartford but he does say that he was refused permission to go through the works to enquire into the character of his father's experiments. It was made very clear to him that Trevithick's relatives were not welcome.[653] We can only surmise that those at Hall & Co. thought Trevithick's family had deserted him in some way.

Little detail is known of Trevithick's time at Hall & Co. but indications are that he made an impact and was appreciated for the contribution he was making to his employer's company. We have no evidence of those disputes that so frequently beset his earlier lifestyle; he appeared to be relaxed. It is thought that, once Trevithick reached Dartford he did not travel again. It had been thirty years since he first demonstrated his self-propelled locomotive climbing Camborne Hill. In the intervening years he had led the life that circumstances and his inner self dictated. He had seen universal acceptance of his invention and its application in more ways than he could have dreamt possible.

His story telling about the strange things that had happened to him was always great entertainment in The Bull.

> Twas almost nightly that the writer of this paragraph sat *vis-a-vis* in the Bull coffee-room and talked with him over the olden times in the far-western land of 'Jack, the Giant Killer', comparing it with the wild and weird world of the southern hemisphere.[654]

Trevithick was in his sixties, ideas still flowed as they had always done but now he was mellowing. Trevithick's life can be easily described as one of endeavour, success, failure and disappointment but it is not until he reached Dartford that we detect him eventually experiencing happiness, probably tainted with some forgiving.

Was he happy at Dartford? His short time there is remembered there with affection in the town and commemorated with plaques at the railway station, in the church and the burial ground, inside and outside the Victoria & Bull Hotel and in a mighty mural in Dartford's main street; as this is being written there is talk of a commemorative statue. As a remark of respect for the great man, a Trevithick centenary memorial service was held at Holy Trinity Church on Sunday 23rd April 1933 and Trevithick steam traction events are held there annually.

The success of his various engines spread throughout the land and, had Trevithick been sensible to patent the many features of this new power source, develop the design, supply his eager customers, move to Birmingham from Illogan in Cornwall as the Tangye Brothers did, and keep an eye on his burgeoning business, it is likely he could have become one of the wealthiest industrialists of the nineteenth century. But this was not in his nature; the profit that he was making from his original idea enabled him to develop other ideas rather than pursue the expansion of a manufacturing company. He had difficulty in appreciating that his income was coming from mining and industrial customers who were, in turn, making profits from his engines. Trevithick wished to pursue his original vision of horseless carriages, something he eventually realized that few people wanted.

Investigations by others into his life and achievements were slow to gain any momentum. These were the beginnings of the Steam and Railway Ages; Trevithick's contribution was not fully understood or appreciated. Many others from Cornwall successfully followed a more conventional route through engineering. James Tangye, for instance was employed at William Brunton's Works between 1848 and 1854, before joining his brothers at Cornwall Works, Smethwick, Birmingham, 1857.

275

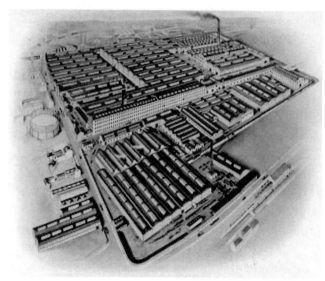

Recognition of his achievements by the engineering fraternity came throughout Trevithick's life but it was probably unnoticed by the man himself. There was also criticism of his successes as they were not in everyone's interests. There is little evidence that Trevithick took notice of either recognition or criticism; he accepted the former as his due and the latter as ill informed from those who were unable to see the future as clearly as he did.

The substantial account of Trevithick's achievements appeared ten years after the Rainhill Trials in which Stephenson established himself as a public figure. The remarkably detailed account in *The Civil Engineer & Architect's Journal* of March 1839 accorded Trevithick respect and honour for being the inventor of the high-pressure steam engine and boiler. Its most quoted lines are:

> ... for, it must be observed, that however he may have been remunerated, and how much so ever he may have derived to advance his own interests, yet the apathy of his countrymen ever prevented him from carrying out his own wishes, ... He died, indeed comparatively poor, and left, we believe, little other inheritance to his family than the grandeur of his name and the glory of his works.[655]

It remarked on his contribution to the Industrial Revolution and the means by which ships such as Brunel's *Great Western* had crossed the Atlantic the previous year. Trevithick's place in the history of mechanical engineering was seen as so important that the lack of a suitable statue and an account of Trevithick's life were frequently noted.

On a page that reported on the erection of statues to Nelson, Wellington and Robert Stephenson there was an editorial comment that,

> We think another name connected with the progress of locomotive power, which is well worthy of some tribute, we mean Richard Trevithick, the

inventor of the high pressure system.[656]

Similar respect was shown in a Cornish publication,

> To Trevithick we owe the invention of the high-pressure steam-engine; of the steam carriage; and of that boiler without which, or a modification of which, no steamer could have cross the Atlantic.[657]

The Institution of Civil Engineers offered a reward to anyone who would produce a suitable book. A Trevithick Memorial Fund was established to erect a statue in Westminster Abbey along with that of Watt and Stephenson. The Institution of Civil Engineers stated that,

> In 1888 a fund was established in memory of Richard Trevithick (1771-1833) which was used to provide a memorial window in Westminster Abbey, and to establish a Trevithick Scholarship at Owens College, Manchester. In 1890 the balance of the fund was accepted in trust by ICE Council, and was augmented in 1932 by a gift from Mrs H. K. Trevithick, MD. The income is used to award a money prize and certificate annually for papers presented to the Institution.

The donations included £100 from Mr Tangye. The statue was not erected, probably due to insufficient funds. In 1917 Cmdr Sir Edward Nicholl, RNR, a wealthy ship owner at Cardiff, promised to erect a statue to Trevithick at Redruth similar to the one that Lord Rhondda was planning for Merthyr.[658] As the latter statue was not erected, we can only assume Nicholl saw no reason why he should honour his promise.

James Holman and J. J. Berringer launched a collection to erect a statue to Trevithick but the Great War intervened when £600 had been subscribed.[659] It was not until 1932 that a statue of Trevithick by L. S. Merrifield was unveiled by the Duke of York in Camborne.[660.]

In the following years, a number of learned engineering journals published accounts and memoirs of Trevithick; some printed lengthy letters of appreciation. All were concerned that he should receive rightful praise for his achievements and contribution to the advancement of mankind. During this period, some correspondents would refer to his nature and how geniuses often display similar traits. The accounts were generally consistent and each might add a few more facts. The only reference to his pecuniary status noted the lack of reward that his inventiveness and labours had granted him. No mention was made of his funeral arrangements or the nature of his grave. For all their style, the contemporary comments of these appreciative engineers provide us with a fairer appraisal of Trevithick and his achievements than many of the modern commentators.

We are grateful to Edmund Vale for the research connected to his book *The Harveys of Hayle* into the elusive Trevithick Papers that were at one time in the City Museum, Leicester and were removed in the 1960s. They were reputed to contain another, unpublished account of Trevithick's life by his son, Francis. The papers were withdrawn after a couple of years by a K. Knight with a local village address. However, this may have been identity fraud as John H. Dickinson of the Trevithick Society has traced this deceased gentleman as the former tenant manager of a Co-operative farm with no interests in Trevithick. All efforts by an enquiry to the British Records Association have failed to find the papers. Any trace of them would be appreciated by the Trevithick Society; their contents could be very revealing.

On the 19th April 1934, during the Great Depression, a memorial to Trevithick was unveiled at Penydarren by the Mayor's Chaplain prior to a procession to Merthyr Tydfil Town Hall. There is a plaque at Abercynon to mark the end of his historical railway journey.

The Penydarren memorial.

Trevithick's valediction and grave

So we come to one of the last mysteries to surround Trevithick, that final paragraph. In his book, Francis provides us with few instances of the relationship between Trevithick and his family. Francis was twenty-one when his father died and he was articled to Joseph Locke, the notable civil engineer who had worked with George Stephenson. He must have remembered the reaction within his family but there is not a word about it in his book.

The method Francis uses to complete his book leaves many questions unanswered. The circumstances surrounding the death of Trevithick occupy just a page and a half of the 778 pages in the two volumes. This has presented succeeding writers with opportunities to create their own versions of his life, death, burial and financial status.

In these pages, we have seen parts of many letters that Trevithick wrote. While these are well preserved and frequently documented it is his last alleged words, contained in a letter reputedly sent to Gilbert 'a few months before his last illness',[661] that have attracted the attention of subsequent authors and media presenters. Here we quote the whole document as included in *Beyond the Blaze,* a biography of Davies Gilbert by A. C. Todd. The famous ending to Francis' *Life of Trevithick* is in bold type. Words omitted by Francis are in plain type while those added are in italics.

The first moving cause of my attempt to introduce high steam was in 1802 from a conversation with Mr Gilbert on the probable advantages to be derived by working with high steam: this idea, it appears, had originated to him some time before, because his reply was: "I have long thought that the theory of high steam points out very great advantages, and have often requested the Engineer Mr. Hornblower to put it into practice without effect." Finding Mr. Gilbert's ideas agreeing with my own on the principles, I immediately thought of an entire new arrangement for constructing engines to work with high steam: the old plan, working with low steam, not being calculated to resist its force: this succeeded to the extent that you have in my written report. On my return from abroad, after 11 years absence, I did not find any essential improvements, all the engines being copies of what I had built prior to my going abroad. Mr. Gilbert then requested that I would turn my thoughts to improvements on the Navigation engines: at the same time observing that there was a wide field for improvements and to a boundless extent: that the present engines were very ill constructed, and though they had far exceeded whatever might have been expected: yet to make them of general utility, still further great improvements were required: and after a great expense and time in making different engines and trying experiments, that is accomplished both for Navigation, Locomotion and every other purpose: by entire new principles and arrangements, in addition to my former high pressure steam engine: these new principles have now been carried into effect by a union of Mr. Gilbert's ideas with my own. I have always consulted him in everything new I have brought before the public, and though his practical knowledge could not assist me his theory has been very correct and essential. Nearly thirty years I have contented with steady hard labour, and immense expenses, entirely alone, for the great and even incalculable benefit to my country, without receiving any reward; but *[I]* **have been branded with folly and madness for attempting what the world calls impossibilities: and even from the great engineer, the late Mr. James Watt, who said to an eminent scientific character still living that I**

**deserved hanging for bringing into use the high pressure engine: this
so far has been my reward from the public: but should this be all, I shall
be satisfied by the great secret pleasure and laudable pride that I have
feel in my own breast from having been the instrument of bringing
forward and maturing new principles and new arrangements,** to
construct machines **of boundless value to my country:** and, **[H]owever
much I may be straitened in** my **pecuniary circumstances, the great
honour of being a useful subject can never be taken from me, which
far exceeds riches.**[662]

There is no source reference in either *Beyond the Blaze* or *The Life* for this passage
although Todd suggests that it was written by Trevithick and sent to Gilbert in 1831.
He described it as 'a sincere and thoughtful tribute to the selflessness of Gilbert'.
It is also remarkable for the mistakes it contains by way of content and the lack of
spelling mistakes but that will be dealt with shortly.

Burton and other subsequent authors quoted *The Life* as their source for these
final lines and did not offer a reference. Todd referred to the above passage as
accompanying a letter from Trevithick to Gilbert dated 18 August 1831 in the
Trevithick papers held in the Courtney Library of the Royal Institution of Cornwall.
While that letter exists the other single document in the file is not the above passage
and a search in the library failed to find it.[663]

In Todd's biography of Davies Gilbert he quotes the passage in full and we are grateful
to him. When Todd quoted the work of others, he meticulously copied the passages,
warts and all. In this case, we have nearly five hundred words, reputedly written by
Trevithick without a spelling mistake: that is very unusual. Todd is not at fault for not
noticing the historical discrepancies; he was studying and writing about Gilbert and
was unlikely to have all the facts about Trevithick's development of the steam engine
to hand.

Did Trevithick write it?
The most unlikely possibility is, as Francis claimed, that Trevithick wrote it about
himself.

Before dismissing that possibility entirely, there is something about the content of the
passage that leads one to suppose that Trevithick did have a hand in its composition;
it blesses Gilbert but makes no reference whatsoever to the support he received
throughout his life from members of his family or the many friends and relatives like
Vivian, Harvey and West who went out of their way to assist him in his chosen tasks.
On the other hand, it vigorously applauds Gilbert; so perhaps the writer did not know

these Cornish people: or preferred to ignore them. Against that, we have to bear in mind Gilbert's approach to valedictions when he writes his own; he also avoids any reference to his wife, family and friends when looking back on his life.

Had Trevithick been the author it would have been his only document that did not concern the specification and superiority of his inventions, their detailed performance and associated matters.

The thoughtful little paragraph chosen by Francis to conclude his book was eloquently written in the style prevalent at the time of Trevithick's death. It appears to be the final prayer of a cultured, educated engineer who looks back over a lifetime of unappreciated achievement and is willing to forgive those who had failed to be grateful for all he had done for them. Francis does not suggest that it is part of a longer document, which we now know it was.

These words and the message they convey as a dramatic closure to Trevithick's life are completely at odds with his writings as we know them. There were few people in history whose response to a situation was more predictable than Trevithick's.

> In sixty years he never changed his attitude to technology, people or circumstances.
>
> If there was an opportunity, he would take it.
>
> If there was a challenge, he would take it.
>
> If there was no challenge, he would make one.
>
> He would see success in the last dying ember of a failing enterprise.
>
> He always had confidence in his ability to succeed.
>
> He would welcome people he thought could aid him even though that was not their intention.
>
> He had no time for people who opposed him in word or deed. While we have no evidence that he ever harmed anyone, he successfully threatened and frightened many.
>
> He had no tact and his sensitivity was limited to his prime interest in life.
>
> He would put his principles before any compromise.
>
> He would rather walk away from a situation than try to improve a relationship.
>
> His memory of matters concerning high-pressure steam was excellent.

It is those three last 'virtues' that make the passage in question so unbelievable. Had he written it, it is likely that he would have started the story much earlier, probably in the 1790s. He was more likely to have used the phrase 'strong steam', one he used throughout his lifetime, not 'high steam', a phrase used by John Farey when explaining something that Watt wrote about his proposed steam carriages.[664]

We do not see him ever obtaining ideas from Gilbert, they flowed continually in the other direction to be encouraged or denounced. He did not need Gilbert to tell him, after returning from South America, to 'turn his thoughts to improvements on the Navigation engines'. It is likely that, after sailing in the Pacific for years and a long sea voyage home his mind would have been full of little else.

He would also have been unlikely to have referred to Watt as, *'the great engineer'*, more likely to have mentioned him in a disparaging manner for resisting progress to his very end. He would have seen little point in forgiving all those who had sinned against him over the years. Remember, Trevithick told it as he saw it; he was not given to limiting his words or political correctness.

Then we have the basic problem with Trevithick's nature, it is unlikely that he would have even thought of writing it, even if he had the time. It would have required considerable diligent self-application and he had many more important things to do before he died, engines to design and problems to solve. Even if he had given the matter some thought, which was unlikely, he would have been more inclined to leave such writing to others.

Supposing Trevithick had drafted it and Francis had tidied up his father's spelling, the use of such sophisticated language was unusual for Trevithick, even after Francis had modified it. To illustrate this, here is an authentic letter from Trevithick to Gilbert, read some of the 'the' as 'they'.

> I was at the admeraltrie office and was order'd to wait a few days before the culd say mee what the wanted. I call 5 or 6 days foll'ing and never received a satisfactorey answere, only to still wait longer. But I left them without knowing what the wanted of mee for I was tired waiteing, and was wanted much at Coalbrookedale at the time. When the send for mee again, the shall say what the want before I will again obey the call.[665]

So, if it is doubtful that Trevithick wrote it we must consider who did, and why. The candidates would have known or studied Trevithick in the years following his departure from Cornwall. It is improbable that it was written in Cornwall; had it been, there would have been fewer mistakes about the early years. The reasons why it was written are not clear: was it satire or someone's quest for benediction?

Did Gilbert write it?

The passage is reported as being addressed to Davies Gilbert but there is no trace, other than Todd's view, that Gilbert received such an important and out-of-character letter. We know by a study of the dates of his correspondence that he was very diligent about such matters and replied at the first opportunity. Todd also questions as he says, 'What Gilbert thought of this remarkable document and its picture of genius dying penniless for his country, we do not know'. Todd adds to the general belief of the situation surrounding Trevithick's death by employing the word 'penniless'. As Gilbert did not apparently acknowledge it, did he write it?

In one way, Gilbert was seen as an unlikely writer as it appeared to be so unlike the character described by his biographer and others who applauded him. Although he was a politician, he seldom indulged in such obvious self-aggrandisement. However, on another occasion and because it was the fashion for those who faced the Almighty, he allowed himself the luxury of carefully penning a few lines about his own life. In it, he gave thanks for the good fortune of his birth and regretted the things he had failed to complete. This has a comparable tone to the passage Francis says was written by his father. In a manner similar to the Trevithick passage, he fails to mention his life's companion or his family, choosing to lay emphasis on his opinion of the Poor Laws and, as he saw it, their depressing effect on the willingness of the working classes to work. This probably concealed his dislike of the fact that the costs of the workhouses, their upkeep and merger payments to their inmates fell on the property-owning middle classes.

We know that it was written at some point in Gilbert's latter years when he was inclined to make more than the odd error. During the same time, he also edited the *Parochial History of Cornwall* and that was noted in October 1837 as 'suffering from an extensive Table of Errata, due to "want of early habits, dimness of sight and absence from the Press".[666] Historian Charles Thomas in his introduction to *Lake's Parochial History of the County of Cornwall* quotes Joseph Polsue's criticism of Gilbert's work and offers a 'side-swipe' at the popular *genre* of Cornish writing, that of folk-lore and popular tradition.[667] Thomas says, 'His *Parochial History of Cornwall,* however, was literally spoilt through typographical errors of the most extraordinary and complicated nature'; today we might be more straightforward and say that Gilbert was writing rubbish.

The reader will see that the written quality of Gilbert's own valediction is higher than that purported to be Trevithick's but we can assume that Gilbert would have toned down the writing he attributed to Trevithick. However, a wordsmith such as Gilbert was would have baulked at having to incorporate Trevithick's mistakes by inventing misspellings and permitting the ultimate horror: inaccurate punctuation. The reader could be forgiven for thinking that Gilbert, on eventually hearing the news of Trevithick's death, considered, for all his faults and foolish ways, that the inventor deserved an epitaph for his service to mankind. He may also have seen an opportunity, guessing that Trevithick was very unlikely to have written a valediction, to write something in the name of Trevithick that would express his own views on a number of subjects and draw attention to his contribution to the establishment of the steam engine, as he had been advised to do by Davy. Francis does not say when he received the valediction from Gilbert but we must read it was after his father's death as it was supposedly written 'a few months before his last illness'.[668]

In the line about 'high steam' and Trevithick's supposed relationship with Hornblower, 'and have often requested the Engineer Mr. Hornblower to put it into practice without effect', we read of Gilbert's attempts to influence Hornblower's development of his advanced two cylinder steam engine that he patented in 1781. Hornblower would have derived his futuristic technology from his father, his elder brother and his own years of experience in steam, not from a mere, inexperienced fourteen-year-old like young Gilbert; or from Trevithick, who would have been only ten-years-old.

Gilbert was probably more aware than anyone in the country that Trevithick was unlikely to receive credit for his inventiveness and hard work; he had done his best to ensure that he did not. Although he had been closely linked to Trevithick over the years, we cannot trace any attempts by Gilbert to publicise his achievements. In spite of Gilbert's attempts to denigrate those achievements, there was always the chance that Trevithick's engine would one day become famous. Gilbert saw it as important that the world understood it was his involvement that was the contributing factor to steam locomotion; he had to be sure his participation was not overlooked. Here we go back to Davy's advice on the importance of guaranteeing Gilbert's place as the source of all knowledge connected to Trevithick's engine. If Trevithick was to be forgotten, there was a chance that Gilbert may also sink with him. By writing what was, in effect, Trevithick's epitaph, something that might attract attention, Gilbert would have the opportunity to include his own name four times together with the satisfaction of displaying what he saw as his important contribution to engineering history in his own well-chosen words. It would be a fitting end and sign of gratitude from Trevithick to Gilbert for his thirty years of being beleaguered by his continual questions. Gilbert would have gone to his grave a disappointed man had he known that his carefully planned and executed subterfuge had gone astray and, when Francis eventually wrote the story of his father he would only quote the final small part of the passage, one that omitted any of the references to Trevithick's ideas being those of Davies Gilbert. The abridged passage has been quoted by numerous authors as being by Trevithick but the full transcript has seldom been seen.

We must also ask how Francis came by the passage. Had Trevithick written it and sent it to Gilbert 'a few months before his last illness',[669] it must have been held between

284

Gilbert and Francis for nearly forty years before Francis published it. A problem would have arisen for Gilbert if he had written it; Francis would have known that it was not his father's writing. Perhaps Gilbert had thoughtfully had the important passage typeset: we may never know.

The reader will have to detect if there is a similarity between the valediction attributed to Trevithick and that which we know Gilbert wrote and delivered as his leave-taking to the RGSC at Penzance in 1839. This farewell of Gilbert's is part of the seventeen pages of preface to his editing of the *Parochial History of Cornwall* written in 1837 and published in 1838; only a section of which is reproduced here. Working in a manner similar to Francis, Todd uses only the parts in bold type in Gilbert's biography.

> As this must in all probability be the last time of my addressing the inhabitants of my native county through the medium of any permanent work, I shall so far presume as to offer a few lines respecting myself, nearly in the words used by two among the most distinguished of modern writers. Since it has pleased Almighty God so to constitute the world, that the human race should every where increase up to the very limit of subsistence, all countries must witness by far the greater proportion of their inhabitants exposed to the dangers of privation, of poverty, and of distress, incapable of being mitigated in any way, except by the prudence, the care, and the general good conduct of the themselves; but easily and fatally susceptible of being augmented, almost to an unlimited degree, by the establishment of permanent charities, by distributions in the shape of largesses, and above all, by the greatest and most melancholy achievement of human weakness and short-sighted folly, the English system of poor laws, extending premiums to idleness and improvidence, on the basis of infinite relief to claimants multiplying without end.

> "My lot might have been thrown among these; it might have been that of a savage or a slave: **nor can I reflect without gratitude on the bounty of Nature, which has cast my birth in a free and civilized country, in a family decently endowed with the gifts of Fortune, in an age of science and philosophy, where years outrun in discoveries and in improvements the advances of former centuries**.

> It is not for me to determine how far these advantages have been improved by myself; but at the age of threescore years and ten, I may justly say with the other writer alluded to --

285

> **The retrospect of life recalls to my view many opportunities of good neglected, much time squandered upon trifles and much lost in idleness and vacancy. I leave many quasi-designs unattempted, and many great attempts unfinished: but my mind being free from the burden of any heavy crime, I compose myself to tranquility: I endeavour to abstract my thoughts from hopes and cares which, though reason knows them to be vain, still try to keep their old possession of my heart: I humbly expect the hour which Nature cannot long delay: and with the most profound adoration of the Divinity, I hope to possess in a better state of existence that happiness which here I could not find and that virtue which here I have been unable to attain."**

Gilbert could have written so much more. He chose to include something on his aversion to the Poor Laws; something he considered simply enabled the poor, with whom he associated the word 'idle', to do little more than multiply. He speaks of his own good fortune but there is nothing about his lifelong ambition to enable a few less fortunate than himself to improve their status.

Gilbert reveals his method of including a nameless person as an approving mentor as in, 'I may justly say with the other writer alluded to --' and uses a similar procedure of anonymity when writing Trevithick's valediction, as in, 'who said to an eminent scientific character still living'. One feels this is a well-developed and practised technique that Gilbert may have honed over the years to get his own way in Parliament, the Royal Society and elsewhere.

It is interesting to compare the following passages for similarities of style,

> The Editor is desirous of preserving them in their actual forms, however distorted by false grammar or by obscurities, as specimens of times now passed away, and of religious feelings superseded by others of a different cast.
> *Some Ancient Christmas Carols,* edited by Davies Gilbert
> I leave many quasi-designs unattempted, and many great attempts unfinished: but my mind being free from the burden of any heavy crime, I compose myself to tranquility: … or can I reflect without gratitude on the bounty of Nature, which has cast my birth in a free and civilized country, in a family decently endowed with the gifts of Fortune, in an age of science and philosophy …
> Address to the *Royal Cornwall Geological Society*, written by Davies Gilbert

... this so far has been my reward from the public: but should this be all, I shall be satisfied by the great secret pleasure and laudable pride that I have feel in my own breast from having been the instrument of bringing forward and maturing new principles and new arrangements ...
Trevithick's reputed valediction, written by Davies Gilbert?

Even if there are doubts whether these passages are all written by the same man, they are certainly very unlike anything written by Trevithick.

It appeared to be the destiny of inventors and scientists to feel that they had not been recognised for their contributions to mankind. The American, Oliver Evans, who developed flourmills and high-pressure steam engines about the same time as Trevithick, had similar doubts about deserved appreciation. He wrote,

> He that studies and writes on the improvements of the arts & sciences labours to benefit generations yet unborn, For it is improbable that his Contemporaries will pay any attention to him.

In fact, Evans was well known and well-to-do when he died in 1819.[670]

Did Francis write it?
Did Francis write the passage as a fitting end to the story of his father? It probably did not suit Francis' sensitive attitude that his father, one of the world's greatest engineering geniuses, should die alone away from home. There is evidence that Francis copied it from another source, probably the same as Todd. Todd tells us that it was written in 1831, when Trevithick was 60 and a couple of years before his death. That would have made it forty-two years old when it was published. We believe he was fit and well at that time and it was probably a little earlier than Trevithick might have been considering reviewing his life. Gilbert suggests a date when it was written but, again, neither Todd nor Francis provides that date or a source. We suspect that it was written between Trevithick's death and the publication of *The Life.* Perhaps the answer lies in the elusive Leicester papers.

Neither in the passage nor elsewhere in Francis' book is there any mention of the family's reactions at the time of Trevithick's death. We do not know Jane's response to the news of her husband's demise, was it sadness or relief? She had been his wife for thirty-six years, borne his six surviving children and brought them up by her endeavour and hard work with the help of her immediate family. Had she eventually had enough? Francis must have known but could not bring himself to speak ill of anyone. While this may be an admirable trait when used judicially, here we are deprived of a great deal of information about Trevithick and those who surrounded him.

We may never know what Francis was holding back. It was clearly in his nature to be pleasant to everyone and he went out of his way to be so. Just how corrupt he would become to be pleasing to people we will never truly know and how much that generosity has affected the true story of his father will have to be a matter of conjecture. We must suppose that he was doing this as a favour to his late father but did he do him a service? We have a situation similar to the stance taken by James Watt's son James. In that case his father's reputation was established during his lifetime but did young James over-egg the pudding by whipping up support that was not proportional to his father's achievements?

Stephen Buckland says that the Trevithick valediction 'is so totally unlike him, that I wonder if he really wrote it. I think it's the son's invention, a kind of fictional valedictory address'. Elsewhere Buckland talks of Francis' 'embroidery' and 'elaboration for literary effect'.

The lack of information about Trevithick has left us with an enigma, one that subsequent authors have been all too willing to replace with their fiction and fancy. Francis, as a well-established railway engineer, was likely to have received and read the many articles about his father contained in learned engineering periodicals. These would have supplied him with a great deal of information that might not have been directly available to him at home or at work. For instance, a detailed account of the tunnelling disaster and the subsequent enquiry had been published but Francis chooses to use the rather brief, bullish letter from his father to Gilbert to describe what happened. This clearly avoids having to explain what might have been an embarrassing error of judgement by his father who made a decision quickly without reference to Gilbert.

Francis was coming to the end of the book about his father; a man who had never received the recognition that both he and his son thought he richly deserved. Francis needed something to conclude the book. He retrieved the passage he needed from his file of Gilbert correspondence and extracted a small, but significant, part of it. He doctored it slightly, changed some punctuation and attributed it to a letter written by his father to Gilbert. This tidied up the story of his father's life and provided, as he thought, an informative and fitting end. He writes nothing after quoting the passage, trusting that the reader will believe in his father's ability and sanctity.

Francis was being clever by not quoting the passage in full as this would have revealed the errors it contained. It would also have attributed all of his father's genius to someone else. By choosing that extract, he had honoured him in a way that few others had done. Both his father and Gilbert were long dead and Francis was in his final years. We must suppose he thought he would not be discovered and, anyway, he had led a relatively blameless life; would a small indiscretion matter now if it served his father well?

288

Whoever wrote the passage knew that Trevithick had died with little of this world's goods. It is unlikely they would have had access to the letter written by the landlord of The Bull at Dartford to John Tyack; that would have been in Cornwall.

All great men have biographers; Churchill, for instance, had many. In his case, they take apart the decisions he made, the campaigns he fought, his disputes with his generals, his tantrums, his unpleasant habits and the effects on his family. In many ways, they reveal the important weaknesses as well as the strengths that make up the character we honour. Those who achieve something important are as mixed up as the rest of us; they are no less for that. Had we, who found Trevithick interesting in subsequent years, known more about his failings and foibles we would have been in a better position to judge the man for his achievements and not continually refer to his failings. What he accomplished he did with his own thoughts, ability and determination.

Today we have a much better understanding of the troubles probably faced by Trevithick. In his time, it is likely that he was aware of his problems and, when faced with the decisions he had to make, considered he was choosing his best course through life.

Francis could have written an inspiring tale of a lifetime's work mixed, as all full lifetimes are, with success and failure. It could have been an inspiration to those who followed him. It is a pity that some opportunities have been lost and, in peeling back some of the folklore and romanticism we find a much more interesting character than that portrayed by the imagination of the novel writers. There is still an opportunity for someone to write the full story; what an opportunity the media has with Trevithick.

Was Trevithick estranged from his wife and family? We have no evidence of correspondence between Trevithick and his home at Hayle. There are apparently no letters that he might have written home during his time with John Hall & Co. This could well be because the recipients did not keep them. We can only liken his behaviour in London to that in South America when it was reported that he did not write home once in eleven years.

The death scene
Ironically, Trevithick died on the day that Walter Hancock inaugurated his first steam bus service in London. His *Enterprise* ran between London Wall and Paddington via Islington on Monday, the 22nd April 1833, thirty years after Trevithick led the way.

Following Trevithick's death, we discover that he had made a will and drawn up a list of creditors. This is very uncharacteristic of the inventor and one is left supposing that someone at Hall & Co. was advising him and keeping a watchful eye on his affairs. Trevithick must have co-operated whole-heartedly in the making of the will and the list

289

of creditors. Rowley Potter, the innkeeper at The Bull, found the address of John Tyack of Copperhouse, Hayle, Trevithick's nephew and sole executor, within the will and wrote informing him of the death. Francis does not mention his cousin John Tyack but prefers to say that 'the family received a note dated 22nd April, from Mr Rowley Potter of Dartford, stating that he had died on the morning of that day'.[671] William Gittings of Lauderdale House also wrote to Henry Harvey concerning the demise and advised him of the list of Trevithick's creditors.

Trevithick was deeply in debt when he died.[672] Gittings was owed money for lodgings and sums lent to Trevithick to facilitate his experiments. Rowley Potter of The Bull was also listed as a creditor. This is remarkable as it is likely Trevithick would have been paid regularly by Hall & Co. and could have settled the charges for accommodation weekly. Was the will made just a couple of days before Trevithick's death or is there the unlikely situation that Potter lent him money? Nephew John Tyack was also on the list. Henry Harvey's name was not mentioned, perhaps because the total amount was simply incalculable or Trevithick felt so detached from his family at the time that he ignored it. One gets the impression that there were few who had association with Trevithick who did not lend him money at some time.

A search for Trevithick's will in Kent, Exeter, Cornwall and other places has been unsuccessful although Jane's will and that of her father-in-law have been traced to the Cornwall Record Office after they were found in the office of a London solicitor.

Jane was also Francis' mother; she must have had something to say of her husband's death but *The Life* recounts nothing. Is Francis silently bearing his mother's guilt? If Trevithick's grave was unmarked, and we have some evidence to the contrary, was it Jane's decision to leave it that way? Trevithick was buried on the Friday following his death on Monday morning. A letter informing the family of the death would normally have taken three days so we can understand why they were unable or unprepared to attend the funeral. We have no evidence that anyone from the Trevithick family visited Dartford until Francis did, as he puts it, 'some years later'. Did Francis stay at The Bull during his visit?

The character of Rowley Potter has not been examined and he is seen as a hard-working hotelkeeper who was left out of pocket as a result of his house guest dying before settling his account. It may be unfair to balance this often quoted view of his character but publicans at that time were frequently regarded as rogues. It is unlikely that the innkeepers of Paris were much different from those in London and Victor Hugo's portrayal of the notorious M. Thenardie as 'Master of the House' in *Les Misérables* illustrated their personality. The following characterisation is just a small part of a very revealing lyric that the reader is invited to read on the World Wide Web.

Watering the wine, making up the weight
Pickin' up their knick-knacks when they can't see straight
Everybody loves a landlord
Everybody's buxom friend
I do whatever pleases
Jesus! Won't I bleed 'em in the end!

Burton tells us that the often quoted gold watch from South America went some way to pay for the funeral expenses, the balance being covered by Hall. Trevithick was well liked in Dartford by his workmates. Hall would have been wise to ensure that he got a suitable funeral; Burton describes it as 'a very grand affair'.[673] Such an event would normally have been marked by the erection of a gravestone. The dispute concerning the location of the grave pointed out two areas some considerable distance apart.

We do not know Francis' reasons for being so off-hand. He is usually effusive about his father. Did he wholeheartedly believe the account by Rowley Potter.[674] Alternatively, was it remorse because his beloved father had been ill for some time and had died without any attention from his family? It would be a few years before Francis visited Dartford to be refused permission by Hall & Co. to go through the works to ascertain the nature of the experimental work being undertaken by his father at the time of his death.[675] Although Francis's was probably no more than curious, Halls could have been suspicious that his intentions were industrial espionage as they had no recollection of him showing any interest in his father whilst he was alive. On the other hand, Francis says he received a great welcome from the people of Dartford. Here again, as in Cornwall, Trevithick was appreciated by his workmates but his former employers had little time for his family. It was unfortunate for the ensuing debate that Francis did not tell us if he tried to find his father's grave[676] and we are again left with disputed myth and imagination instead of history.

Tributes and an unmarked grave

It is interesting to see the way authors dealt with Trevithick's financial situation before one of them introduced the word 'pauper'. The first account of Trevithick's life, travels and achievements appears in the *Civil Engineer & Architects' Journal,* Vol II, 1839. It said,

> He died, indeed, comparatively poor, and left, we believe, little other inheritance to his family than the grandeur of his name and the glory of his works.[677]

Richard Edmunds, the son of Trevithick's solicitor in Penzance, said something very similar,

291

He died at Dartford, in Kent, on the 22nd April 1833, leaving no inheritance to his family but the grandeur of his name and the glory of his works.

This is a good example how one author will copy another without making due reference.

In the *Edinburgh New Philosophical Journal* of October 1859, Richard Edmunds reprinted a letter written by Michael Williams, MP in 1853, who said,

Mr Trevithick's subsequence absence … deprived him of much of the pecuniary advantage to which his labours and inventions justly entitled him.

Williams demonstrates how the word 'pecuniary' should be used and continues with an excellent, lengthy account of Trevithick's life and achievements. This account also appeared in the 5th volume of the *Railway Register, 1847*

Even after his death Trevithick continued to create controversy. Whoever was the original writer of the valediction that contains the line, 'straitened in my pecuniary circumstances' has provided the media and later writers with the opportunity to proclaim that he died a 'pauper' and they have frequently added the sad assumption that he was alone. Described as 'the final stamp of failure' by Thomas Laqueur,[678] the use of the word pauper may have been encouraged by the alliteration between 'pecuniary, poverty, penniless, poor, paucity, penurious' and 'pauper'. The use of these words was the final insult in the description of Trevithick's errant lifestyle. 'Pecuniary'* is merely an alternative word for 'financial' and in this case is unnecessary tautology. 'Straitened[†] circumstances' would have been sufficient. The word 'poverty' is used with relish by many subsequent writers; Arthur Mee used it in *1,000 Heroes*, in 1934. At the time of his death, Trevithick was regular employment, working for one of the most respected employers in the industrial town of Dartford as a well-paid designer and innovator. He was not, as could be deduced from those who describe his circumstances, in poor lodgings or a doss house but accommodated in what passed for luxury in those days. He may not have been in the finest room of the Bull Hotel, a hostelry that was patronised by Queen Victoria six years later but he was in the best hotel of a busy industrial town. It is true that Trevithick owed considerable sums of money at his death, but he usually did. Also, Burton doubts that he was the pauper the world would have us believe.

Gilbert was not in evidence during Trevithick's last year at Dartford and, when asked about the inventor's demise thought that it had probably occurred in the autumn of 1833 while we know it was in April. Did Gilbert truly not know the date of Trevithick's

* The Concise OED explains *pecuniary* as *relating to or consisting of money*.

† *Straiten* is explained as *restricted because of poverty*.

death or was he trying to deprecate him? There was apparently little to be gained from an association with him. With Gilbert's final dismissal of the departed Trevithick one might have thought we had heard the last of his intervention in the life of his errant pupil and great inventor, but that would not be Gilbert's way.

True engineers and those who create tangible advances usually have to rely on the written words of their admirers for immortality. It is not the same with writers; they have the ability and often the desire to pen their feelings and achievements for the entire world to see. So we have copious writings from the scribes over the millennia but very little on the one man who made the greatest single advance in steam engineering.

Francis adds to the confusion over his father's grave by saying that it 'was among those of the poor buried by the charitable; no stone or mark distinguished it from its neighbours'.[679] He does not give a date for his visit to Dartford. His report, if it is true, could well be one of the first accounts we have of the appearance of the grave. It raises one or two questions. Firstly, the obvious one, did he go to the cemetery, he didn't say he did. If he did, and it was without headstone or marker, how did he know where to look? Supposing the location was indicated to him by people in Dartford who, at that time would certainly have been able to recall its position without the dispute that surrounded later claims, why did he not arrange for a stone to be prepared and erected, he could surely have afforded it. Had he done so, the story of Trevithick's end would have been much clearer and not left to the imagination of subsequent writers. Francis spent little time on the circumstances surrounding his father's death, barely a page and a half. It is possible that the brief account suited his purposes. Francis survived his father by 44 years in financial comfort; he did not erect a headstone.

The financial status of the deceased is not relevant to whether a headstone is erected on the grave; it is the responsibility of the deceased family or the community to erect a memorial to their loved one. In this case, his widow may have desisted. However, it is unlikely that, after such an ostentatious funeral John Hall would have allowed the grave of someone so popular,[680] who had contributed to the fortunes of his business, to go unmarked. Sixty years later the company thought it advisable to re-mark the grave but Everard Hesketh, a director of J. & E. Hall Limited was surprised when he was unable to trace the expected location of a gravestone so a memorial brass plaque, that introduced the word 'poverty', was erected in 1894 in the church. His unsuccessful attempt to find the stone revived the question whether or not it had ever existed.

The reported absence of a grave at the time would serve no purpose because all graves are unmarked for some time after burial. This allows the ground to settle and for a tombstone to be made. It was many years after his death that we see the first records of the controversy surrounding the existence of a headstone and we are grateful to Dr

Michael C. W. Still of Dartford Museum who has reproduced all the letters and offered his best assumptions.

There is a press cutting on the subject dated 11th October 1890 from W. A. Chandler who pointed out that the graves had been levelled some years previously and there was currently no stone erected to 'the great inventor'. He did not suggest whether there had been a gravestone prior to the levelling.

A number of letters followed in the *West Kent Advertiser*. One was from Hesketh, who published a book in 1935 that celebrated the first 150 years of J. & E. Hall Limited. He recounted his search of the churchyard accompanied by two knowledgeable local residents of Dartford and offered a reward for authentic details of the grave's location. His companions had suggested two locations.

Hesketh also provided us with an account of the funeral in his book. He devoted a chapter to the relatively short time that Trevithick was associated with the company. While he depends on Dickinson & Titley's account of Trevithick's life he makes it clear that the inventor's presence was an influence on the future development of the company and the brass plaque claimed that Trevithick's 'splendid gifts shed a lustre on the town'; Trevithick would have liked that.

Following Hesketh's appeal there was a letter in the press referring to the *'History of Dartford'* published in 1844 that stated Trevithick's grave was next to that of Henry Pilcher. This location of the grave next to a respected citizen refutes the suggestion that Trevithick was buried with the paupers. It stated that a subscription was raised to create a cast iron monument over the grave but the funds were inadequate.

Another letter, signed with the Cornish *non-de-plume* of Tre-Pol-Pen, objected to the frequently used term 'pauper' and pointed out the value of Trevithick's watch at 30 Guineas and other goods. The writer also mentioned that there was one remaining inhabitant of Dartford who attended the funeral.

In early January 1902[681] Thomas Aldous wrote of his memories along with those of other people now deceased, and was prepared to swear to the location of the rather small headstone. He called for a public subscription to raise a monument to 'the greatest engineer of the 19th Century'.

A little later a letter from 'Tregothan' (later identified as a Dartford printer called T. C. Reed) and first published in the *Cornish Telegraph* asserted that the former chief draughtsman at Hall's knew the location because he was at the funeral. This letter was accompanied with a plan of the grave.

This elicited a report in September 1903 from Thomas Aldous who stuck to his assertion of the correct location and suggested that the headstone could be found in the levelled ground.

T. C. Reed, replied and again quoted the *'History of Dartford'*.[682]

Back came Aldous[683] and quotes his father's claim to know the location. He then wrote another letter on the subject.[684]

T. C. Reed was equally assertive later that month[685] and Aldous was back at him[686] clinging onto his claim to the location. After this the correspondence thankfully ended.

Everard Hesketh gave a lecture to the Dartford District Antiquarian Society in 1914 entitled 'The Life of Richard Trevithick'. This included the matters raised in the above letters with further evidence of Thomas Aldous, the authenticity of which Hesketh clearly doubted.

Never one to let the dead lie peacefully, T. C. Reed was back in 1931 and referred to his journey with Mr Snowden of 30 years previously and Snowden's categorical claim to know the exact location of the grave. Subsequent research suggests that Snowden was too young to have either worked at Hall's or to have attended the funeral.

Finally, Mr T. A. Ochiltree, formerly of Reading and later of Penzance, carried out his research into the subject in 1969 and provided an account similar to that of Snowden's. He supplies us with a plan of the churchyard but it adds nothing to a subject that has occupied the attention of the residents of Dartford for many years.

The words, 'pauper's grave', are often used to describe Trevithick's financial status and his eventual resting place. During the first century following his death, the word 'pauper' does not appear in any report on his life or his demise, even in relation to the possible location of the grave. At the time of Trevithick's death, a pauper would have been a 'penniless person' buried at public expense by the Board of Guardians for five shillings. Such people were often buried in the same graves as those who could afford their own plots[687] and this accounts for the unanticipated remains that are sometimes found in graves beneath those of the expected incumbent. Although Trevithick died in debt, he was certainly not penniless and his funeral was not conducted by the parish.

At the time, the location of Trevithick's grave was well known as the body was reputed to have been covered in iron as a protection against the 'Resurrectionists', a group of opportunists who robbed graves for the cadavers they could sell in their interests

Dartford Cemetery, now a garden of rememberance.

and that of medical science. It is interesting that there was such concern about this possibility as the Anatomy Act had been passed by Parliament the previous July to outlaw such activities.[688] Grave robbery still existed in exceptional circumstances and perhaps Trevithick's workmates were concerned that his large physique was likely to fetch a good price from an unscrupulous surgeon.

According to Thomas Aldous, whose father worked at Hall & Co. and was a pall bearer at the funeral, the coffin was rather complicated and so its description is usually disregarded. He told how it was fitted with two stout pieces of timber placed at right angles to the coffin above and two pieces below; these were strongly bolted together so as to clamp the coffin between them. As a further precaution the nuts on the bolts were under the bottom timbers so could not be disturbed from above. It is obvious that to get the body out the whole structure would have had to be removed, necessitating the excavation of an enormous hole.

The skies over Dartford are now clear but in the 150 years following the death of Trevithick, they were blackened by industrial smoke. Their present condition is the result of the Clean Air Act of 1956, which forbade the burning of coal in the area. This was too late to save the tombstones, probably made of poor quality Kentish ragstone in the Dartford cemetery and they suffered badly from the effects of chemical decay in the form of acid rain. While Thomas Aldous may have been able to locate where his grandfather had pointed out the Trevithick's grave in 1902 all trace of the inscription was missing by the time other researchers arrived. Apart from those made of slate there are now few legible tombstones left in what was the cemetery.

In the past century almost all the gravestones have been discarded or relocated. There have been various road widen schemes, subsidence and alterations to the earth retaining wall below the cemetery. It is now virtually impossible to recreate a plan of the churchyard in 1833. We simply know that Trevithick lies in Dartford, let him rest in peace.

There are many accounts of Trevithick's life written since that of Francis Trevithick; the one by Conrad Matschoss in 1970 is a typical example.

> His associate [John Hall] buried him and also paid the costs of the funeral. He was interred in a pauper's grave, now unknown.[689]

Then he ends with a direct copy of Francis' 'folly and madness' valediction; so much for research.[690]

Memorial to Trevithick in the wall of East Hill Cemetery, Dartford.

Whatever the truth, Francis has ensured that Trevithick is remembered along with his valediction. The chosen paragraph has painted a picture of a poor, pious, thoughtful man of great integrity and ability, doing his best for Mankind, forgiving and caring for his fellows. It would be unfair of us to say that Trevithick did not exhibit some of those noble qualities but he would probably did not go out of his way to write a long legend about them.

Francis died on the 27 October 1877 at The Cliff, a house that still stands on Chyandour Cliff, Penzance.[691] where he overlooked the picturesque St Michael's Mount and the bay. He must have felt some comfort as the trains his father had initiated ran daily services from the station before him to London and other parts of the nation.

Oliver Evans, 1755 – 1819.

It would be unfair not to explain something about Trevithick's contemporary inventor, Oliver Evans in the United States. As is frequently the case, historians often find a reference to a design or patent and elaborate it into a fiction of their own imagination. Trevithick's lack of interest in such diversions as patent applications meant his steam engines that worked in the mines prior to 1800 and his Camborne locomotive of 1801 were never patented. For this reason most historians tend to ignore their existence, concentrate on his patent of 1802 and claim that to be the date he built his first steam engine.

The situation was no different in the case of Oliver Evans. Evans was an exceptionally fine inventor whose visions for the ultimate use of the steam engine were very similar to Trevithick's. However, he was more rational in his approach and he made a point of writing descriptions of his works and applying for patents long before the inventions physically existed. This provided material for historians to claim his achievement before its time. A great deal has been written about Evans' engine being the first in the world but his biography, previously published in the Mechanic's Magazine, edited by its principal partner Joseph Clinton Robertson, 1755 – 1819, offers a clearer account. The following extract is a fair summary of Evans' work on steam and suggests an interest in Evans' other achievements.

> In North America the use of steam-carriages was early advocated by the ingenious Oliver Evans, who applied, in 1786, to the legislature of Pennsylvania for an exclusive right to use steam-waggons, and certain other inventions in that state. His ideas representing steam-locomotion appeared so strange that he was considered insane; and though in the following year his petition was granted as far as regarded his improvements in flour-mills, no notice was taken of the steam wagons. A similar application in Maryland was more favourably received; the required privilege being granted for fourteen years, on the ground that it could injure no one, and might lead to the production of something useful. Evans however could not obtain such encouragement and assistance as would enable him to build a steam-carriage; and therefore he turned his attention more to the application of his improvements in the steam engine to mill-machinery. In a curious

autobiographical notice of his inventions, which has been published in No. 372 of 'Mechanics' Magazine and in several other English works, Evans states that in 1804, he demonstrated the practicality of his steam carriage project by applying temporary wheels to a machine which he constructed for the purpose of cleaning docks, and connected these with the steam-engine which was intended to work the apparatus for raising mud into lighters.

With this cumbersome and necessarily imperfect steam-carriage, [known as the Oruktor Amphibolis] he succeeded in obtaining a satisfactory though slow motion. [Robert] Stuart's account of Evan's scheme *(Anecdotes of Steam-Engines, p 391)* intimates that he sent drawings and descriptions of his machinery to England. The views of this projector were far in advance of his age, for he expressed his belief that the time would come when carriages propelled by steam would be in general use, as well for the transport of passengers as goods, travelling at the rate of fifteen miles per hour, or three hundred miles a day, upon good turnpike-roads.[692]

National patriotism plays a great part in the support inventors receive from historians. Many American-favoured writers applauded Oliver's notable achievements. In particular there was Dr. Ernst Alban of Mecklenburg University, a man who standardised his own size of bushel and made a very robust defence of Oliver in 1848, placing Trevithick and Vivian 'clumsily in his wake'.[693]

Dickinson says, '... in 1803 not more than six engines could be mustered in the whole of the States; mechanical construction and skill were at least fifty years behind those of England.'[694]

More recently Peter Tertzakian of the ARC Financial Corp, Alaska, has also been apposite about progress in the States with, 'The American railway was born about 20 years after Trevithick's Penydarren'.[695] Tertzakian's may be an optimistic conclusion, the British passenger railway was not born until 25 years after Penydarren, at the Rainhill Trials. Evans' engine of 1804 consisted of a three foot cylindrical boiler made of copper with an internal fire tube strengthened by iron rings. The exterior was lagged with wood surrounded by iron rings.[696] Evans wrote of many uses to which the engine was applied in a stationary capacity such as, '... sawing at the rate of 100 feet of marble in 12 hours ...'.[697]

In 1805 Evans designed the first refrigeration machine in America that used vapour instead of liquid. He never constructed his machine, but one similar to it was built by John Gorrie, an American physician, and he patented it in 1851.

Trevithick, the meaning of life

Trevithick was single-minded, a man driven by a cause. As a young man he had a fixation connected to steam engines and it drove him on relentlessly, all his life.

> The mind, once strengthened by a new idea, never regains its original dimensions.[698]

The evolution of steam power took a tremendous step forward in Trevithick's mind and hands. He created a power that is in use to this day. His relationships with people suffered while his engineering changed the world. He scorned the good friendship of many who would have helped him, and chose others who sealed his fate and oblivion.

Trevithick, unlike most people, was a genius and, to some extent, a social misfit. He saw the same world as everyone else but he saw it differently. He was unaware that he saw things differently and would sometimes be short-tempered because he thought others were stupid or blind to the obvious, simple things that he could clearly see.

Dedicated people are tolerated today because their ability often interests others. This was seldom the case in Trevithick's day and his true worth was not fully appreciated.

Of those people Trevithick met along the way we have two groups, his family and friends, and the others. Of his family, we have his wife Jane, her brother Henry Harvey and two other relatives, Andrew Vivian and William West. Although relationships were sometimes strained and even intermittent, as family relationships frequently are, they were steadfast almost until the end; just what happened then Francis refuses to tell us. Apart from remembering his immediate search for Francis after returning from South America, Francis tells us little or nothing about love within the Trevithick family.

Trevithick's friendships blossomed with people like John Rastrick and John Hall; they, like Davies Gilbert could see what he saw. Of the rest it is difficult to find anyone who is not using Trevithick's combination of genius and gullibility for their own purposes. Throughout his life Trevithick placed his faith in Davies Gilbert, a man of learning and social standing whom he respected.

Gilbert and Davy did nothing to raise Trevithick above his original station in life, to establish his name as the true inventor of the steam engine and to perpetuate it. In fact, there is evidence that Gilbert avoided any mention of Trevithick in the context of the steam engine.

For over a hundred years we have been told what life had meant to Trevithick and what he had derived from his relationships was contained in his much quoted valediction, but we have discovered that he never wrote it. By dismissing it we are left to consider our own views about Trevithick's thoughts. Until now we have believed that Trevithick forgave Watt and all those who had failed to acknowledge his achievements but now, without any true indication of that forgiveness, we do not know that he forgave Watt or even thought of forgiving anyone. Life was too short and there were better things to be done. Similarly, in the absence of any evidence we will never know whether he held any grudges or considered that he should be forgiven for anything. What we have tended to believe about his personal feelings has been based on myth and conjecture. Apart from the chance remark about the quality of someone's work we see little evidence of his condemnation or criticism of anyone. He had a temper, Henry Harvey said so, but it was short-lived and he turned to other matters that were of greater concern to him.

Never short of an intellectual opinion, Gilbert saw Trevithick from a different angle and said that he had failed to reach the rank to which his ability entitled him through his restless and turbulent inner self.

Memories
Trevithick belonged to that handful of human beings who clearly and decisively changed the history of the world in the nineteenth century. However, he did little to establish his name amongst the great engineers of all time, a mistake few others have made. It is interesting, and it reveals a portion of his character, that he never named any of his inventions after himself. This is unusual amidst inventors who are usually only too keen to broadcast a connection to their creation. For instance, we have Stephenson's Rocket and, today, the Dyson vacuum cleaner. Wirelesses and motor cars were, almost invariably, named after people who, if they did not actually invent the contrivance, were certainly instrumental in its development and promotion.

The products of man's ingenuity are often recognised without identification of their inventors. We may know the names of Oscar Wilde and Charles Swinburne but few people are sufficiently well read to recognise their poetry. On the other hand, we all identify a steam engine but few can recall its true inventor.

It was Trevithick's habit to name his inventions according to their purpose; we have the 'plunger pole engine' and the 'werling engine'; he was satisfied to call them 'Cornish'. Many engines around the world are called by their generic name 'Cornish' although they were not necessarily built in Cornwall.

By the time the Railway Age arrived, the name of George Stephenson was synonymous with its development and Trevithick would seldom be associated with the world's first railway locomotive.

In fairness, Stephenson said,

> The locomotive has not been the invention of one man but of a race of mechanical engineers.

Those who believed in Stephenson as the true inventor of the railway locomotive, and they do exist just like those in America who shun evolution and solemnly believe that Henry Ford invented the motor car, saw this remark by Stephenson as a sign of his modesty and applauded him for it. When Stephenson did invent something, and we think of the miners' lamp, we know that he very determinedly claimed it for himself. In the case of the railway locomotive he knew very well that its invention was not entirely his work but he was happy to build an improved engine, receive the plaudits and reap the financial rewards. Claiming to invent something is not as rewarding as claiming to develop it. Remember, it is the second mouse that gets the cheese.[699]

Trevithick slipped away from this world, a departure noticed only by his friends at Dartford, his creditors and, at a distance, his family. The *West Briton* did not carry a notice of his death. It is not thought that there was more than the one simple obituary notice in the *Mechanics' Magazine*.

> Mr. Trevithick. We regret to learn that this distinguished engineer, who may justly be regarded as the father of steam locomotion in England, died on the 22nd inst. at Dartford in Kent after a few days' illness. He was in his 67th year.[700]

During Trevithick's lifetime, there were many people who took advantage of his technology but offered little or nothing in return. It was in the *Civil Engineer & Architect's Journal* of March 1839 that the first account of Trevithick's life appeared. It published an anonymous but frequently quoted *Memoir of Trevithick* in its *Civil Engineer & Architect's Journal, Scientific and Railway Gazette,* Volume II.

> In his person and his manners he seemed formed to sustain the arduous conquests to which he was destined. Blunt, but not rude, he maintained his opinions with honesty and power, and was only in fault that too frequent success made him adhere to them with pertinacity. In his moral character he maintained with propriety all the social duties. … while as a friend none, perhaps, could be more relied upon, for his feelings of confidence survived constant disappointments and betrayals. … so few have done remarkable things without having in some degree participated in their greatness.
>
> That the memory of Trevithick has not received the honours that have been conferred on others is a neglect which has been shown to many of our

greatest names, and proceeds less from our want of veneration for men of genius than from our national character. ... The English, in acceding to their suggestions, while they commemorate inferior names, create mementos of their own neglect. While, therefore, there are three memorials to Walter Scott to one of Shakespeare and to Milton none, we must not consider the many tributes to Watt as emblems of superiority but as proofs of a better fate.[701]

Elsewhere in the Journal, it acknowledged the contribution the Age of Steam had made to architecture and the opportunities it presented. It is clear that steam had been fully embraced as a part of the advancing world and there was mention of the engine in many articles such as the dredging of the River Thames and the Caledonian Canal; Trevithick would have felt his work during the three previous decades to have been fully vindicated. There are also many references to the various railway companies that had been set up throughout the country and abroad. As it said, it is against this background of steam power in industry, shipping and rail transport that, we find the memoir of Richard Trevithick.[702]

This work is all the more remarkable because it is apparently the first history written about the inventor and must have influenced Francis to produce his more extensive work. The depth of the research mentions the personalities involved in Trevithick's life, even his activities in South America, and it leads one to believe that the imaginative writer must have interviewed extensively. For instance, it says,

> But neglect him as we may the name of TREVITHICK will live while his engines annihilate space in the Old World and in the New control the current of the Mississippi and disgorge the mountain riches of the Cordilleras.[703]

It was written in the flowery, patriotic prose of the day that allied the thoughts and achievements of heroes with greater, unseen forces. Today we find this rather amusing but must wonder if, in these chosen paragraphs, the author has not managed to capture the full nature of Trevithick, his endeavours and disappointments, something all these pages have sought to achieve, and a fitting ending that Francis might have chosen for his father's biography.

> While the biography of literary men has received full attention although rarely presenting any object of interest, the lives of men of science, deeply envolved as they are with the history of the pursuits in which they are engaged, have frequently remained unknown, or too often neglected. Nothing, however, can be more interesting to the student, or better calculated to animate him in his career, than the impediments apparently

unconquerable, or create a giant work from the rudest and most incongruous material … When, too, our own countryman is the theme, we warm as we take pride from the halo shining on our native land, and we feel the exalted nature of that genius fame which is not restricted to selfish enjoyment but brightens the whole human race …

It is not unaccountable that Oblivion should after encloud the memory of the greatest practical geniuses, for their early labours are hidden in the obscurity of the study or the workshop, and then, after battling against the efforts of the malignant, or the immovable resistance of solidarity, the inventor is long dead before the contest is ended, or his works are successfully established. In the meanwhile, the progress has been slow and so graded, that, like a plant, casts off all semblance of its seed, so the name of the author has ceased to keep company with his labours. Often, too, where a name survives, we are led to distrust, when, like that of an Arkwright, it has surplanted that of the rightful owner.

One of the neglected benefactors of the human race is the subject of the present notice, where memory, except in his native mines among his fellow-countrymen almost consigned to oblivion. At the present period therefore when we are beginning to enjoy the benefits of steam locomotion, we have thought that it would be acceptable to present some account of the engineer to whom the country is so indebted for his efforts in promoting this improvement. We can only regret that this task had not fallen to the lot of others possessed of the ample materials for doing justice to the subject. Although we see Trevithick during a most active portion of his career, yet the later years soon renders the memory of incidents vague and imperfect. I know no one, indeed, who could better have fulfilled this task than the late President of the Royal Society [must be Sir Humphry Davy, Gilbert was still alive in March 1839], Trevithick's fellow countryman and friend.

Towards the end it says,

That his name is but slightly known, and his labours consequently little appreciated, is by no means a result of their unimportance, but the effect of concurrent circumstances, which, as they can elevate insignificance, too often obscure merit.

The *Journal* went on to call for a full story of Trevithick's life and achievements to be written so that the world might appreciate what he had done. This theme was followed by articles and calls for an account to be written by a number of magazines including the *Mechanics' Magazine & Gazette*, 1847; *Mining Almanac*, 1849, the *Edinburgh New Philosophical Journal*, 1859 and so on. Sir Edward Watkin, the chairman of four railway tunnel companies who founded The Channel Tunnel Company in 1875, was impressed by Trevithick and contemplated writing his biography.

Loughnan St. L. Pendred's eulogy given in Dartford Parish Church near the centenary of his death (23 April 1933) contained some somewhat florid biographical information:

> ... there is no figure so romantic as Richard Trevithick. A man of great stature and great strength. Blue eyes in a firm rugged face, with a large good-natured mouth.

Professor Charles Inglis, speaking in 1933 in a lecture to the Institution of Civil Engineers to commemorate the centenary of Trevithick's death, said,

> In the brief period between 1799 and 1808 he totally changed the breed of steam engines. From an unwieldy giant of limited ability he evolved a prime mover of universal application.

> In its many forms, the steam engine became the major source of power in the nineteenth century, both in manufacturing industry and in transport whether on land or at sea.[704]

Industrialists and transport operators adopted Trevithick's remarkable invention. The engine enabled more work to be done and more products to be made. The ages of mass production and travel were created by the many opportunists who saw ways in which they could utilize the high-pressure steam engine. In the hands of such people the engines generated previously unknown progress in industrial and economic activity. The demand for the high-pressure steam engine was insatiable and every day more uses were found for its remarkable virtues.

The famous prediction of Erasmus Darwin in 1765 was coming to pass,

> Soon shall thy arm, unconquer'd steam! afar
> Drag the slow barge, or drive the rapid car;
> Or on wide-waving wings expanded bear
> The flying chariot through the fields of air.
> Fair crews triumphant, leaning from above,
> Shall wave their fluttering 'kerchiefs as they move;
> Or warrior-bands alarm the gaping crowd,

And armies shrink beneath the shadowy cloud.
The Botanic Garden.[705]

And, …

Believe me, 'ere long we shall see a pan of coals brought to use in place of a feed of oats,' Bishop Berkley, c 1740.[706]

It will be possible to construct chariots so that without animals they may be moved with incalculable speed. Roger Bacon, C13th.[707]

There are numerous quotations that describe the rise of the high-pressure steam engine and the following, translated from the Italian, is as simple and good as it comes.

Watt never developed engines that were powerful for their weight, because he refused to use high-pressure steam. He feared that he could not make the boiler and the engine strong enough to withstand such pressure with the iron and sealants of the time.

The Rise of the High-Pressure Steam Engine

Following Boulton and Watt's stranglehold on the supply of engines, the arrival of Trevithick's new, lightweight, compact, cheap engine was a boost to industrial manufacturing. Factories sprang up all over the country building steam engines. It was estimated that there were five thousand steam engines at work in British factories, mills and mines within twenty years of Watt's retirement against only two hundred in France and fewer than one hundred in Prussia.[708]

Advertisements for the new technology were everywhere. Neither Trevithick nor Cornish were mentioned as brand names but the implications were clear and crediting the design would have made the manufacturer liable for the payment of a royalty. There are records of some payments to Trevithick but it is unlikely that many were made. Here is a typical advertisement from May 1816.

Wm Heath, Engineer, Burslem.
Begs to offer his entire new principle of STEAM ENGINE, founded upon a sure basis, occupying only half the usual space, yet open and free; the materials are of the first qualities, which from the mode of adoption, with packings, grease, oils, &c, will exceed all others in point of durability, in near treble capacity.[709]

There was, of course, no control over the quality of the materials used or statutory testing of the pressure capacity of the boiler. There were many unfortunate incidents but, along with the opportunities to make money, the advance of the new high-pressure engine throughout the world was relentless.

The steam engine was welcomed by engineers and industrials who could see opportunities to make a great deal of money. Just how the engine could be improved to achieve that aim was always a matter for experiment, heated discussion and dogged determination. At the last meeting of the Institute of Mechanical Engineers before his death a couple of weeks later, its President, George Stephenson steadfastly condemned the various attempts to build a steam turbine although a number had been proved to operate satisfactorily. He contended,

… that the fallacy of Mr. Onion's principle was pretty conclusively proved by the fact, that fifty patents, at least, had been taken out for Rotary Engines, every one of which had failed. No man who ever lived could improve on the lever principle, as there was no power but in the lever.[710]

In 1835 Sheffield had 74 steam engines working in the steel industry consuming 38,000 tons of coal a year.[711] This would have been in addition to the steam engines used for other purposes and together they would have accounted for a great deal of atmospheric pollution.

By 1835 [in the United States] … 50 times as many people were travelling by rail as had travelled by all other means put together just five years earlier.[712]

From virtually nothing in 1830, the mileage of American railway rose to 30,000 by 1860 -- that is, more than all the rest of the world put together – and to a staggering 200,000 by 1890.[713.]

By 1850 practically every town in England was linked by rail with London,[714] and by 1855 over £300 million had been invested in the railways [of England].[715.]

1851, The Great Exhibition and the clamour for high-pressure steam
The Great Exhibition of 1851 brought together all that was moving the British Empire forward and the benefits that had accrued. The driving force was undoubtedly the steam engine and an examination of the exhibition's official catalogue shows,

In **'Class 5. Machines for direct use, including carriages, railway and marine machines'**, we find,

'4.   **Stothert, Slaughter & Co. Bristol.** Marine engine, intended to meet the assured requirements of machinery for propulsion by screw, in which it is imperative to drive the propeller shaft at a speed unsuited to the speed of the vacuum apparatus.'

This is clearly a promotion of the type of high-pressure engine that the company has chosen to make as being suitable for the purpose of their clients. It is also an attack on the vacuum engine, advising prospective customers that it maybe unsuited for their purpose. The entry in the catalogue for Watt comes next but one. It is interesting to note that the name Boulton is missing and that the influence of Murdoch, an engineer and company director who died in 1839, is retained.

'6. **Watt, James & Co. 18 London Street, London and Soho, Birmingham**. Marine engines, of the collective power of 700 horses, designed for driving the screw propeller by direct action. Models made in 1785, showing the early application of steam power to locomotion & Co.'

According to the Royal Society,[716] Watt's 700 horse-power four cylinder engines weighed over 100 tons without boilers and other ancillary equipment. So impressive was this mass of machinery that Karl Marx mentioned it in Das Kapital, saying 'Boulton and Watt, sent to the exhibition of 1851 steam-engines of colossal size for ocean steamers'.[717]

The inclusion in the Great Exhibition of Murdoch's 1785 model steam locomotive and oscillating engine of 1784 was quite remarkable. The former was the engine with which he was reputed to have frightened the clergyman in Redruth one dark night sixty-six years previously. It hints at a form of desperation within the Watt camp as they see dozens of companies successfully building the new-fangled Trevithick-type steam engines in competition to their outmoded atmospheric engines. In some way they must have been trying to assert their belated place in the development of high-pressure steam locomotion as they had also exhibited Murdoch's engine at the Institute of Mechanical Engineers the previous year.[718] Griffiths says that this carriage was ascribed to Watt by that calculating obfuscator, Watt's relative, Muirhead, who noted deviously, 'that the models were made by Murdoch to illustrate Mr. Watt's patent'.[719]

James Watt, Junior, had taken control of the company in 1840 and died just eight years later. His place was taken by W. H. Blake who capitalised on the fame of Watt by changing the company name to James Watt & Co. The company had clearly lost its impact in the engineering scene and its building of the screw engines for Brunel's mighty *Great Eastern* in 1857 shows some remarkable departures from its previous standard practice. The engines comprised four 84″ horizontal cylinders, producing 1600 h.p. and driving a 24′ propeller without gearing. They were fed by multi-tube, 'tubular' boilers working at 25 lbs/sq″. The 1,000 h.p. engines built by Scott Russell &

Co. for the 56′ paddles were composed of four oscillating 74″ cylinders, also working at 25 lbs/sq″ from similar boilers. It is clear that Brunel was specifying the engines he needed and the pressure at which they would work. There is no mention of condensers in any account of the *Great Eastern's* specification. In a similar manner Brunel insisted on the ill-fated funnel heaters that cost a funnel and nearly took his life.

In 1861 the Government of Peru ordered a steam gunship of 300 tons displacement from James Watt & Co. for use on the 3,100 square miles of Lake Titicaca, at 12,500 ft the highest navigable lake in the world. This was later amended to two ships of 180 tons. The ships were to operate transport routes and offer some protection against Bolivia in the mineral trade. The *Yavari* and *Yapura* were supplied in 'flat pack' form and shipped to Arica in Peru where they finished their journey on mules and were then fuelled by llama dung. The *Yavari* was in service until 1977 and, after a period of neglect, has now been restored to be a prime tourist attraction. A brief summary can be found at http://www.yavari.org

In 1811 Boulton & Watt had advised Uville that their atmospheric engines would not operate satisfactorily at 14,000 feet. This was due to the partial loss of the essential atmospheric pressure. The fact that these ships operated for many years at 12,500 feet confirms a departure by James Watt & Co from atmospheric to Trevithick's high-pressure steam engines.

James Watt & Co. was unable to survive on large bespoke engineering projects in the days of advancing mass production. In 1895 W. & T. Avery acquired the foundry with the company name of James Watt & Co.[720] and subsequently cast the iron bodies of their industrial and personal scales.

Yavari in the Bay of Puno.

In the latter years of the nineteenth century some electric motors were introduced to industry but it was far from the end of the steam engine. Where real, raw power was required the steam engine was supreme and many saw this as the industry's heyday. The internal combustion engine in diesel or petrol form had yet to appear and steam lorries would be made in Shrewsbury for a further hundred years. It was, however, long past the age of Watt's atmospheric engine and steam power was seen universally as being high-pressure.

Most of the companies building steam engines and exhibiting in the Great Exhibition made a point of emphasizing that their engines were of the portable, expansion variety. For instance,

'37   **Evans & Son, 104, Waldour Street, Soho.** Steam engine, six horse-power, simple in construction, portable and economical in working.'

Another, typical, example of the listings in the catalogue was,

'38.   **Maudslay, Son & Field, Lambeth.** A small double-cylinder, direct-acting high-pressure steam engine.'

Maudslays concentrated on building steam engines for maritime use and in 1823, a Maudslay engine powered the *Lightning*, which they claimed to be the first steam-powered vessel to be commissioned by the Royal Navy. By 1850, they had supplied engines for over 200 steam vessels including the 750 horse power engines for Brunel's paddle steamer *Great Western*, the first transatlantic liner. Note the contract awarded to Harvey & Co. in 1831 to re-boiler HMS *Echo*.

An American visitor in London in 1851 said, 'It is astonishing to see the immense travel there is by steam boats on the Thames. They go, as omnibuses do, from one part of the city, upon the river, to another … and carry passengers for four-pence.'[721]

The years leading up to the Great Exhibition saw a remarkable and irreversible change to industrialisation and marketing. The new engines enabled goods to be manufactured in quantity. The making of goods moved from the home or small workshop into manufactories. Watt's atmospheric engines were modernised with the new high-pressure steam and took on new lives. As the designs of steam engines became smaller and more efficient they also became cheaper. Smart industrialists like Henry Maudslay and the Tangye Brothers saw that demand for the steam engine was going to outstrip supply. They built large factories and commenced volume selling in a way hitherto unknown in the engineering business.

Enterprising manufacturers aimed at the mass market, reasoning that it was better to make a little money from many people than a lot of money from a few. They continued to design their engines to be better and cheaper and so eliminated the many makers of inferior engines who were simply looking for a quick profit. The previous attitude of manufacturers like Boulton & Watt was to milk a successful product for all that it was worth. If competitors came along with something better, they either bought them out or tried to get rid of them with lengthy patent battles or other bullying tactics. They did not create new products that made existing lines obsolete; as Maudslay and the Tangyes did.*

The international demand for the new steam engines and the benefits they brought to industry and the public was tremendous. Much of this requirement was satisfied by British factories making goods from its iron with the aid of its coal while it created horrific conditions for its workforces. Mining industries flourished. This was the Industrial Revolution and, in its success were the seeds for its demise. Machines and railways were exported to countries that preferred to make their own. The new steam ships carried the countries exports and looked for return cargoes. They carried cotton, exotic cloths, new foodstuffs and also imported metals and ores in competition with home industries.

In Cornwall, Harvey & Co. had been joined by Holman Brothers and Perran Foundry as foundries making the world's finest mine pumping and lifting machinery. Cornish miners left their homeland in their thousands to spread their skills throughout the world and they called for the mighty Cornish mine engines to follow them. Thousands of people were employed in the Cornish foundries and factories where countless tons of iron and coal were imported from South Wales and elsewhere. Trevithick did not benefit at all.

In later years Harvey & Co. used their shipping interests and building material connections to import wood and become builders' merchants with branches throughout Cornwall. The Fox family, who were involved with Perran foundry and shipping at Falmouth, became timber merchants and followed a similar trade in the form of Fox, Stanton & Co Ltd.[722]

In 1934 a memorial was unveiled at Penydarren to commemorate the first powered railway journey and followed by a plaque at Abercynon in 1978, at the end of the journey. The Minister of Transport, Arthur Stanley, also unveiled a tablet on the walls of the University College London in 1934[723] to mark the location where, in 1808, Trevithick operated his 'Catch-me-who-can' railway and sold the world's first railway passenger tickets.

By the time the Rainhill Trials paved the way for passenger transport, the increased

* It is acknowledged that this paragraph owes a lot to Bill Bryson's account of George Eastman's development of his Kodak camera company in *Made in America*, p 335. It may be impossible to find a more succinct description of the Boulton & Watt approach to marketing compared with that of the successful steam engine manufacturers who replaced them.

use of mechanical power in the labour intensive agricultural industry was remarkable. This was not appreciated by those who laboured on the land. In an agricultural version of Luddite attacks on looms, farm workers smashed steam threshing machines, burnt ricks and maimed cattle. Machines and cheap Irish labour were alleged to have taken the jobs of thousands of workers. Three years of poor harvest were followed in 1830 with over 100 threshing machines reported as being destroyed in East Kent alone.

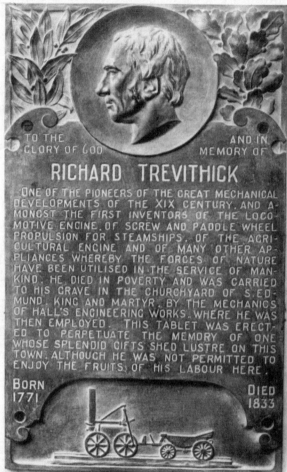

These deeds illustrated the expansion in the use of steam in agriculture.[724] The government extended the Frame Breaking Law that imposed the death penalty for Luddites[725] to agricultural machine smashing. The actions of the rioters caused nineteen to be executed, 505 transported to the Colonies and 644 sent to prison.[726]

The riots were to divide opinions on the subsequent Poor Laws, something that Davies Gilbert considered encouraged idleness and improvidence. They also revealed another side of the changes brought about by the introduction of high-pressure steam. In burgeoning factories the machines could be used to manufacture an increased number of desirable consumer goods at low prices, something the industrialists realised was the recipe for increased profits. On the land, the story was different, the demand was unlikely to increase significantly but there was an opportunity for the industrialists

The 1934 Catch-me-who-can memorial in Gower Street, London.

(farmers) to make greater profits by using machines instead of manual labour, even if the wage for the majority of workers was ten shillings (50p) a week or less. We are looking at the time of the Tolpuddle Martyrs. Ultimately, the surplus labour force on the land would move to the towns, work for a pittance in the factories, create uncontrolled slums and provide justification for the Poor Laws. While we tend to glorify the versatility and economic advantages of Trevithick's invention as a mighty step of progress, these revolts plainly illustrated that his engine was seen as a disaster by a large proportion of the working population.

Japan bought a quantity of British railway locomotives in component form and assembled them on arrival. In 1874, one of Trevithick's grandsons arrived in Japan as an engineer and supervised the building of the first thirty-three entirely Japanese built railway locomotives. His brother joined him three years later and surveyed a great part of the railway system. These two young men were the sons of Francis Trevithick.

The conjectural replica of Trevithick's 1801 steam carriage, built by the Trevithick Society that has climbed 'Camborne Hill' every year since 2001. *Photo Martin Fry, FRPS, 2009.*

Contrary to the popular notion of petrol driven motor cars being restricted to 4 m.p.h. by the 'Red Flag Act' all the vehicles were steam-driven. The 1865 Locomotion Act was repealed in 1896, just in time for the internal combustion engine and the power of the oil companies to oust steam power from the roads, but that is another story.

Westminster Abbey

There is a note in the Blight Collection[727] that an 1883 committee including the Prince of Wales, later King Edward VII, was formed to discuss the commemoration of Trevithick. An objective was to establish a fund to provide a memorial window in Westminster Abbey. The 1888 window, next to those of Brunel and Stephenson[728] was composed of a number of saints associated with Cornwall: St Michael, the patron saint of Cornwall, St Piran, the patron saint of Cornish miners (who in this instance looks like Trevithick), St Petroc, St Pinnock, St German, St Julian, St Constantin, St Nonna and St Geraint.

In 1897 the Institution of Civil Engineers, always a very supportive body where the memory of Trevithick was concerned, commissioned a marble bust of him from C. H. Mabery for its London headquarters.[729]

It was not until a century after the demonstration of his steam carriage in Camborne in 1801 that there was public celebration of his achievements. On Christmas Eve, 1901, the rain fell just as it had a hundred years before while a parade of steam traction engines included those of Hosken, Trevithick, Polkinhorn & Co. and Harvey & Co. in leading positions. A century later the Trevithick Society organised a similar parade of steam traction that included its full-sized conjectural replica of Trevithick's 1801 road locomotive. On this occasion the rain held off and all concerned enjoyed a goose luncheon. They included Francis (Frank) Masahiro Trevithick Okuno, a great, great grandson of Trevithick, and John Sawle, the remarkable Cornish engineer who prepared the drawings for the Trevithick Society's replica of Trevithick's 1801 Camborne steam locomotive and supervised its construction in 2001. The locomotive had been constructed on time, within budget and operated without subsequent modification for Camborne Trevithick Day in April of that year; Trevithick would have been proud of it. On Sunday April 23rd 1933 members of the Cornish Institute of Engineers met in the square at Pool near Camborne, formed a procession, and walked to the Methodist Church, Tregajorran, where they held a Trevithick memorial service. The Order of Service included the following,

> … By his introduction of high pressure steam, the previously impossible was made possible. His invention of the Road Locomotive in 1801, was the foundation on which our modern transport system has been built, and from which we derive so many advantages.

References

334. *Life of Richard Trevithick,* Volume I Francis Trevithick p52

335. *Ibid*

336. *Trevithick* Edith K. Harper, 1913, p10

337. *Ibid*

338. *Physics for Game Programmers,* Grant Palmer, 2005, p22

339. *Life of Richard Trevithick* Volume I Francis Trevithick p32

340. *Ibid* p33

341. *Ibid,* p55

342. *Ibid* p56

343. *Ibid* p55

344. *Ibid* pp54-56

345. *Early Tin Ingots, Ores and Slags from Western Europe.* Beagrie 1983, p107

346. *Life of Richard Trevithick,* Volume 2 Francis Trevithick p249

347. *Ibid* Volume 1 p62. Gilbert to Enys 29 April 1839

348. *Richard Trevithick, new light on his earliest years and family origins* Charles Thomas, The Journal of the Trevithick Society, 1974, p51

349. *Ibid* p52

350. *Ibid* p51

351. *Ibid* p51

352. *Life of Richard Trevithick.* Volume 1, Francis Trevithick p62

353. *Richard Trevithick, new light on his earliest years and family origins* Charles Thomas, The Journal of the Trevithick Society, 1974, p51.

354. *The Engineer* 11 March 1921 p269

355. *Life of Richard Trevithick* Volume 1, Francis Trevithick p103

356. *Ibid* p103

357. *Motor cars and the application of mechanical power to road vehicles* Rhys Jenkins, 1902, p58

358. *Steam Cars 1770-1970* Lord Montagu and Anthony Bird 1971 p43

359. *Life of Richard Trevithick* Volume 1, Francis Trevithick, p143

360. *West Briton* newspaper January 1902

361. http://en.wikipedia.org/wiki/North_River_Steamboat

362. *A Treatise on the Steam Engine* Farey Volume 2 p69

363. *Encyclopaedia of World Environmental History* Sheppard Krech p99

364. *The Engineer* 21 December 1866, p482

365. *Ships of the World,* Lincoln Paine, p106

366. *Richard Trevithick, Giant of Steam* Anthony Burton, p18

367. *News from Cornwall* Notes written by William Jenkin, Quaker, 1738 -1820, p 37, edited by A. K. Hamilton Jenkin, 1951

368. James Watt to Wilson October 1791

369. Wilson to James Watt 27 February 1794

370. Boulton &Watt Papers 26 November 1796

371. *Life of Richard Trevithick* C. E. Hyde Clarke The Mining Almanak, 1849 p303

372. Gundry to Boulton & Watt 6 July 1796 *James Watt & the Steam Engine* Dickinson and Jenkins p311

373. James Watt Jnr. to Wilson 5.01.1796 CRO AD1583/9/1

374. *Ibid* 5.01.1796 CRO AD1583/9/3

375. *Ibid* 4.05.1796 CRO AD1583/9/22

376. *Ibid* 9.05.1796 CRO AD1583/9/23

377. *Ibid* 19.07.1796 CRO AD1583/9/23

378. *The Life of George Stephenson and his son Robert.* Samuel Smiles, 1868

379. *Life of Richard Trevithick,* Francis Trevithick. Volume 1 p96

380. Edmund Vale's notes for *Harveys of Hayle*

381. Life *of Richard Trevithick* Volume I Francis Trevithick p64

382. *Ibid, p 65*

383. *Memorials & Commemorations in Camborne & District* J. F. Odgers, 1956, p7

384. *Life of Richard Trevithick,* Volume 1 Francis Trevithick p64

385. *Richard Trevithick, Giant of Steam* Anthony Burton p55

386. *Life of Richard Trevithick,* Francis Trevithick Volume 1 p271

387. *Harveys of Hayle* E. Vale, p67

388. *Life of Richard Trevithick* Francis Trevithick Volume 2, p209

389. Cornwall Family History Society J. Higgans, Company Secretary, Harvey & Co.

390. *John Brunton's Book* pp11-15

391. *Biographical dictionary of civil engineers in Great Britain,* Skempton, p545

392. *Life of Richard Trevithick,* Francis Trevithick Volume 2 p257

393. Harveys of Hayle notes Edmund Vale 26 August 1810

394. *Ibid* 10 December 1810

395. *Harveys of Hayle.* Edmund Vale pp69 & 74

396. *Harveys of Hayle notes* Edmund Vale 17 March 1810

397. *Life of Richard Trevithick* Volume 1 Francis Trevithick p237

398. *National Railway Museum. Francis says 1796 or 7,* Life Volume 1 p103.

399. *Life of Richard Trevithick* Volume 1,Francis Trevithick p105

400. *Ibid* pp 237-8

401. Grace's Guide, The Best of British Engineering website URL

402. *Inst of Civil Engineers.* Volume 59, 1880, pp308-313

403. *Arthur Woolf* T. R. Harris p101

404. *Vivi*an *to Trevithick* 23 Mar 1802

405. *Richard Trevithick, the Engineer and the Man* H. W. Dickinson & Titley 1934. p273

406. *Vivian to Trevithick* 23rd April 1802

407. *Life of Richard Trevithick Francis* Trevithick Volume I p115

408. *Richard Trevithick, Giant of Steam* Anthony Burton p77

409. *Gilbert to Thomasin Dennis 3rd and 10th March 1802*

410. *Mechanics Magazine* Volume 37, 1842

411. *Life of Richard Trevithick* Volume I Francis Trevithick p53

412. *Richard Trevithick, Giant of Steam* Anthony Burton p107

413. *Beyond the Blaze* A. C. Todd, p84

414. *Ibid* p 138.

415. *Gilbert to Thomasin , March 1802*

416. *Andrew Vivian Cashbook Courtney Library 17 April 1834*

417. *Ibid Courtney Library 8 April 1834*

418. *Harveys of Hayle* E. Vale

419. http://www.steamindex.com/people/trevith.htm

420. *Crewe Locomotive Works & its Men.* Brian Reed, 1982, p48.

421. *Railway Magazine 1899,* 5, 232

422. *The Railway Record* 31 January 1846, p111

423. *Crewe Locomotive Works & its Men* Brian Reed, 1982, p47

424. *An Illustrated History of Steamships.* A. F. L. Deeson, p16

425. *Arthur Woolf* T. R. Harris 1966 pp 22-3

426. *Biographical Dictionary of the History of Technology* L. Day, I. McNeil p233

427. *An Illustrated History of Steamships,* A. F. L. Deeson, p40

428. *Reflexions sur la puissance motrice du feu* Sadi Carnot, Robert Fox

429. *Journal of Modern History,* Volumes 21-22 JSTOR, Rhys Jenkins p137

430. *A Treatise on the Steam Engine,* Farey Vol 2 p91

431. *Biographical Dictionary of the History of Technology* L Day, I McNeil p233

432. *Arthur Woolf* T. E. Harris, Bradford Barton, 1966

433. *Harveys of Hayle* Edmund Vale pp89 & 91

434. *Links in the history of engineering and technology from Tudor times;* The collected papers of Rhys Jenkins. p126

435. *Arthur Woolf: the Cornish engineer, 1766-1837* Thomas Roberts Harris, p64

436. *Arthur Woolf.* T. E. Harris, p66

437. *Richard Trevithick, Giant of Steam* Anthony Burton p148

438. *History & progress of the steam engine* Galloway & Hebert, 1829. p164. Google Books

439. *Arthur Woolf,* T. R. Harris, p27

440. *History & progress of the steam engine* Galloway & Hebert, 1829. p157. Google Books

441. *Civil Engineer & Architect's Journal,* 1850, p95 Original italics.

442. *Arthur Woolf,* T. R. Harris, p64

443. *A treatise on the Cornish pumping engine,* Parts 1-3, Wm Pole, p49

444. *Arthur Woolf,* T. R. Harris, p65

445. *Ibid,* p100

446. *Ibid,* p26

447. *Reflexions on the motive power of fire* Pierre-Sadi Carnot, trans Robert Fox 1986, p7

448. *The Circle; or, Historical Survey of Sixty Parishes and Towns in Cornwall 1819,* William Penaluna

449. *Arthur Woolf,* T. R. Harris p64

450. Camborne Old Cornwall Society website

451. *Life of Richard Trevithick* Volume 1 Francis Trevithick p109

452. *Ibid* p111

453. *Glossary of Derbyshire Terms* J. H. Rieuwerts, p 140, 1998

454. *Derbyshire Archives D2067/1*

455. *Full report of Parliamentary Select Committee in Elemental Locomotion by means of Steam Carriages on Common Road, Chapt 5,* Alexander Gordon, 1832

456. *The Mining Almanack for 1849* Henry English p304

457. *The Falmouth Post Office Packet Service, 1689 – 1850,* John Beck, p261

458. 'The Mystery of Trevithick's London Locomotive http://www.steamindex.com/magrack/newcomen.htm

459. *Civil Engineer & Architects' Journal March 1839*

460. *Life of Richard Trevithick* C. E. Hyde Clarke The Mining Almanak, 1849 p304

461. http://www.steamcar.net

462. *Life of Richard Trevithick* C. E. Hyde Clarke The Mining Almanak, 1849 p304

463. *Life of Richard Trevithick,* Francis Trevithick Volume 1 p211

464. *Trevithick, Giant of Steam Chap 7,* Anthony Burton

465. *Steam Cars 1770 -1970* Lord Montagu and Anthony Bird p33

466. *Treatise on Elemental Locomotion by means of Steam Carriages on Common Road ,* Alexander Gordon 1834 p46

467. *Ibid* p50

468. *Steam on the Common Roads* Wm Fletcher, p63

469. *Treatise on Elemental Locomotion by means of Steam Carriages on Common Road* Alexander Gordon, p56

470. *Steam Cars 1770-1970* Lord Montagu & Anthony Bird p35

471. *Ibid* p36

472. *Treatise on Elemental Locomotion by means of Steam Carriages on Common Road ,* Alexander Gordon 1834

473. *April 29 1839, Life of Richard Trevithick,* Francis Trevithick Volume 1, p117

474. *Ibid* p111

475. *Ibid* p119

476. http://www.genuki.org.uk

477. *Gilbert's Journal* CRO

478. *The Richard Trevithick Memorial Committee of 1833,* R. Trevithick, p7. Cornwall Centre, Redruth

479. http://www.yourmotorcar.com

480. *July 1 2008 issue of Arteriosclerosis, Thrombosis and Vascular Biology*

481. http://www.napoleon-series.org/research/abstract/population/vital/c_heights1.html *and The Ascent of Money* Niall Ferguson. p 191. Penguin 2008/9

482. *Histoire des populations de "Europe, 1997*

483. *Unicef, Decline of infant mortality in Europe, 1800-1950*

484. Cornwall Online Census Project, Civil Parish of Camborne, 1841-1861

485. *Inst Civil Engineers, Obituary, J. U. Rastrick, 1780-1856.* Minutes of the Proceedings, Volume 16, January 1857, p128

486. *The 3rd Man Griffiths* p167

487. *Ibid* p155

488. *History & Progress of the Steam Engine* Elijah Galloway & Luke Hebert, p418

489. *Ibid,* p418

490. *1st October 1803 Life of Richard Trevithick.* Francis Trevithick Volume 1, pp149 -50

491. *The Story of Merthyr Tydfil* Merthyr Tydfil Traders' Assoc, 1932, p177

492. *The Times* 20 April 1934

493. *Industrial Railway Record No 59,* p12, April 1975

494. *Beyond the Blaze,* A. C. Todd p85.

495. *Richard Trevithick to Davies Gilbert Richard Trevithick, Giant of Steam* Anthony Burton p93

496. *Ibid* 27 February 1804 p91

497. *The Engineer, 29 March 1867* p263

498. *The Edgar Allen News July 1940,* p581

499. *The most powerful idea in the world – the steam engine.* William Rosen 2010 p306

500. *Trevithick to Gilbert 22 Feb 1804 Life of Richard Trevithick,* Francis Trevithick Volume 1 pp161-2

501. *Ibid* p171

502. *Ibid* pp117-8

503. RCM Collection

504. *Transfer of Industrial Technologies to America Darwin Stapleton,* American Philosophical Society, 1987 p124

505. *The Engineer 16 June 1876,* p445

506. *The Story of Merthyr Tydfil* Merthyr Tydfil Traders' Assoc, 1932, p177

507. *James Watt.* Dickinson and Jenkins p311

508. *Stationary Power* Laurance Ince No 1 1984 p72

509. *The History of the iron, steel, tinplate, and other trades in Wales* Charles Wilkins. 1903

510. *Ibid*

511. *The Times, Wednesday May 14th 1834,* p6, column F

512. *Life of Richard Trevithick,* Francis Trevithick Vol ? p186

513. *Ibid Vol; 1 p157*

514. *Trevithick Society Newsletter No 36* Miles Tomalin Feb 1982

515. *Trevithick Society Newsletter* No 36, Rodney Law, Feb 9182

516. *Newcomen Journal 1970-71* p 140

517. *Ibid* p 146

518. *W. Smith, Richard Trevithick & Sam Homfray, correspondence, 1804-06.* Prof Hugh Torrens to the Newcomen Society, pp21-25

519. *Wyatt to Gilbert* 30 June 1807 Courtney Library

520. *SB Papers*

521. *Royal Cornwall Gazette* August 1804

522. *Ibid*

523. *Biographical dictionary of Civil Engineers in G.B. & Ireland,* A. W. Skempton, p88

524. *Memoir of the Life of Marc Isambard Brunel,* Beamish, 1862, p205

525. *RIC Trevithick to Gilbert,* 11 August 1807

526. *Trevithick Papers,* Courtney Library

527. *Beyond the Blaze* A. C. Todd p90

528. *Memoir of the Life of Marc Isambard Brunel,* Beamish, 1862, p205

529. *RIC Courtney Library* 2 February 1808

530. *The Mechanics Magazine* 1847 p304

531. *The Temple Anecdotes* p285

532. *Trevithick, Giant of Steam* Anthony Burton p127 & RIC Library

533. *Memoir of the Life of Marc Isambard Brunel,* Beamish, 1862, p205

534. *Civil Engineers' Journal* Volume II p 94

535. *The Mechanics' Magazine* January-June 1847

536. *SB Papers*

537. *Memoir of the Life of Marc Isambard Brunel,* Beamish, 1862, p206

538. *Ibid.*

539. Links in the *History of the Locomotive* E. A. Forward, *The Engineer, 22nd Feb 1952. pp 266-268 and* Dr Sanjay Rana, http://www.steamcircus.info

540. *The Locomotive* 14 June 1830, p207

541. *Life of Richard Trevithick* Francis Trevithick Volume 1 p196

542. *An Illustrated History of Steamships* A. F. L. Deeson, p48

543. *Richard Trevithick, the Engineer and the Man* H. W. Dickinson & Titley 1934. p118

544. *Richard Trevithick to Gilbert,* RIC 5 October 1804

545. *Life of Richard Trevithick* Francis Trevithick Volume 2 p57

546. *Ibid* pp45-48

547. *The High-Pressure Steam Engine* Dr Ernst Alban, trans William Pole 1848 p207

548. *Life of Richard Trevithick* Francis Trevithick Volume 1 p155

549. *Beyond the Blaze* A. C. Todd p 93

550. *Obit, New Zealand Spectator* 24 January 1849

551. *13 January 1811 Courtney Library*

552. *A treatise on the Cornish Pumping Engine. 1844.* William Pole p 50

553. *Ibid*

554. *Ibid*

555. *Technological Revolutions and Economic Growth: The "Age of Steam" Reconsidered* Carolina Castaldi & Alessandro Nuvolari p13.

556. *Gilbert's diary 19 September 1813*

557. *The Civil Engineer & Architect's Journal.* Volume 2, 1839 p95

558. *Life of Richard* Trevithick Francis Trevithick Volume 2, p211

559. *Ibid* p 256

560. *Ibid* Volume pp 366-7

561. *Ibid* Volume 2 p220

562. *Underground Life, or Mines & Miners* L. Simonin, trans H. W. Bristow, London, 1869

563. *Life of Richard Trevithick* Francis Trevithick Volume 2 p246

564. *Richard Trevithick to Uville 15* March 1814 RIC

565. *Royal Cornwall Gazette* 17 March 1804

566. *Life of Richard Trevithick* Francis Trevithick Volume 2. p270

567. *Uville's Last Will & Testament 30 July 1814, SBPapers*

568. *SBPapers*

569. *Mechanics' Magazine 1847*, pp378-9

570. *Royal Geological Society of Cornwall* Henry Boase p212, 11 February 1814

571. *SBPapers*

572. *Travels in South America* Alexander Calcleugh, Volume 2, p75

573. *Lawyers & Legislation,1825*, p55

574. *Travels in South America* Alexander Calcleugh, Volume 2, p75

575. *Lawyers & Legislation,1825*, p57

576. *SB Papers*

577. *Trelawny* Margaret Armstrong, New York, 1940, p5

578. *Ibid,* p6

579. *Ibid,* p29

580. *Ibid,* p165

581. *Life of Richard Trevithick* Francis Trevithick Volume 2 p30 20 May 1813

582. *Ibid* Volume 2 p30

583. *Ibid Gilbert to Trevithick,* Volume 1 p351

584. *Trevithick, Giant of Steam,* Anthony Burton Chapter 14

585. *Life of Richard Trevithick* Francis Trevithick 23rd December, 1815. Volume 2, p 263

586. *Ibid* Volume 2 p88

587. *Ibid* Volume 2 p98

588. *Richard Trevithick to Phillip.* Life Volume 2 p89 13th December, 1815

589. *The business of abolishing the British slave trade, 1783-1807* Judi Jennings

590. *Life of Richard Trevithick* Francis Trevithick Volume 2 p90

591. *Plymouth & West Devon Record Office, ref 710/395*

592. *West Briton* Ashley Rowe 24 August 1953

593. *Life of Richard Trevithick* Francis Trevithick Volume 2, p244

594. *Trevithick, Giant of Steam* Anthony Burton p186

595. *Life of Richard Trevithick* Francis Trevithick Volume 2, p254

596. *Trevithick, Giant of Steam* Anthony Burton p194.

597. *Lawyers & Legislation,1825*, p57

598. *Civilization Builders* Frederick Houk Law 1939 p25

599. *Richard Trevithick, the Engineer and the Man* H. W. Dickinson and Titley 1934. p259

600. *James Liddell to Francis Trevithick,* 3 November 1869

601. *Civilization Builders* Frederick Houk Law 1939 p26

602. *The Ascent of Money* Niall Ferguson p99

603. *The British Empire BBC TV Time-Life books* #45 p1257

604. *The Life of Richard Trevithick,* R Trevithick. Richard Trevithick Memorial Committee. 1883

605. *Life of Richard Trevithick* Francis Trevithick Volume 2 p260

606. *Costa Rica before coffee* Lowell Gudmundson, 1986, p70

607. *Coffee and Power; revolution and the rise of democracy in Central America.* Geoffrey M. Paige 1998 p16

608. *The Illustrator and the book in England from 1790 to 1914.* G. N. Ray, 1976, p 55

609. Courtney Library 4 May 1819

610. Courtney Library RIC

611. *SB Papers*

612. *Life of Richard Trevithick* Francis Trevithick Volume 2, p271

613. *The Industrial Revolutionaries,* Gavin Weightman, 2010, p64

614. *Life of Richard Trevithick* Francis Trevithick Volume 2 p273

615. *Ibid*

616. *Harveys of Hayle.* Edmund Vale, p158.

617. *The Engineer* 1March 1867 p178

618. *Sketch of Richard Trevithick* J. J. Beringer, p209

619. *Richard Trevithick, Giant of Steam* Anthony Burton p208

620. *Harveys of Hayle.* Edmund Vale p160.

621. http://www.theshipslist.com/ships/fares/1849.htm

622. *Life of Richard Trevithick* Francis Trevithick Volume 2 p281

623. http://www.measuringworth.com

624. *Richard Trevithick, Giant of Steam* Anthony Burton p217

625. *Edinburgh New Philosophical Journal, 1859,* p327

626. *Life of Richard Trevithick* Francis Trevithick Volume 2, p276

627. *Ibid* p277

628. *Trevithick to Gilbert* RIC 18 June 1828

629. *Trevithick to Gilbert* RIC 29 June 1828

630. *Harveys of Hayle* Edmund Vale 17 Jan 1829 p ??

631. *John Brunton's Book 1812-1899.* p14

632. *Richard Trevithick, Giant of Steam* Anthony Burton p224

633. *Ibid,* p 225

634. *13 April 1830 Harveys of Hayle* Edmund Vale

635. *Life of Richard Trevithick* Francis Trevithick Volume 2, p356

636. *Ibid* p362

637. http://en.wikipedia.org/wiki/HMS_Echo

638. *The most powerful idea in the world – the steam engine* Wm Rosen, Jonathan Cape 2010

639. *Biographical dictionary of Civil Engineers in G. B. & Ireland.* A. W. Skempton, p723

640. *Beyond the Blaze* A. C. Todd p 104

641. Public Record Office, Admiralty Section, DG letter 17 June 1830

642. *Trevithick Papers*, RIC 20 August 1830

643. *Trevithick* Dickinson and Titley, pp243-5

644. *Richard Trevithick to Gilbert RCM* 9 January 1832

645. Trevithick Papers, Leicester

646. Dr Mike Still, Dartford Museum, 2008

647. *J. & E. Hall Limited, 1785 – 1835* p9. Everard Hesketh

648. *Trevithick Papers RIC* 14 May 1832

649. *The Engineer* 29 March 1867 p263

650. *SB Papers*

651. *Ibid*

652. *A Short History of Gateshead. Chapter 6. Gateshead MBC*

653. *Life of Richard Trevithick* Francis Trevithick Volume 2 p395

654. *Richard Trevithick, Giant of Steam* Anthony Burton p 228

655. *Civil Engineer & Architect's Journal* March 1839. p95

656. *Ibid* .March 1839, p114.

657. *Cornish Worthies* Walter H. Tregellas 1884

658. *The Engineer* 18 May 1917, p 447.

659. *Heroes of Invention, 1750-1914* Christine MacLeod p345

660. *Engineering* Volume 137, January-June 1934

661. *Life of Richard Trevithick* Francis Trevithick Volume 2 p395

662. *Beyond the Blaze* A. C. Todd p 106-7

663. *P. M. H. Sept 2008*

664. *A Treatise on the Steam Engine,* Volume 2. John Farey p5.

665. *Trevithick to Gilbert 15 Jan 1808* RIC

666. *Beyond the Blaze* A. C. Todd p274

667. *Lake's Parochial History of the County of Cornwall* pxi

668. *Life of Richard Trevithick* Francis Trevithick Volume 2 p395

669. *Ibid*

670. *The Engines of Our Ingenuity 1988-1997* John H. Lienhard.

671. *Life of Richard Trevithick* Francis Trevithick Volume 2 p394

672. Trevithick Papers, Leicester.

673. *Richard Trevithick, Giant of Steam* Anthony Burton p229.

674. *Life of Richard Trevithick* Francis Trevithick Volume 2 p394.

675. *Ibid*

676. *Ibid*

677. *Civil Engineer & Architects' Journal,* Volume II, 1839

678. *Death, grief and poverty in Britain,* p131

679. *Life of Richard Trevithick* Francis Trevithick Volume 2 p395

680. *Richard Trevithick, Giant of Steam* Anthony Burton p228

681. MCW Still, Dartford, cuttings 7th January 1902

682. *Ibid* 14 Sept 1903

683. *Ibid* 22 Sept 1903

684. *Ibid* 6 *Oct 1903*

685. *Ibid* 12 Oct 1903

686. *Ibid* 21 Oct 1903

687. http://www.*ancestryaid.co.uk*

688. *Death, grief and poverty in Britain* Julie-Marie Strange 2005, p132.

689. *Great Engineers.1970* Conrad Matschoss, p169

690. *Ibid* p171

691. *History of Penzance* P. A. S. Poole p196

692. *The Penny Cyclopaedia of the Society for the Diffusion of Knowledge, 1842*

693. *Civil Engineer & Architects Journal, 1850* p13

694. *A Short History of the Steam Engine,* Dickinson, 1938 p94

695. *A Thousand Barrels a Second p 64* Peter Tertzakian, 2007

696. *A Short History of the Steam Engine,* Dickinson, 1938 p94.

697. *Niles Weekly Register 1813. A Short History of the Steam Engine,* Dickinson, 1938

698. Oliver Wendell Holmes, 1841 - 1935

699. Steven Wright, American comedian.

700. *Mechanics' Magazine, XIX,* April 1833 p80

701. *Civil Engineer & Architect's Journal* William Laxton Volume I 1839 p93

702. *Ibid*

703. *Ibid* p96

704. *Power from Steam,* R. T. Hills pvii

705. *Automobile Biographics, an account of the lives and the work* ...L. H. Weeks, 1904, p16

706. *Ibid,* p11

707. *Ibid,* p11

708. *Steam Cars, 1770 – 1970* Lord Montagu & Anthony Bird , p34

709. *Staffordshi*re *Advertiser*

710. Stephenson 26 July 1848

711. *Hunt's Handbook to the Official Catalogues,* 1851. p97.

712. *Made in America.* Bill Bryson, p230

713. *Ibid,* p230

714. http://www.webrarian.co.uk

715. *John Brunton's Book* p171

716. *Lectures on the Great Exhibition of 1851 by the Royal Society*, p307

717. http://digilander.libero.it/calchic/marx/marxenglishb.html

718. *The Temple Anecdotes* p255

719. *The Third Man* John Griffiths p344
720. *Matthew Boulton* H. W. Dickinson 1936 p170
721. *Glimpses & Gatherings...Summer of 1851.* William Allen Drew, p186.
722. *A Quaker Record of Maritime Falmouth in World War One* Pamela Richardson, p8
723. *The Times* 25 April 1934
724. *The farmer's magazine.* D. Willison, All editions from 1802
725. *Britain, 1750-1900* Fiona Reynoldson, David Taylor, p89
726. *Britain in the Hanoverian Age, 1714-1837* Gerald Newman, Leslie Ellen Brown
727. Cornwall Record Office
728. *Trevithick* Edith Harper p57
729. *Richard Trevithick* Dickinson and Titley p262

IV   Summary

We bring together the three most important characters in this book. Two have been shown to be devious while the other was straightforward to a fault. While all came from humble Cornish backgrounds, two departed this life as rich men having married wealth while the third died in debt. They all made considerable contributions to the world although it was the latter who made the greatest and yet he received the least reward. Here we will see how the other two conspired against him.

Along the way we have met a great number of people including Boulton, Watt, Harvey, Rastrick, Homfray and a host of others, many were very influential. Then there were the lesser individuals, Gerard, Anna Beddoes, the sons of Boulton, Watt and Wedgwood, Thomasin, the assorted Fellows of the Royal Society and, dare we put her in this category, Trevithick's wife Jane. These and many others have helped us to reveal the personalities of our three main characters.

In their way Davy, Gilbert and Trevithick were all exceptionally clever but they never worked together for their common good. While Davy and Gilbert moved in different circles they both met people of power in parliament, various institutions and the Royal Society. Trevithick worked in engineering and was the greatest traveller of the trio. In spite of their collusion, the other two failed to stop Trevithick's engine powering the world; but they did ensure that he did not receive credit for it.

Although Gilbert had the opportunity to introduce Trevithick to notables there is just the one letter to Davy in connection with a patent application in January 1802. It was Trevithick and Vivian's first application and Gilbert had hurriedly but carefully prepared it after the outstanding demonstration of the steam carriage in Camborne at the end of the previous month. Davy simply passed him onto a Mr Nicholson and Vivian was unable to see Davy on subsequent visits to London.

At the time Gilbert had been encouraging Trevithick and established a solid base of understanding that would last throughout their lives. Trevithick responded with his absolute faith in Gilbert's ability and wrote to him after the patent meetings in London imploring him to be nearby should his influence be required.

Mr. Davy says that a Mr. Nicholson, he thinks, will be a proper person to assist … We shall not specify without your assistance, and all our friends say that if we meet with any difficulty nothing will be so necessary as your presence.'[730]

In the event, the grant of the patent was seriously delayed and Trevithick left the completion of the application to Andrew Vivian.

In 1804, Trevithick was enjoying the success of having built and operated the first self-propelled railway locomotive. It is very unlikely that he ever knew of the following words written by Humphry Davy to Gilbert but they were to influence and control the relationship between Trevithick and Gilbert for the rest of their lives.

In October of 1804, Davy wrote to Gilbert and said of Trevithick's invention, '… remembered that your reasoning and mathematical enquiries led to the discovery'

We can only wonder at the dismissive thoughts that went through Gilbert's mind on receiving this letter but he continued to maintain a façade of dealing faithfully with Trevithick's pleas for assistance.

This letter from Davy contains crucial interference in the relationship between Gilbert and Trevithick. These conspiratorial words stuck in Gilbert's mind throughout the following years as he silently guided Trevithick's inventions into obscurity and unattributed fame.

In the year of his death, Gilbert eventually let his guard down when writing to his son-in-law and explained how, in about 1796, Richard Trevithick had come to him with the idea for a high-pressure steam engine exhausting to air.[731]

Gilbert's position at the seat of national power was assured. Sir John Barrow, in his Sketches of the Royal Society & the Royal Society Club said of him,

> Gilbert omitted no opportunity of being useful to society and more particularly to the inhabitants of his native county, Cornwall.[732]

Gilbert had the ear of all those with influence; he could so easily have dropped a word in for Trevithick. The fact that he chose not to mention him ensured his oblivion; if Gilbert overlooked a man, those about him would also overlook him. Gilbert was a clever man whose decisions tactfully maintained his position in society.

In 1827, after a quarter of a century of working with Trevithick and being theoretically involved in the substantial improvements to Trevithick's engine, Gilbert delivered an address to the Royal Society and published his 'Observations on the Steam Engine'. In this he investigated the operation and efficiency of various steam engines, referred to other learned papers, the work undertaken by James Watt and developments by Jonathan Hornblower of Penryn. While a great number of the observations are based upon the operation and efficiency of engines in Cornwall, there was no reference whatsoever to Trevithick and his development of more efficient steam engines. It should be remembered that by 1827 the high-pressure engine had made tremendous changes possible in industrial Britain. This was at a time when the adulation of Watt was a driving force in the establishment and it would not have aided Gilbert's prestige to cause trouble where the simple omission of a reference to Trevithick suited his purpose. Members of Gilbert's audience who knew the facts must have wondered what he was doing but he got away with it. We do not know if Trevithick knew about this deception, if he had, he would have been rightly surprised and very annoyed.

In the same year, Trevithick asked his solicitor to petition Parliament on the 20th December 1827 to recognise the value of his inventions to the country.

Soon after the petition had been prepared, Trevithick met with a partner who supplied him with the money he required for perfecting his never-ceasing inventions. This being all he wanted, he lost interest in the petition and gladly resumed the kind of life he had pursued for so many years.[733] There is another account that refers to the petition being presented and the advantages to be gained from Gilbert's intervention as an M.P. and President of the Royal Society. Not surprisingly, Gilbert did not appear and there is a record of a well-prepared petition failing in February 1828. These were difficult days for Gilbert and Davy at the Royal Society and other things could have been on his mind. On the other hand, the debate on the petition in Parliament could have raised questions amongst those members who would have asked if Trevithick was so important and deserving of the nation's money, why he was not mentioned in Gilbert's lecture to the Royal Society a few months earlier, which would never have done.

A further unsuccessful petition was made[734] in 1831 and put in the hands of Gilbert. J. J. Beringer, one time principal of Camborne School of Mines, said, 'What exactly happened we do not know; all we learn about it is … that it was unsuccessful and Gilbert sent a letter saying, 'I cannot get the Lords of the Treasury to agree to remunerate or assist me in any way.' Beringer was obviously mystified by this outcome and raised some doubts over the circumstances surrounding the application, he said that, 'there must have been some misdirection of activities; yet it is difficult to believe that when Trevithick had behind him an M.P. who "knew the ropes" like his friend Giddy, any such misdirection had occurred'.[735] Beringer's reasonable assumption that Gilbert would have been on Trevithick's side in this petition is not borne out in reality. If Gilbert gave the petition a blessing, Beringer found it to be a surprisingly ineffective one.

In the early nineteenth century the activities in Cornwall were much respected for their technological and financial importance. Gilbert developed his connection with Cornwall as much as he could and in 1830 had the opportunity to present a paper to the Royal Society entitled *Progressive Improvements Made in the Efficiency of Steam Engines in Cornwall*.[736] This would be an opportunity to tell the assembled intelligentsia about Trevithick's achievements. After all, it had been twenty-six years since Davy had written his harmful letter; surely a mention now would cause no harm.

His choice of a paper on the progress of the steam engine in Cornwall provided the renowned author with a respected title and an opportunity to study design, manufacture and operation. Such a paper requires a great deal of time and thought together with research into all known documents and reports on the progress of steam engine. Gilbert started with an explanation of the Newcomen engine and the subsequent introduction of Mr Watt's improved engine together with a copy of the report on the test held at Poldice Mine, 30th October 1778, into the efficiency of the Watt engine. This included a detailed explanation of the Watt design, the dimensions of its components and the performance of the engine against the quantity of coal it consumed. This was followed by a turgid ten-page exposition on the operation of machines, the advantages and disadvantages of cog mechanisms and the amount of friction to be encountered. All the calculations were based on the medium of the Watt machine.

It is remarkable that, by 1830 when the paper was given, Watt had retired thirty years previously and been dead for eleven of them. Although the title of this paper depicted the developments in Cornwall, Gilbert made no mention of Hornblower, Trevithick or Woolf, all of whom could have found a place in an address on the improvements to the steam engine. Gilbert continued to use Watt's name to cover the years when steam engine development was in the hands of the much more progressive and freethinking Cornish inventors. As in his previous address to the Royal Society in 1827, entitled *Observations on the Steam Engine*, Gilbert had taken the opportunity to ally himself with Watt, the hero of the engineering age and so avoided any pitfalls connected to the lesser-known Cornish engineers.

In Volume One of his 1838 edition of the *Parochial History of Cornwall* Gilbert inserted the following update as the only reference to Trevithick in all four volumes. He tended to avoid Trevithick's actual achievements and used an entry of about a hundred words to exalt Watt, mentioned philosophy, the state of Trevithick's mind and discussed the political circumstances of the South American nations. Thirty-seven years after Trevithick's steam carriage climbed 'Camborne Hill', his entry about Camborne read,

> I cannot close my short additions to Camborne without noticing Mr. Richard Trevithick. No one, with the exception of Mr. Watt, has probably contributed in so great a degree to the improvement of steam-engines, the most important and philosophical of all mechanical inventions. His enterprise has also equalled the abstract powers of his mind, and for several years he laboured in South America to give the mines of that great continent the advantage of European machinery; but civil wars, and the instability of

Governments, defeated his best endeavours, so as to render them, up to the present time, unavailing either to those mines or to himself.

Five years after Trevithick's death, nine years after Davy's death and thirty-four years after Davy had written his damning letter Gilbert failed to give Trevithick any credit for his achievements. These had been the years when the name of Watt had been on everyone's lips and had been joined in the last nine years by Stephenson. Gilbert was in his decline and he had secretly been bound into Davy's connivance for over thirty years; he was not going to change now.

Gilbert died the following Christmas Eve and took his secret with him.

References
729.   *Trevithick, Giant of Steam,* Anthony Burton p76
730.   Gilbert to JS Enys 29 April 1839
731.   Sketches of the RS and RS Club, Sir John Barrow, pp 110/111
732.   Richard Edwards The Land's End District, July 1862.
733.   *Life of Richard Trevithick* Francis Trevithick Volume II p 311
734.   Sketch of Richard Trevithick, John Jacob Beringer, 1902, p 228
735.   RS 4th March 1830

Appendix I

Attendees at the meeting held in the Freemasons' Hall, 18th June 1824 to raise funds for the statue to the late James Watt, FRS.

Earl of Liverpool KG
Earl of Aberdeen
Richard Arkwright
Matthias Attwood
Charles Babbage FRS
Geo. H Barker FRS
Alex Baring
H. H. Birley
Sam. Boddington
Henry Brougham FRS
John Boulton
Matthew R Boulton FRS
W. T. Brande SecRS FRS
George Canning MP FRS
Wm. Clayfield
Rev. John Corrie FRS
Wm. Cotton FRS
John W. Croker FRS
D. S. Dugdale
Heneage Coffin
John Dalton FRS
James Davies
Humphry Davy PRS
Peter Ewart
Kirkham Finley
Francis Freeling
Geo. H. Freeling
Rev T. Lane Freer
Davies Gilbert MP FRS
Benj. Gott
Sir James Graham FRS
Charles Hatchett FRS
Wm Henry FRS
J. F. W. Herschel SecRS FRS
Wm. Huskisson MP
Francis Jeffery

John Kennedy
T. F. Kennedy
Geo. A. Lee
Sir Thomas Lawence FRS
Francis Lawley
Sir T. Frankland FRS
Lewis FRS
Baron E. J. Littleton FRS
Sir James Mackintosh FRS
Thomas Murdoch FRS
Wm. Murdoch
Wm. Mylne FRS
Robert Peel
Rt. Hon Robert Peel FRS
Geo. Philips
Geo. Philips Jnr
George Rennie FRS
Joseph Reynolds
Earl F Robinson FRS
Sir Walter Scott
Joshua S. S. Smith
Richard Storp FRS
Wm. Strutt FRS
Thomas Telford FRS
J. H. Tremayne
C. H. Turner FRS
Wm. Wilberforce MP
John Vivian FRS
James Walker FRS
James Watt Jnr FRS
Sir John Woolmore FRS
Josiah Wedgwood FRS
Baron John Wrottesley FRS

Appendix II

The details in this account of the explosion at Greenwich in 1803 have been extracted from an article on the East Greenwich Tide Mill written some years ago and kindly supplied by Mary Mills of Blackheath. It was intended for the Greater London Industrial Archaeology Society.

In 1802 Trevithick set up in an office in Southampton Street, near the Strand. Sales were handled by Andrew Vivian one of the family involved in metal mining in the West Country and, latterly, in Wales. In 1803 a George Russell ordered an 8 horse power high pressure engine from Andrew Vivian. Russell was the promoter of a large tide mill on the Greenwich peninsula and the engine was to be used during construction work and for other purposes. The engine cost Russell £75 12s 0d.

Russell's engine was used for pumping out water during the construction of the tide mill. It was on the East Greenwich marshes on the river side at the end of the lane, known then as Marsh Lane and today as Riverway. Building work went on during 1803 in the charge of the foreman, a Mr. Dryden. The steam engine began to give some concern. The fire was directly in contact with the cast iron of the boiler and on Sunday 4th September it overheated. The boiler became red hot and some joints burnt out. Despite this the engine was kept working and was the responsibility of an apprentice-whose name is not known.

On the following Thursday, the 8th September, this boy was called away from minding the engine and asked to catch eels which had congregated under the foundations of the building. It is not clear why he went - perhaps they were a nuisance and he had been told to go and clear them by the foreman. However it was dinnertime and eels can be very tasty spit roasted, or even steamed. Workmen have always found ways of adapting equipment to cookery (my father used to describe using the steam hose to cook shrimps caught in Northfleet off Harmsworth's jetty). For whatever reason the boy went off and left the steam lever - which vented the waste stream - fastened down. He had in fact wedged a piece of timber between the top of the safety value and then bent it down so that it could not rise to let the steam escape.

A labourer was asked to mind the engine while the boy was gone and noticed that it had begun to run too fast. He was alarmed by this and shut it down but he did not remove the wedge that was jamming the safety valve.

The result was inevitable and fatal. The boiler burst 'with an explosion as sudden and as dreadful as a powder mill'. One piece of the boiler, an inch thick and weighing 5 cwt was thrown 125 yards in the air and 'landing on the ground made a hole eighteen inches deep'. Bricks were thrown in a 'circle of two hundred, no two of them stayed together'. Three men were killed instantly, and three more were injured.

In my attempts to research this incident I have never managed to trace the inquest records on the three who died. I do not know their names or anything about them. Of the three who were injured, one went deaf but was soon to able to return to work. One, the boy, also fully recovered. The third, Thomas Nailor, had been showered with boiling water and was badly scalded. A wherry was called and he was taken to St. Thomas Hospital. St. Thomas was then still on its old site in the Borough, on the site now occupied by the southern part of London Bridge Station. It was near the river and easy to reach by wherry. Thus Nailor went to one of the best hospitals in the country as quickly and efficiently as he could he could be got there. The incident illustrates

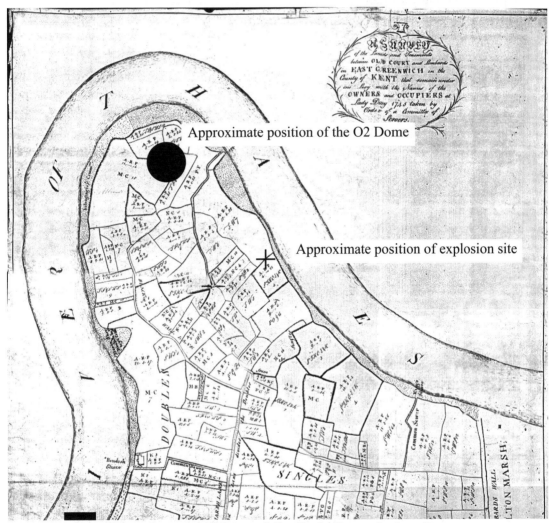

Location map (tithe map) for the boiler explosion site.

something about the response to 'casualties' - something rarely mentioned in works about nineteenth century medicine. Despite the work of Mr. Bingham, the surgeon, Nailor died three days later. It may be of interest that he, and those who gave evidence at his inquest, did not live in Greenwich but across the river in Poplar.

The newspapers were quick to report the accident - although there is the suspicion that the story was given to them by those who did not wish Trevithick well. In particular, he thought, James Watt and his partner, Matthew Boulton, were against him. He said that 'Boulton and Watt are about to do me every injury in their power for they have done the best to report the explosion both in the newspapers and in private letters very different to what it really was'. When The Times ran the story a week after the incident it was with the rider that Mr. Watt's engines would not explode in this way.. However reports in the press, so far as they can be traced, do not really differ very much from Trevithick's account of the accident based on his inspection of the site a week or so later.

Trevithick quickly made some changes to the design of his engine boilers. It had been said in the press that the accident should be a 'warning to engineers to construct their safety valves so that common workmen cannot stop them at their pleasure'. In future Trevithick's boilers had more than one safety vent and were constructed differently. It was, however, an accident that was well remembered and is recounted in almost every account of Trevithick and the steam engine. Few of these accounts are very clear as to where it happened - giving locations anywhere between Woolwich and Deptford! What none of them have realised is the importance of the tide mill that was under construction at the time and that this accident was only one of several which took place on that site in the next hundred years.

It has been said 'history vindicated Trevithick for it was his high pressure engines that made the steam locomotive possible'. The real victims were the nameless men who died at East Greenwich.

The location of the explosion was in a road once called Riverway SE10 which has now disappeared but a small stretch of it appears as a slip road off West Parkside going to a pub called the Pilot. When the explosion took place it would have been the middle of nowhere and reached by a footpath down Blackwall Lane and then Marsh Lane. Then the tide mill itself was built, and the Pilot and some cottages (Ceylon Place which are also still there). In the 1840s the mill was sold to a chemical company and became part of a vast chemical works and then around 1900 the gas works bought the chemical works and the mill but part of the site became an electric power station - which remained there until the mid-1980s. By then Marsh Lane was Riverway and on the other side was a steel works. Now that has all gone. Most of the area round the pub is now Park Lane but housing is going up nearer the river over the site which would once have been the mill and the steel works. When the [Millennium] Dome was built the landscape architects were told to wipe away all signs of the past and create a new environment - but we managed to get English Heritage to step in and save the pub and the cottages - the power station is also still there, disused, but it is the only thing left which is roughly near the site of where the explosion must have taken place, map reference TQ39716.79574.

This is the human story found amongst all the machinery.

Appendix III

Trevithick locomotives

1801   Camborne carriage, ran on the road up Fore Street, Camborne on Christmas Eve. Two or three subsequent journeys before being involved in an accident on the way to Tehidy, 28th December. Not used again.

1802   Patent taken out by Trevithick and Vivian for a carriage to be propelled by steam.

Coalbrookdale tram locomotive. Little is known other than it did exist in August.

1803   London Road Carriage. Chassis constructed in Camborne and carriage body fitted in London. Driven through the streets of London during July. Involved with some railings and engine subsequently employed in the manufacture of hoops for barrels. Conveyed the first London 'bus passengers.

1804   Penydarren tram locomotive, design unsure. In February it famously pulled a train with 10 tons of iron and 70 passengers 9½ miles to Abercynon, the world's first railway journey. Several similar journeys resulted in broken tracks and the engine was put to use within the iron foundry.

Wylam locomotive built at Gateshead to Trevithick designs. Some significant improvements over the locomotive that probably ran at Penydarren. Little used because track would not bear weight.

1808   'Catch me who can' demonstration locomotive operated on a circular track in the vicinity of Gower Street, London. Sold first railway tickets.

Index